Concepts in Computer Science
Implemented in MATLAB®

by David Smith, Georgia Institute of Technology

PEARSON

Custom
Publishing

10 9 8 7 6 5 4 3 2 1

ISBN 0-536-94164-5

2005200011

EH/CS

Please visit our web site at *www.pearsoncustom.com*

PEARSON CUSTOM PUBLISHING
75 Arlington Street, Suite 300, Boston, MA 02116
A Pearson Education Company

This book is dedicated to the glory of God

"That of all the several ways of beginning a book which are now in practice throughout the known world, I am confident my own way of doing it is the best—I'm sure it is the most religious—for I begin with writing the first sentence—and trusting to Almighty God for the second."
LAURENCE STERNE (1713–1768), British author, clergyman

Both the underlying philosophy of this book and the material that forms its skeleton originated in the work of Professor Russell Shackelford around 1996. Russ was then the Director of Lower Division Studies at the Georgia Institute of Technology, and developed the introductory course in Computer Science for students majoring in CS. While the course numbers have evolved over time, I can safely refer to this course in all its forms as "CS1." Russ believed that the capabilities of a student's first programming language shaped their view of programming in a very strong way. If they began with a language of limited capability (as I did with FORTRAN) they would see subsequent languages through glasses with the same tint. He really wanted the Tech students' first language to be as rich and easy to use as possible. Since no real programming languages could fit that bill at the time, he designed a pseudo-language that combined all of the computer science concepts he felt to be important, and we taught CS1 in that style for a number of years.

Dr. Melody Moore, currently an Assistant Professor in the Computer Information Systems Department of the College of Business Administration at Georgia State University, was instrumental a) in persuading me to join the instructional staff at Georgia Tech's College of Computing, and b) in creating many of the teaching materials (then as overhead transparencies) from which this class was first taught.

When Russ moved on to other opportunities, we retained the emphasis on teaching richness, but moved to a "real" language—Scheme—to give the students instant feedback on the results from running their programs. The authors of the Scheme book, "How to Design Programs," added another dimension to our concepts—the importance of matching the form of the solution to the form of the data, and the concept of programming to a template.

Around that time frame, the University mandated that all students at Georgia Tech were required to take introductory programming, and CS1—still taught in Scheme—was then offered not only to the CS majors, but to all the engineers, science majors, architects, etc. After not too many semesters, it became clear that "one size fits all" was not working well, and we began to offer different versions of CS1—one for CS majors, one for the engineers, and one for the non-CS, non-engineers. The College of Engineering made it very clear that they wanted their version of CS1 to be taught in MATLAB. I am deeply endebted to Prof. James Craig from the Aerospace Engineering department who joined me in co-teaching CS1(E), the Engineering version, taught me much about MATLAB, and pioneered this class from the original 35 students to its current size, teaching almost 1,000 engineers per semester. This engineering class became a vessel for introducing the students to the MATLAB language (although I clung grimly to the idea that we should teach object-oriented programming in Java).

The CS1 material has benefited from the efforts of every teaching assistant (TA), graduate student, instructor and professor who has taught this class, a list too long to enumerate. In particular, those wonderfully creative TAs who developed the ideas for examples in this text have enriched it immeasurably. I do wish to personally credit Prof. Aaron Bobick with an important contribution, made in the course of one short conversation. That conversation was responsible for pulling the class back from the brink of being merely a MATLAB programming class to its roots in CS concepts. Prof. Bobick taught this class with me in the Fall of 2004. Early in the semester, he made a very simple request—he said it would be easier for him to teach the class if we explicitly expressed the computing concepts inherent in each lesson, rather than leaving him—and the students—to tease the concepts out of the teaching materials. So the class returned to Russ Shackelford's roots—using MATLAB, a very flexible, enormously capable language that is easy to use—to deliver the computer science concepts that will enable students to transition rapidly to other programming languages.

Perhaps just a word about the object-oriented concepts. As late as the end of 2004, I was convinced that we should use Java to teach OO. However, to switch language syntax in the middle of an introductory class was arguably the most difficult challenge for our students. So I reluctantly agreed to attempt to express the OO concepts in MATLAB's emerging OO capabilities. The initial version of this book uses those capabilities in MATLAB R14. As we go to press with this version, I am helping to Beta test a vastly improved MATLAB OO implementation. As soon as that capability makes it into the version of MATLAB available on campus and to the students, the OO syntax in this text will be upgraded to this improved version. This will be a powerful test of the structure of this book in which concepts are presented first, followed by the MATLAB implementation.

Beyond the historical background, I would like to acknowledge the personal contributions of a number of people without which this book would not exist. My wife and best friend, Julie, has been an unwavering source of strength and encouragement during the process of writing this text. Bill Leahy was a student in the first CS1 class I taught in the Spring of 1997. In spite of this beginning, he continued to earn a MS in Computer Science from Tech, and is now an Instructor in the College of Computing. During that period of time, he was a Teaching Assistant for the class, and has subsequently taught the class on a number of occasions. Beyond his uncountable technical contributions to the material now in this book, I want to acknowledge the friendship, encouragement and wise judgment that have been an inspiration to me during this arduous process. Most of all, if there is any enduring wisdom in this text, I give all the credit to Almighty God and His son, Jesus. "For the LORD giveth wisdom: out of his mouth cometh knowledge and understanding." Proverbs 2:6.

CONTENTS

1. Introduction...1

   1.1. History of Computer Architectures...............................2

   1.2. Computing Systems Today..3

      1.2.1. Computer Hardware...4

      1.2.2. Computer Software..5

      1.2.3. Operating Systems..5

      1.2.4. Software Tools..6

      1.2.5. Computer Languages..7

      1.2.6. Executing a Computer Program.............................9

      1.2.7. Executing a MATLAB Program.............................11

   1.3. The Architecture of the CPU.......................................11

   1.4. Memory Management...12

   1.5. Problem Solving..12

   1.6. Programming Language Background................................13

      1.6.1. Abstraction..13

      1.6.2. Algorithms...14

      1.6.3. Programming Paradigms...................................14

      1.6.4. Assigning Values to Variables.............................15

      1.6.5. Data Typing..17

      1.6.6. Classes and Objects.......................................19

   1.7. Outline of the Book..19

      1.7.1. Book Content...20

      1.7.2. Teaching Outlines...20

      1.7.3. A Final Thought Before We Go On........................20

Part I—Programming Fundamentals................................21

2. Getting Started with MATLAB....................................23

   2.1. Student Edition of MATLAB.......................................24

   2.2. MATLAB Windows...24

      2.2.1. Command Window...25

      2.2.2. Command History..26

      2.2.3. Workspace Window..27

      2.2.4. Current Directory Window.................................31

      2.2.5. Document Window...31

      2.2.6. Graphics Window..32

2.2.7. Edit Window 33
2.2.8. Start Button 33
2.3. Examples 33

3. Scripts **35**
3.1. Concept—Text Files 35
3.2. Implementation—m Files 35
3.2.1. Creating M Files 35
3.2.2. The Current Directory 35
3.2.3. Running Scripts 36
3.3. Examples 37

4. Vectors **39**
4.1. Concept: Data Collections 39
4.1.1. Data Abstraction 39
4.1.2. Homogeneous Collection 39
4.2. MATLAB Vectors 39
4.2.1. Definition of Terms 39
4.2.2. Creating a Vector 40
4.2.3. Size of a Vector 41
4.2.4. Accessing the Elements of a Vector 41
4.2.5. Shortening a Vector 42
4.3. Operating on Vectors 42
4.3.1. Scalar Arithmetic Operations 42
4.3.2. Logical Operations 44
4.3.3. Operator precedence 45
4.3.4. Concatenation 45
4.3.5. Defining Ranges of Indices 46
4.3.6. Slicing 47
4.4. Examples 49

5. Conditional Statements **55**
5.1. Concepts 55
5.2. If Statements 56
5.2.1. General Template 56
5.2.2. MATLAB Implementation 57
5.2.3. Logical expressions 57
5.2.4. Short-circuit evaluation 58

5.3. Switch Statements 58

    5.3.1. General Template 58

    5.3.2. MATLAB Implementation 59

5.4. Examples 60

6. Iteration **65**

6.1. Concepts 65

6.2. MATLAB Constructs 65

6.3. For Loops 66

    6.3.1. General for Loop Template 66

    6.3.2. MATLAB Implementation 66

    6.3.3. Indexing Implementation 68

6.4. While Loops 69

    6.4.1. General while Template 69

    6.4.2. MATLAB while Loop Implementation 69

    6.4.3. MATLAB loop-and-a-half Implementation 70

6.5. Examples 71

7. Functions **75**

7.1. Concepts 75

7.2. Black Box View of a Function 76

7.3. Implementation 76

    7.3.1. General Template 76

    7.3.2. MATLAB Function Definition 77

    7.3.3. Storing and Using MATLAB Functions 78

    7.3.4. Returning Multiple Results 78

    7.3.5. Auxiliary (Local) Functions 79

    7.3.6. Encapsulation in MATLAB 79

7.4. Examples 80

8. Generic Arrays **87**

8.1. Concept 87

8.2. Implementation 87

    8.2.1. MATLAB Cell Array Creation and Access 87

    8.2.2. Uses for Cell Arrays 88

    8.2.3. Operations on Cell Arrays 89

8.3. Examples 91

9. Structures **95**

   9.1. The Concept of Structures.. 95

   9.2. Basic MATLAB Structures 95

      9.2.1. Constructing and Accessing One Structure 95

   9.3. Structure Arrays 97

      9.3.1. Constructing Structure Arrays 98

      9.3.2. Manipulating Structures.................................. 98

   9.4. Examples 101

10. Principles of Problem Solving **107**

   10.1. The Character of Solution Steps 107

   10.2. Summary of Operations 108

      10.2.1. Building 108

      10.2.2. Traversal.. 109

      10.2.3. Mapping 111

      10.2.4. Filtering 112

      10.2.5. Folding 113

      10.2.6. Searching 114

      10.2.7. Sorting 116

   10.3. Assembling Solution Steps 116

11. Arrays **117**

   11.1. Properties of an Array 117

   11.2. Creating an Array 118

   11.3. Accessing the Elements of an Array 120

   11.4. Removing Elements of an Array................................ 120

   11.5. Operating on Arrays 121

      11.5.1. Scalar Arithmetic Operations........................... 121

      11.5.2. Array Logical Operations 122

      11.5.3. Concatenation 123

      11.5.4. Defining Ranges of Indices 123

      11.5.5. Linearizing Arrays 123

      11.5.6. Slicing 124

   11.6. Examples.. 127

12. Character Strings **131**

   12.1. Character String Concepts...................................... 131

   12.2. MATLAB Implementation 132

      12.2.1. Slicing and Concatenating Strings 133

12.2.2. Arithmetic and Logical Operations 133

12.2.3. Simple Data Output: The disp(...) function. 134

12.2.4. Simple Data Input: The input(...) function 134

12.2.5. Complex Input and Output. 136

12.2.6. Comparing Strings 137

12.2.7. Arrays of Strings 138

12.3. Examples 139

13. Recursion **143**

13.1. Concepts 143

13.1.1. A Stack. 143

13.1.2. Activation Stack 143

13.2. Recursion Defined. 144

13.3. Recursion Implementation 145

13.3.1. General Template 145

13.3.2. MATLAB Implementation. 145

13.4. Wrapper Functions 146

13.5. Tail Recursion 148

13.6. Mutual Recursion 149

13.7. Generative Recursion 150

13.8. Examples of Recursion 150

13.8.1. Fibonacci Series. 150

13.8.2. Detecting Palindromes 151

13.8.3. Other Recursive Examples. 152

13.9. Examples. 152

14. Exceptions **155**

14.1. Historical Approaches. 155

14.2. Concepts 155

14.3. MATLAB Implementation 156

Part II—Procedural Programming **159**

15. Plotting **161**

15.1. In General 161

15.1.1. A Figure—The Plot Container. 161

15.1.2. Multiple Plots on One Figure—Subplots. 161

15.1.3. Manually Editing Plots 161

15.2. 2-D Plotting. 163

15.3. 3-D Plotting 166

    15.3.1. Linear 3-D Plots 166

    15.3.2. Surface Plots 168

    15.3.3. Simple Exercises 170

15.4. Parametric Surfaces 172

15.5. Examples 175

16. Matrices **179**

16.1. Concept: Behavioral Abstraction 179

16.2. Matrix Operations 180

    16.2.1. Matrix Multiplication 180

    16.2.2. Matrix Division 182

    16.2.3. Matrix Exponentiation 183

16.3. MATLAB Implementation 183

    16.3.1. Matrix Multiplication 183

    16.3.2. Matrix Division 184

16.4. Applications 186

    16.4.1. Rotating Coordinates 186

    16.4.2. Solving Simultaneous Linear Equations 188

    16.4.3. Curve fitting 188

16.5. Examples 191

17. File I/O **193**

17.1. Concept 193

17.2. Approach 194

17.3. Implementation 194

    17.3.1. Exploration 195

    17.3.2. Reading and Using the Data 195

    17.3.3. Processing the Data 197

    17.3.4. Saving Results to a File 197

17.4. Examples 198

18. Sounds **201**

18.1. Concept 201

18.2. Recording and Playback 201

18.3. MATLAB Implementation 202

18.4. Time Domain Operations 203

    18.4.1. Slicing and Concatenating Sound 203

18.4.2. Changing Sound Frequency—Poorly 207

18.4.3. Changing Sound Frequency—Well 208

18.5. The Fast Fourier Transform. 211

18.6. Frequency Domain Operations 215

18.6.1. Analyzing Instrument Sounds 215

18.6.2. Adding Sounds to the Spectrum 217

18.6.3. Manipulating the Spectrum 219

18.6.4. Truncating the Spectrum 221

18.6.5. Digital Filtering 221

18.7. Examples 221

19. Images **225**

19.1. Concepts 225

19.2. Image Types 226

19.2.1. True Color and Gray Scale Images 226

19.2.2. Color Mapped Images 226

19.2.3. Reading and Writing Images 227

19.3. Operating on Images 227

19.3.1. Creating a Collage 227

19.3.2. Changing Color Maps 231

19.4. Advanced Image Manipulation 231

19.4.1. Creating a Kaleidoscope 232

19.4.2. Detecting Edges 234

19.5. Examples 235

20. Numerical Methods **239**

20.1. Interpolation 239

20.1.1. Linear Interpolation 240

20.1.2. The `interp1` Function 240

20.1.3. Cubic-Spline Interpolation 244

20.1.4. The `spline` Function 244

20.2. Curve Fitting 244

20.2.1. Linear Regression 244

20.2.2. Polynomial Regression 247

20.2.3. The `polyfit` and `polyval` Functions 247

20.3. Using the Interactive Fitting Tools 249

20.3.1. Basic Fitting Tools 250

20.3.2. Curve Fitting Toolbox 253

20.4. Numerical Integration 254
    20.4.1. Trapezoidal Rule and Simpson's Rule 255
    20.4.2. Solving Practical Problems 256
20.5. Numerical Differentiation 259
    20.5.1. Difference Expressions 260
    20.5.2. The `diff` Function 261
    20.5.3. Estimating Critical Points of a Function 263
20.6. Putting It All Together 264
20.7. Examples 268

21. Big O **275**
21.1. Definitions and Symbology 275
21.2. Specific Big O Examples 276
    21.2.1. O(1)—Independent of N 276
    21.2.2. O(N)—Linear with N 276
    21.2.3. O(logN)—Binary Search 276
    21.2.4. O(N^2)—Proportional to N^2 277
    21.2.5. O(2^N)—Exponential Growth or Worse 278
21.3. Analyzing Complex Algorithms 278

22. Sorting **279**
22.1. Insertion Sort 279
22.2. Quick Sort 281
22.3. Merge Sort 282
22.4. Bucket Sort 284
22.5. Performance Analysis 285
22.6. Applications 287
    22.6.1. Insertion Sort 287
    22.6.2. Quick Sort 287
    22.6.3. Merge Sort 287
    22.6.4. Bucket Sort 287
22.7. Examples 288

Part III—Object-Oriented Programming **289**

23. Object-Oriented Programming **291**
23.1. Background 291
23.2. Definitions 292
23.3. Concepts 293

23.3.1. Behavioral Abstraction 293

23.3.2. Abstract Data Type... 293

23.4. MATLAB Observations 294

23.5. Categories of Classes 294

23.5.1. Modeling Objects... 295

23.5.2. Modeling Collections... 295

23.5.3. Objects within Collections 295

23.6. MATLAB Implementation of Classes and Objects......................... 296

23.6.1. MATLAB Classes 296

23.6.2. MATLAB Objects 297

23.6.3. MATLAB Attributes 297

23.6.4. MATLAB Methods 298

23.6.5. Encapsulation in MATLAB Classes 298

23.6.6. Inheritance in MATLAB Classes.................................. 299

23.6.7. MATLAB Parent Classes.. 300

23.6.8. MATLAB Child Classes 300

23.6.9. Polymorphism in MATLAB 301

23.7. Examples 303

24. Modeling Objects 305

24.1. The Base Class 305

24.2. Inheritance by Extension... 308

24.3. Inheritance by Redefinition 310

24.4. Practical Example of Modeling...................................... 312

24.4.1. A Vehicle Hierarchy... 312

24.4.2. The Containment Relationship 313

24.5. Examples.. 314

25. Dynamic Data Structures.. 317

25.1. Concepts 317

25.1.1. Static Memory Allocation 317

25.1.2. Dynamic Memory Allocation 318

25.1.3. Dynamic Data Structures....................................... 319

25.2. Linked Lists.. 319

25.2.1. The LLNode Class 320

25.2.2. The LinkedList Class 321

25.3. Processing Recursive Data Structures.................................. 321

26. Implementing a Linked List in MATLAB **323**

    26.1. Building a Linked List..323

        26.1.1. Adding at the Head of the List.................................323

        26.1.2. Adding to the Tail of the List..................................323

        26.1.3. Adding to the List in Order....................................325

    26.2. Traversing a Linked List 326

    26.3. Mapping a Linked List 328

    26.4. Filtering a Linked List...329

    26.5. Folding a Linked List 331

    26.6. Searching a Linked List...332

    26.7. Queues..334

    26.8. Stacks 335

    26.9. Priority Queues 336

    26.10. Summary of Ideas 338

    26.11. Examples..338

27. Binary Trees **345**

    27.1. Concepts 345

    27.2. Processing Binary Trees 346

    27.3. Processing Binary Search Trees 348

    27.4. Traversing a Binary Tree...348

        27.4.1. Depth-first Traversal 348

        27.4.2. Breadth-first Traversal 350

    27.5. Building a BST 352

    27.6. Mapping a Binary Tree 353

    27.7. Filtering a BST 354

    27.8. Folding a Binary Tree 357

    27.9. Searching Binary Trees 358

        27.9.1. Breadth-first Search 358

        27.9.2. Depth-first Search 358

        27.9.3. Searching a BST 360

    27.10. Combining Complex Operations...360

    27.11. Examples..361

28. N-ary Trees **363**

    28.1. Processing N-ary Trees 363

    28.2. Traversing an N-ary Tree...365

        28.2.1. Depth-first Traversal 365

        28.2.2. Breadth-first Traversal 366

28.3. Building an N-ary Tree 367

28.4. Folding an N-ary Tree 368

   28.4.1. Counting an N-ary Tree 368

   28.4.2. Finding the Largest Item in an N-ary Tree 369

28.5. Searching an N-ary Tree 370

   28.5.1. Breadth-first Search 370

   28.5.2. Depth-first Search 371

28.6. Testing the N-ary Tree Methods 372

28.7. Examples 274

29. Graphs **375**

29.1. The End of the Line 376

29.2. Searching Graphs 376

   29.2.1. Depth-first Graph Search 377

   29.2.2. Breadth-first Graph Search 380

   29.2.3. Optimal Graph Search 382

29.3. Examples 386

30. Cost of Computing **389**

30.1. Comparing Algorithms and Collections 389

30.2. Reasonableness of Algorithms 390

   30.2.1. Polynomial Algorithms 390

   30.2.2. $O(2^N)$ 390

   30.2.3. $O(N!)$ 391

   30.2.4. Unreasonable Algorithms 392

30.3. Tractability of Problems 392

   30.3.1. Definitions 392

   30.3.2. Closed vs. Open Problems 393

   30.3.3. More Definitions 393

30.4. N-P Complete Problems 393

   30.4.1. Yet More Definitions 393

   30.4.2. Illustrations 394

   30.4.3. The Opportunity 394

Part IV—Appendices. **395**

31. MATLAB Reserved Words and Symbols. **397**

32. The ASCII Character Set. **405**

33. Internal Number Representation **407**
    33.1. Integers 407
    33.2. Floating Point Numbers 408
    33.3. Parameters of Each Storage Type 408

34. Web Reference Materials **409**

35. Solutions to Selected Examples **411**

Figure 1—Babbage's Difference Engine 2

Figure 2—Colossus at Bletchley Hall 3

Figure 3—von Neumann Architecture 3

Figure 4—Internal Organization of a Computer 4

Figure 5—Interactions Between Software and Hardware 5

Figure 6—Program Compilation/Loading, Linking and Execution 10

Figure 7—Internal Computer Architecture 11

Figure 8—Types of Memory Usage 12

Figure 9—Generalized Problem Solving 12

Figure 10—MATLAB Opening Window 25

Figure 11—The Current Directory Window Lists All the Files in the Current Directory 31

Figure 12—The Document Window Displays the Array Editor 32

Figure 13—MATLAB Makes It Easy to Create Graphs 33

Figure 14—A Vector 39

Figure 15—A Simple **if** Construct 55

Figure 16—Generalized **if** Statement 55

Figure 17—Simple **for** Loop 65

Figure 18—A Simple **while** Loop 69

Figure 19—Abstract View of a Function 75

Figure 20—Assembling Kaleidoscope Steps 116

Figure 21—A 2-D array 117

Figure 22—The Transpose of an Array 118

Figure 23—Behavior of a Stack 143

Figure 24—Fibonacci Rabbit Population 150

Figure 25—Fibonacci in Nature 151

Figure 26—Subplots 162

Figure 27—Simple Plot 164

Figure 28—Styles of 2-D plots 165

Figure 29—Rotated 2-D plot 166

Figure 30—Simple 3-D Plots 166

Figure 31—3-D Parametric Curves 167

Figure 32—A Surface Plot 168

Figure 33—peaks(30) 171

Figure 34—Added Color Bar 171

Figure 35—Illuminated Curvature Plot 172

Figure 36—Parametric Cylinder 172

Figure 37—Simple Cylinder 173

Figure 38—A Sphere. 173

Figure 39—A Solid Disk. 174

Figure 40—Klein Bottle 175

Figure 41—Scalar Multiplication 180

Figure 42—Matrix Multiplication in General 181

Figure 43—Simple Example of Matrix Multiplication 182

Figure 44—Coordinate Rotation 186

Figure 45—Rotation Output 187

Figure 46—Gas Mileage Results. 190

Figure 47—Polynomial Fit Results. 191

Figure 48—Reading a Data File 193

Figure 49—Writing to a File 193

Figure 50—Sound Recording and Playback 202

Figure 51—Cropping the Problem Speech 205

Figure 52—Removing 'My Dear' 206

Figure 53—The Final Speech 206

Figure 54—Structure of a Tune File 208

Figure 55—Constructing a Tune Vector 210

Figure 56—A Typical Amplifier 211

Figure 57—Overview of the Fast Fourier Transform 212

Figure 58—Basic Sine Wave Relationships 214

Figure 59—Instrument Analysis Results. 216

Figure 60—Adding Sine Wave in the Spectrum 218

Figure 61—Synthetic Muting Spectra. 219

Figure 62—Details of Trumpet Spectrum 221

Figure 63—Image Basics 225

Figure 64—True Color Image Storage 226

Figure 65—Color Mapped Image 227

Figure 66—Original Images 228

Figure 67—Collage Layout. 228

Figure 68—Resulting Collage 229

Figure 69—A GIF Image 231

Figure 70—Bone Color Map. 231

Figure 71—Creating a Kaleidoscope 232

Figure 72—Kaleidoscope Pictures 232

Figure 73—C-130 Image. 234

Figure 74—C-130 Outline. 234

Figure 75—Interpolation between Data Points 239

Figure 76—Linear Interpolation 240

Figure 77—Cubic-spline Interpolation 241

Figure 78—Interpolated Data Points. 242

Figure 79—Cubic-spline Interpolation 243

Figure 80—A Linear Estimate 245

Figure 81—Data and Best-fit Line 246

Figure 82—Polynomial Fits 249

Figure 83—Interactive Basic Fitting Window. 250

Figure 84—Plot Generated Using the Basic Fitting Window 251

Figure 85—Residuals Plot. 251

Figure 86—Basic Fitting Window. 252

Figure 87—Data Statistics Window 252

Figure 88—The Curve Fitting and Data Windows 253

Figure 89—Curve Fitting Windows 254

Figure 90—Integrating a Function 255

Figure 91—Velocity of a Sounding Rocket. 256

Figure 92—Trapezoidal Rule Implementation 257

Figure 93—Results from Integration Test. 258

Figure 94—Derivative of f(x) at x = a. 259

Figure 95—Example of a Function with Critical Points. 259

Figure 96—Techniques for Computing f' (x_k). 260

Figure 97—Slope of f(x) 264

Figure 98—Velocity, Altitude and Acceleration of a Rocket 265

Figure 99—Order Study Results 266

Figure 100—Smoothing Results 267

Figure 101—Binary Search Example 277

Figure 102—Insertion Sort 279

Figure 103—Quick Sort 281

Figure 104—Merge Sort 283

Figure 105—Bucket Sort. 285

Figure 106—Comparison of Sorting Algorithms 286

Figure 107—ADT Illustration—A Queue Class 293

Figure 108—ADT for the Class Double 294

Figure 109—ADT for a Stack 295

Figure 110—Example Classes. 296

Figure 111—Functionality of a Child Class 300

Figure 112—ADT for the Bank Account 305

Figure 113—The SavingsAccount Class. 308

Figure 114—The Delux Savings Account. 310

Figure 115—A Vehicle Hierarchy 313

Figure 116—An Activation Stack 317

Figure 117—Dynamically Allocated Memory 318

Figure 118—Dynamically Linked Data 319

Figure 119—ADT for the LLNode 319

Figure 120—The LinkedList Class 321

Figure 121—Recursive Processing 322

Figure 122—Initial List. 324

Figure 123—First Recursive Call 324

Figure 124—At the End of the List 325

Figure 125—Returning the New List 325

Figure 126—Queue Implementation. 334

Figure 127—Priority Queue Implementation 336

Figure 128—Structure of a Binary Tree 345

Figure 129—A Binary Tree Node 346

Figure 130—Processing a Binary Tree 347

Figure 131—Deleting from a BST 355

Figure 132—Structure of an N-ary Tree 363

Figure 133—An N-ary Tree Node. 363

Figure 134—Processing an N-ary Tree Node 365

Figure 135—A Typical Graph. 375

Figure 136—Map of the London Underground. 375

Figure 137—Typical Graph Example 377

Figure 138—Performance of Operations on Collections 389

Figure 139—Towers of Hanoi. 391

Figure 140—Towers of Hanoi Solution. 391

Figure 141—Reasonable and Unreasonable Algorithms 392

Figure 142—Integer Number Representation 407

Figure 143—Number Formats. 408

Table 1—Assembly Language Instructions. 8

Table 2—Comparison of Software Statements 8

Table 3—The MATLAB Command Window 16

Table 4—Variable Storage. 18

Table 5—A Simple Script 36

Table 6—Constructing Arrays. 40

Table 7—Scalar Matrix Operations. 43

Table 8—Matrix Logical Operations. 44

Table 9—Bit-wise **and** and **or** Operations 44

Table 10—Operator Precedence 45

Table 11—Concatenating Arrays 46

Table 12—Vector Slicing Script 47

Table 13—Vector Slicing Results 48

Table 14—Template for the if Statement. 56

Table 15—Typical MATLAB Implementation 57

Table 16—Implicit Call to **all(...)** from the **if** Statement 58

Table 17—Generalized **switch** Template 59

Table 18—Typical MATLAB **switch** Implementation 59

Table 19—General **for** Loop Template 66

Table 20—A MATLAB **for** Loop 67

Table 21—General **while** Template. 69

Table 22—MATLAB **while** Loop Code 69

Table 23—Generic Function Template 77

Table 24—Normal MATLAB Function Implementation 77

Table 25—Returning Multiple Results 78

Table 26—Cell Arrays. 88

Table 27—A **switch** Clause. 89

Table 28—Passing Cell Arrays as Parameters. 89

Table 29—Exercising Cell Arrays. 90

Table 30—Building a Structure. 95

Table 31—The makeCD Function. 96

Table 32—Operating on a Structure 97

Table 33—Building a Structure Array "By Hand" 99

Table 34—Building a Structure Array—One Structure at a Time 99

table 35—Using a Structure Array 100

XXIV | LIST OF TABLES

Table 36—Building a Structure Array Using the Function `struct(...)` 101

Table 37—Taxonomy of Solution Steps 107

Table 38—The Custom CD Read Function. 108

Table 39—Traversal Template. 109

Table 40—Printing a Selected CD Attribute 109

Table 41—Writing to a Text File. 110

Table 42—Template for Mapping 112

Table 43—Mapping a CD Collection 112

Table 44—Template for Filtering 112

Table 45—Filtering CDs 113

Table 46—Auxiliary Function to Test for Equality 113

Table 47—Template for Folding 114

Table 48—Finding the Best CD 114

Table 49—Template for Searching 115

Table 50—Searching for a CD 115

Table 51—Constructing Arrays. 119

Table 52—Scalar Matrix Operations. 121

Table 53—Array Logical Operations 122

Table 54—Concatenating Arrays 123

Table 55—Linearizing Arrays 124

Table 56—Slicing Arrays 125

Table 57—Array Slicing Results. 126

Table 58—Converting Characters 132

Table 59—Slicing and Concatenating Strings. 133

Table 60—Logical Operations on Strings 134

Table 61—MATLAB String Representations 135

Table 62—C based I/O Functions 136

Table 63—String Comparison. 137

Table 64—Arrays of Characters 138

Table 65—General Recursive Template 145

Table 66—MATLAB Listing for Factorial 146

Table 67—Template for a Wrapper Function 147

Table 68—MATLAB Implementation of a Factorial Wrapper 147

Table 69—Tail Recursion Template 148

Table 70—Tail Recursive Factorial in MATLAB 149

Table 71—Illustrating a `try ... catch` Block 156

Table 72—Exception Handling in MATLAB 157

Table 73—Executing the Example 158

Table 74—Subplots 162

Table 75—Simple 2-D Plot 164

Table 76—Simple 3-D Plots 167

Table 77—Parametric 3-D Plots 167

Table 78—The Bowl Plot 169

Table 79—**meshgrid** Results 170

Table 80—Using **peaks(n)** 171

Table 81—Drawing a Simple Cylinder 173

Table 82—Drawing a Sphere 174

Table 83—Drawing a Solid Disk 174

Table 84—Matrix Multiplication 183

Table 85—Matrix Division 184

Table 86—Matrix Division output 185

Table 87—Coordinate Rotation 187

Table 88—Linear Curve Fit 189

Table 89—Polynomial Fit Test 190

Table 90—File I/O Operations 194

Table 91—Typical Spreadsheet Data 195

Table 92—xlsread Importing Data 196

Table 93—csv Data File 196

Table 94—Trying to Use **csvread(...)** 197

Table 95—Processing the Grade Data 197

Table 96—Processing Results 197

Table 97—Sound Resolution Experiment 203

Table 98—Finding the Problem 204

Table 99—Extracting the Problem 204

Table 100—Removing 'My Dear' 205

Table 101—Assembling the Speech 206

Table 102—Playing a Scale 207

Table 103—Playing a Simple Tune 208

Table 104—Changing a Note Frequency 208

Table 105—Playing a Scale 209

Table 106—Building a Tune File 210

Table 107—Transforming a Simple Sine Wave 213

Table 108—Instrument Analysis Function 215

Table 109—Instrument Script 216

Table 110—Adding a Sine Wave 217

Table 111—Synthetic Muting 220

Table 112—Collage Script 229

Table 113—Script for Kaleidoscope 233

Table 114—Diagonal Mirror Function 233

Table 115—Edge Detection Script 235

Table 116—Trapezoidal Integration 257

Table 117—Testing Numerical Integration 257

Table 118—Plotting the Derivative df/dx 262

Table 119—Finding the Critical points 263

Table 120—Combined Differentiation and Integration 264

Table 121—Study of the Polynomial Order 266

Table 122—Effect of Smoothing the Velocity Before Differentiating 267

Table 123—Work for a Binary Search 277

Table 124—Insertion Sort 280

Table 125—Code for Quick Sort 282

Table 126—Code for Merge Sort 283

Table 127—Constructor for the Fred Class 297

Table 128—Fred's Add Method 298

Table 129—Fred Child Constructor 299

Table 130—Child Class Add Method 300

Table 131—Fred Child Test Program 302

Table 132—@Fred\display.m 302

Table 133—@Fred\char.m 302

Table 134—@FredChild\char.m 302

Table 135—Results in the Command Window 303

Table 136—BankAccount Constructor 305

Table 137—The BankAccount Deposit Method 306

Table 138—The BankAccount Withdraw Method 306

Table 139—BankAccount getBalance Method 306

Table 140—BankAccount setBalance Method 307

Table 141—BankAccount Display Method 307

Table 142—BankAccount Char Method 307

Table 143—BankAccount Test Script 307

Table 144—Test Results 307

Table 145—SavingsAccount Constructor 309

Table 146—SavingsAccount calcInterest Method 309

Table 147—SavingsAccount **char(...)** Method 309

Table 148—SavingsAccount Tests 310

Table 149—SavingsAccount Test Results 310

Table 150—DeluxSavingsAccount Constructor 311

Table 151—DeluxSavingsAccount allowOverdraft Method 311

Table 152—DeluxSavingsAccount `char(...)` Method 311

Table 153—Redefined Withdraw Method 312

Table 154—LLNode `char(...)` Method 320

Table 155—Template for Processing a Linked List 322

Table 156—Adding to the Head 323

Table 157—Adding to the Tail of a Linked List 324

Table 158—`ge(...)` operator for the BankAccount Class 325

Table 159—Linked List addInOrder Method 326

Table 160—Iterative LinkedList Processing Template 327

Table 161—The LinkedList `char(...)` Method 327

Table 162—SavingsAccount `update(...)` Method 328

Table 163—Mapping a SavingsAccount List 328

Table 164—BankAccount `keep(...)` Method 329

Table 165—Generic LinkedList `filter(...)` Method 330

Table 166—Testing the Filter Function 330

Table 167—BankAccount `filter(...)` Method 331

Table 168—Generic LinkedList `sum(...)` Method 332

Table 169—LinkedList `find(...)` Method 333

Table 170—Test the `find(...)` Method 333

Table 171—Queue `enqueue` Method 334

Table 172—Queue `dequeue` Method 334

Table 173—LinkedList `peek(...)` Method 335

Table 174—MStack Implementation 335

Table 175—Stack `push(...)` Method 335

Table 176—Stack `pop(...)` Method 336

Table 177—Priority Queue `enqueue` Method 336

Table 178—Stack, Queue and Priority Queue Test Script 337

Table 179—Test Results 338

Table 180—Template for Processing a Binary Tree 347

Table 181—Recursive BinaryTree processing Template 349

Table 182—The Binary Tree `inOrderString(...)` Method 350

Table 183—The Binary Tree `preOrderString(...)` Method 350

Table 184—Template for Breadth-first Traversal 351

Table 185—Breadth-first String Generator 351

Table 186—Inserting into a BST 352

Table 187—Mapping a SavingsAccount Tree 354

Table 188—Deleting from a BST Part I—Finding and Repairing 355

Table 189—Deleting from a BST Part II—Finding the Node 356

Table 190—Testing the BST Functions 356

Table 191—Generic BinaryTree Count Method 357

Table 192—Binary Tree Breadth-first **find(...)** Method 358

Table 193—Binary Tree Depth-first **find(...)** Method 359

Table 194—BST Search 360

Table 195—Template for Processing an N-ary Tree 364

Table 196—Iterative N-ary Tree Depth-first Traversal 365

Table 197—The N-ary Tree **DFString(...)** Method 366

Table 198—Template for N-ary Tree Breadth-first Traversal 366

Table 199—Breadth-first N-ary Tree String Generator 367

Table 200—Generic N-ary Tree Count Method 368

Table 201—Finding the Largest in an N-ary Tree 369

Table 202—N-ary Tree Breadth-first **find(...)** Method 370

Table 203—N-ary Tree Depth-first **find(...)** Method 371

Table 204—Royal Family Tree 372

Table 205—Short Royal Family 372

Table 206—Testing the Royal Family Tree 373

Table 207—Depth-first Graph Search 377

Table 208—Depth-first Stack Trace 378

Table 209—Breadth-first Graph Search 380

Table 210—Breadth-first Queue Trace 381

Table 211—Dijkstra's Algorithm for Optimal Path Search 382

Table 212—Queue Trace of Dijkstra's Algorithm 383

1. INTRODUCTION

The search for new tools is an inescapable part of the life of an engineer. Advances in technology are achieved in two steps:

- a visionary conceives an idea that has never been tried before, and then
- engineers find or invent tools that will bring that vision to reality.

The process of creating tools may well spawn sub-problems which themselves require creative solutions.

The pace of change in our world is growing exponentially, and no field exhibits this change more dramatically than that of Computer Science. In the span of a few generations, computers have invaded every conceivable aspect of our lives, and there is no indication that this trend is slowing.

This book is to help you to become familiar with a specific programming tool: MATLAB. It is intended to bring you to a basic proficiency level so that you are confident to proceed on your own to learn the features of the languages that are useful to your interests.

A word of caution: Learning a programming language is very much like learning to speak a foreign language. In order to find something to eat in Munich, you must be able to express yourself in terms a German can understand—this involves knowing not only some vocabulary words, but also the grammatical rules that make those words comprehensible—in the case of German, this means capitalizing nouns, and putting the verbs at the ends of the phrases.

If languages were a strictly theoretical exercise, you could make up your own vocabulary and grammar, and it would undoubtedly be an improvement over existing languages—especially English with its incredibly complex spelling and pronunciation rules. However, language is not a theoretical exercise; it is a practical tool for communication. We are therefore not free to make up our own, but are constrained to the vocabulary and grammar expected by the people of the culture with whom we wish to converse. Similarly, this book is not an abstract text about the nature of computer languages. It is a user's guide to communicating your problem solutions to extremely complex programs that can translate your inputs into solutions as long as you conform to the vocabulary (definition of key words), and grammar (syntax) of the language.

The overall philosophy used in this text is to approach programming tools in the following manner:

1. Explain a computing concept, and then
2. Delve into the implementation in MATLAB.

The target audience for this text is college freshmen with no previous computing experience with the need to use computing tools for problem solving.

1.1. History of Computer Architectures

The early concepts of computing came about as tools to solve previously intractable problems. This section will trace the growth of computing architectures, with emphasis on their implementation of the memory and arithmetic processes.

Figure 1—Babbage's Difference Engine

Charles Babbage is generally recognized as the earliest pioneer of the modern computer. He was concerned about the process used to develop the tables of logarithms and trigonometric functions that engineers used for design. The only way to develop these tables was for hordes of mathematicians to calculate the values in the tables by hand. While the algorithms were simple, combining tables of the differences between adjacent values, the opportunity for human error was unacceptably high. In 1854, he designed a difference engine able to automate the process of generating tables of mathematical functions. Since the objective was to create numerical tables, the output device was to be a set of copper plates ready to be inserted in a printing press. The memory devices for storing numerical values were wheels arranged in vertical columns. The arithmetic operations were accomplished by ratchet devices cranked by hand. Sadly, the manufacturing tools of the day prevented him from realizing his machine. In 1991, the Science Museum in London undertook the task of building a machine to his specifications, as illustrated in Figure 1. With only minor changes to the design, they were able to make the machine work, although the Science Museum version is driven by an electric motor. While the only programmability was achieved by dialing in constants for the difference equations, the machine was able to compute difference equations up to 7th order with number sizes up to 13 significant digits.

Early in the second world war, Britain was losing the Battle of the Atlantic—German U-boats were sinking an enormous number of cargo ships resupplying the Allied war effort. The Government Code and Cypher School was established at Bletchley Hall in Britain with the goal of breaking the codes Germans used to communicate with their U-boats in the North Atlantic. The

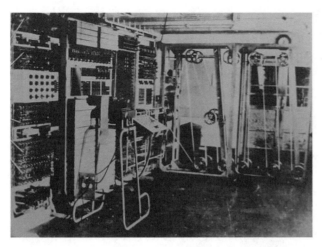

Figure 2—Colossus at Bletchley Hall

Enigma machines were relatively simple devices that encrypted messages by shifting characters in the alphabet. In order to crack the code, it was necessary to rapidly evaluate text shifted by arbitrary amounts. A computer later named "Colossus" (Figure 2) was custom built for this purpose, designed by Max Newman. While not a general-purpose processor, it used vacuum tubes to store data in binary form, and functioned sufficiently fast to enable all but the most sophisticated Enigma codes. Sadly, the machine was completely destroyed when the war ended. However, the dawn of ubiquitous computing was breaking, and general-purpose computers were soon to be available.

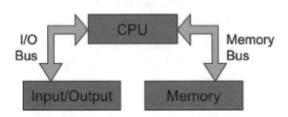

Figure 3—von Neumann Architecture

In 1945, John von Neumann proposed an architecture for general-purpose computing that separated the central processing unit (CPU) from the computer memory and the Input/Output (I/O) devices (Figure 3). Together with the use of binary encoding for storing numerical values, this was the genesis of general-purpose computing as we know it today. While the implementation of each component has improved beyond recognition, the fundamental processing architecture remains unchanged today.

1.2. Computing Systems Today[1]

Before we begin discussing MATLAB, we provide a brief discussion on computing, which is especially useful for those who have not had prior experience with computers. A **computer** is a machine designed to perform operations that are specified with a set of instructions, called a **program**. Computer **hardware** refers to the computer equipment, such as the keyboard, the mouse, the terminal, the hard disk, and the printer. Computer **software** refers to the programs that describe the steps we want the computer to perform.

---

[1] Section 1.2 of Etter, Kuncicki & Moore "Introduction to MATLAB® 7" ISBN 0-13-147492-8.

1.2.1. Computer Hardware

All computers have a common internal organization, as shown in Figure 4. The **Control Unit** is the part of the computer that controls all the other parts. It accepts input values (from a device such as a keyboard) and stores them in the computer's **memory**. It also interprets the instructions in a computer program. If we want to add two values, the processor will retrieve the values from memory and send them to the **Arithmetic and Logic Unit**, or ALU. The ALU performs the addition, and the processor then stores the result in memory. The processing unit and the ALU use internal memory composed of read-only memory (ROM) and random access memory (RAM) in their processing. Most data are stored in external memory or secondary memory using hard disk drives or floppy disk drives that are attached to the processor. The processor and ALU together are called the **Central Processing Unit**, or CPU. A **microprocessor** is a CPU that is contained in a single integrated circuit chip that contains millions of components in an area smaller than a postage stamp.

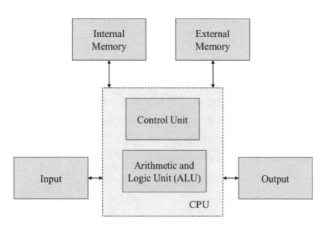

Figure 4—Internal Organization of a Computer

We usually instruct a computer to print the values that it has computed on the terminal screen or on paper, using a printer. Dot matrix printers use a matrix (or grid) of pins to produce the shape of a character on paper, whereas a laser printer uses a light beam to transfer images to paper. The computer can also write information to diskettes, which store the information magnetically. A printed copy of information is called a **hard copy**, and a magnetic copy of information is called an **electronic copy** or a **soft copy**.

Computers come in all sizes, shapes, and forms. Personal computers (**PCs**) are small, inexpensive computers that are commonly used in offices, homes, and laboratories. PCs are also referred to as **microcomputers**. Their design is built around a microprocessor, such as the Pentium microprocessor, which can process millions of instructions per second (mips). Minicomputers are more powerful than microcomputers. **Mainframes** are even more powerful computers that are often used in businesses and research laboratories. A **workstation** is a minicomputer or mainframe computer that is small enough to fit on the top of a desk. **Supercomputers** are the fastest of all computers and can process billions of instructions per second. Because of their speed, supercomputers are capable of solving very complex problems that cannot feasibly be solved on other computers. Mainframes and supercomputers require special facilities and a specialized staff to run and maintain the computer systems.

The type of computer needed to solve a particular problem depends on the requirements of the problem. If the computer is part of a home security system, a microprocessor is sufficient; if the computer is running a military-grade flight simulator, a mainframe is probably needed. Computer **networks** allow computers to communicate with each other, so that they can share resources and information. For example, Ethernet is a commonly used local area network (LAN).

1.2.2. Computer Software

Computer software contains the instructions or commands that we want the computer to perform. There are several important categories of software, including operating systems, software tools and language compilers. Figure 5 illustrates the interactions among these categories of software and the computer hardware. We now discuss each of these software categories in more detail.

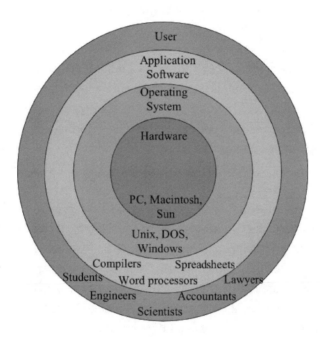

Figure 5—Interactions between Software and Hardware

1.2.3. Operating Systems

The program that controls or "operates" a computer is called the operating system. The operating system manages the computer's hardware such as the disk drives, terminal, keyboard, and modem. Other programs that want to access the computer's hardware must pass their requests to the operating system.

The operating system also manages the programs that are running on the computer. Modern computers may have tens or hundreds of programs running at any one time. The operating system is the traffic cop that schedules one program at a time to have access to the CPU.

Part of the operating system, called the kernel, is loaded when the computer is turned on. The kernel remains running until the computer is turned off. Common modern operating systems are Microsoft® Windows 2000, Microsoft® Windows XP, Linux, UNIX, and Apple Mac OS.

Operating systems also contain a group of programs called **utilities** that allow you to perform functions such as printing files, copying files from one disk to another, and listing the files that you have saved on a disk. Although these utilities are common to most operating systems, the commands themselves vary from operating system to operating system. For example, to list your files using DOS (a disk operating system used mainly with PCs), the command is `dir`; to list your files using UNIX (a powerful operating system frequently used with workstations) or linux (a powerful free operating system that is ported to many different hardware platforms), the command is `ls`. Some operating systems are referred to as *user-friendly,* because they simplify the interface with the user. Examples of user-friendly operating systems are the Macintosh environment and the Windows environment.

Because MATLAB programs can be run on many different platforms or hardware systems and because an individual computer can use different operating systems, it is not feasible to discuss the wide variety of operating systems that you might use while taking this course. We assume that your professor will provide you with information on the specific operating system that you need to use the computers available at your university. This information is also contained in the user's manual for the operating system.

1.2.4. Software Tools

Software tools are the programs that have been written to perform common operations. For example, **word processors**, such as Microsoft® Word and Corel™ Word-Perfect®, are programs that have been written to help you enter and format text. Word processors allow you to move sentences and paragraphs and often have capabilities that enable you to enter mathematical equations and to check your spelling and grammar. Word processors are also used to enter computer programs and store them in files. Very sophisticated word processors allow you to produce well-designed pages that combine elaborate charts and graphics with text and headlines. These word processors use a technology called **desktop publishing**, which combines a very powerful word processor with a high-quality printer to produce professional-looking documents.

Spreadsheet programs are software tools that allow you to work easily with data that can be displayed in a grid of rows and columns. Spreadsheets were initially used for financial and accounting applications, but many science and engineering problems can be solved using spreadsheets as well. Most spreadsheet packages include plotting capabilities, so they can be especially useful in analyzing and displaying information. LOTUS 1-2-3 and Microsoft® Excel are popular spreadsheet programs.

Another popular group of software tools are **database management** programs such as Microsoft® Access, Microsoft® SQL Server, and ORACLE®. These programs allow you to store a large amount of data and then easily retrieve pieces of the data and format them into reports.

Databases are used by large organizations, such as banks, hospitals, universities, hotels, and airlines, to store and organize crucial information. Databases are also used to analyze large amounts of scientific data. Meteorology and oceanography are examples of scientific fields that commonly require large databases for storage and analysis of data.

Computer-aided design (CAD) packages, such as AutoCAD®, ProE®, and Unigraphics®, allow you to define objects and then manipulate them graphically. For example, you can define an object and then view it from different angles or observe a rotation of the object from one position to another. CAD packages are frequently used in engineering applications.

MATLAB®, Mathematica®, Mathcad®, and Maple® are very powerful **mathematical computation** tools. Not only do these tools enable very powerful mathematical commands, but they also provide extensive capabilities for generating graphs. This combination of computational power and visualization power make them particularly useful tools for engineers.

If an engineering problem can be solved using a software tool, it is usually more efficient to use the software tool than to write a program in a computer language to solve the problem. However, many problems cannot be solved using software tools, or a software tool may not be available on the computer system that must be used for solving the problem. Thus, we also need to know how to write programs using computer languages. The distinction between a software tool and a computer language is becoming less clear as some of the more powerful tools, such as MATLAB and Mathematica, include their own languages in addition to specialized operations.

1.2.5. Computer Languages

A computer programming language is a notational form for relating instructions to a computer. Computer languages can be described in terms of levels. Low-level languages, or machine languages, are the most primitive languages. **Machine language** is tied closely to the design of the computer hardware. Because computer designs are based on two-state technology (i.e., computers are devices with two states, such as open or closed circuits, on or off switches, or positive or negative charges), machine language is written using two symbols, which are usually represented by the digits 0 and 1. Therefore, machine language is a binary language, and the instructions are written as sequences of 0s and 1s, called *binary strings*. Because machine language is closely tied to the design of the computer hardware, the machine language for a Sun Microsystems, Inc., computer is different from the machine language for a Silicon Graphics, Inc., computer.

An *assembly language* is a means of programming symbolically in machine language. Each line of code usually produces a single machine instruction. Assembly language is also closely tied to the architecture of a specific processor such as the Intel Corporation 8086 series or the Sun Microsystems, Inc., SPARC series. Programming in assembly language is certainly easier than programming in binary language, but it is still a tedious process.

The assembly code listed in Table 1 demonstrates typical assembly-language syntax. Each instruction is listed on a separate line and consists of an operation, or op code, followed by its operands.

```
mov   cx,bx
shl   cx,8
shl   bx,6
add   bx,cx
add   ax,bx
mov   cx,es: [ax]
```

Table 1—Assembly Language Instructions

High-level languages are computer languages that have English-like commands and instructions and include languages such as C, FORTRAN, Ada, Pascal, COBOL, and BASIC. Writing programs in high-level languages is certainly easier than writing programs in machine language or in assembly language. However, a high-level language contains a large number of commands and an extensive set of syntax (or grammar) rules for using the commands. To illustrate the syntax and punctuation required by both software tools and high-level languages, we compute the area of a circle with a specified diameter in Table 2 using several different languages and tools. Notice both the similarities and the differences in this simple computation. Although we have included C as a high-level language, many people like to describe C as a mid-level language, because it allows access to low-level routines and is often used to define programs that are converted to assembly language.

Languages are also defined in terms of **generations**. The first generation of computer languages is machine language, the second generation is assembly language, and the third generation is high-level language. Fourth-generation languages, also referred to as **4GLs**, are now being deployed with bold promises of programmer productivity. The fifth generation of languages is called *natural languages.* To program in a fifth-generation language, one would use the syntax of natural speech. Clearly, the implementation of a natural language would require the achievement of one of the grand challenges: computerized speech understanding.

FORTRAN (FORmula TRANslation) was developed in the mid-1950s for solving engineering and scientific problems. New standards updated the language over the years, and the cur-

```
Software      Example Statement
MATLAB        area = pi*((diam/2)^2);
C             area = 3.141593*(diam/2)*(diam/2);
FORTRAN       area = 3.141593*(diam/2)**2
Ada           area := 3.141593*(diam/2)**2;
Pascal        area := 3.141593*(diam/2)*(diam/2);
BASIC         let a = 3.141593*(d/2)*(d/2);
COBOL         compute a = 3.141593*(diam/2)*(diam/2);
```

Table 2—Comparison of Software Statements

rent standard, FORTRAN 90, contains strong numerical computation capabilities, along with many of the new features and structures in languages such as **C**.

COBOL (COmmon Business-Oriented Language) was developed in the late 1950s to solve business problems. Many legacy COBOL programs exist today and were a common source of the Year 2000 (Y2K) programming bug. **BASIC** (Beginner's All-purpose Symbolic Instruction Code) was developed in the mid-1960s and was used as an educational tool; in the 1980s, a BASIC interpreter was often included with the system software for a PC. **Pascal** was developed in the early 1970s and during the 1980s was widely used in computer science programs to introduce students to computing. **Ada** was developed at the initiative of the U.S. Department of Defense with the purpose of developing a high-level language appropriate to embedded computer systems that are typically implemented using microprocessors. The final design of the language was accepted in 1979. The language was named in honor of Ada Lovelace, who developed instructions for doing computations on an analytical machine in the early 1800s. **C** is a general-purpose language that evolved from two languages, **BCPL** and **B**, that were developed at Bell Laboratories, Inc., in the late 1960s. In 1972, Dennis Ritchie developed and implemented the first C compiler on a DEC PDP-11 computer at Bell Laboratories, Inc. The language was originally developed in order to write the UNIX operating system. Until that time, most operating systems were written in assembly language. C became very popular for system development because it was hardware independent (unlike assembly code). Because of its popularity in both industry and in academia, it became clear that a standard definition of it was needed. A committee of the American National Standards Institute (ANSI) was created in 1983 to provide a machine-independent and unambiguous definition of C. In 1989, the C ANSI standard was approved. **C++** is an object-oriented programming language that is a superset of the C language. Much of the early development of C++ was made in the mid-1980s by Bjarne Stroustrup at Bell Laboratories, Inc. The major features that C++ adds to C are inheritance, abstract classes, overloaded operators, and a form of dynamic type binding (virtual functions). During the 1990s, C++ became the dominant programming language for applications in such diverse fields as engineering, finance, telecommunications, embedded systems, and computer-aided design. In 1997, the International Standards Organization (ISO) approved a standard for C++. **Java** is a relatively new programming language developed in the early 1990s by James Gosling at Sun Microsystems that has earned a significant popular following. Its primary design goal was to enable programs to be shared across the World Wide Web, and this led to a number of innovative implementation decisions. It can be delivered in machine-independent form, and restricts access to the host computer facilities. We will see more references to Java capabilities further in this text.

1.2.6. Executing a Computer Program

A program written in a high-level language, such as C, must be translated into machine language before the instructions can be executed by the computer. A special program called a **compiler** is used to perform this translation. Thus, in order to be able to write and execute C programs on a computer, the computer's software must include a C compiler.

If any errors (often called **bugs**) are detected by the compiler during compilation, corresponding error messages are printed. We must correct our program statements and then perform the compilation step again. The errors identified during this stage are called **compile errors**, or **compile-time errors**. For example, if we want to divide the value stored in a variable called `sum` by 3, the correct expression in C is `sum/3`. If we incorrectly write the expression using the backslash, as in `sum\3`, we will have a compiler error. The process of compiling, correcting statements (or **debugging**), and recompiling must often be repeated several times before the program compiles without compiler errors. When there are no compiler errors, the compiler generates a program in machine language that performs the steps specified by the original C program. The original C program is referred to as the **source code**, and the machine-language version is called an **object code**. Thus, the source code and the object code specify the same steps, but the source code is specified in a high-level language, and the object code is specified in machine language.

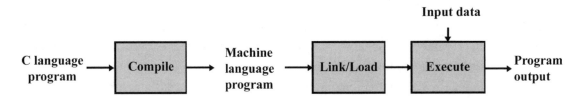

Figure 6—Program Compilation/Loading, Linking and Execution

Once the program has compiled correctly, additional steps are necessary to prepare the object code for **execution**. This preparation involves **linking** other machine-language statements to the object code and then **loading** the program into memory. After these linking and loading steps have been performed, the program's commands are then executed by the computer. New errors, called **execution errors**, **runtime errors**, **logic errors**, or **program bugs**, may be identified in this stage. Execution errors often cause the termination of a program. For example, the program statements may attempt to perform a division by zero, which generates an execution error. Some execution errors do not stop the program from executing, but they cause incorrect results to be computed. These types of errors can be caused by programmer errors in determining the correct steps in the solutions and by errors in the data processed by the program. When execution errors occur because of errors in the program statements, we must correct the errors in the source program and then begin again with the compilation step. Even when a program appears to execute properly, we must check the results carefully to be sure that they are correct. The computer will perform the steps precisely as we specify. If we specify the wrong steps, the computer will execute these wrong (but syntactically legal) steps and present us with an answer that is incorrect.

The processes of compilation, linking/loading, and execution are outlined in Figure 6. The process of converting an assembly language program to binary language is performed by an **assembler**, and the corresponding processes are called assembly, linking/loading, and execution.

1.2.7. Executing a MATLAB Program

In the MATLAB environment, we can develop and execute programs, or scripts, that contain MATLAB commands. We can also execute a MATLAB command, observe the results, and then execute another MATLAB command that interacts with the information in memory, observe its results, and so on. This **interactive environment** does not require the formal compilation, linking/loading, and execution process that we described for high-level computer languages. However, errors in the syntax of a MATLAB command are detected when the MATLAB environment attempts to translate the command, and logic errors can cause execution errors when the MATLAB environment attempts to execute the command.

1.3. The Architecture of the CPU

Figure 7 illustrates the next level of detail in the architecture of a computer. The CPU usually consists of a control unit that performs the instruction decoding and an arithmetic and logical unit (ALU). The memory and I/O implementations are usually merged in a typical architecture since both facilities are implemented by way of data busses, illustrated by the lines linking the system components. Typically, internal data busses move 16, 32, or even 64 data bits in parallel between internal registers and the "outside world" of memory and peripheral devices. The speed of the internal busses usually governs the operating speed of the processor.

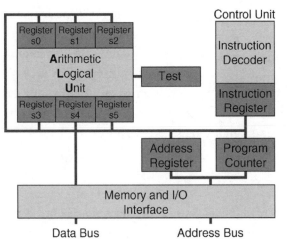

Figure 7—Internal Computer Architecture

Since most processors today are fabricated on a single silicon wafer, enormous amounts of effort go into the design of test circuitry that enables automated test equipment to determine that a particular chip was manufactured correctly. This might be as much as 70% of the total amount of logic on a processor chip.

The basic execution cycle of the system begins with setting the program counter to the address of an instruction. Memory at that address is read and the instruction word or words are moved to the instruction register. That register is decoded by the control unit that then performs the required operation, advances the program counter and begins the next execution cycle. Typical operations might be to move data to or from the ALU registers, command the ALU to perform some mathematical operation on specific registers, or to "jump" conditionally or unconditionally to some other place in memory by putting a new value into the program counter.

1.4. Memory Management

Later in the text, it will be necessary to understand certain aspects of the way computer memory is managed. Figure 8 illustrates a number of these aspects. The operating system (Unix, Windows, OSX or whatever) consumes some memory and determines from the I/O devices available what drivers must be present to enable the application programs to communicate with the outside world. Of the application programs loaded, many are loaded automatically when the operating system starts, and others are loaded upon user request. In addition to the memory needed to store the instructions, each program is allocated some stack space for storing local, static data. The remaining memory, the heap, is accessible to all programs upon request to the operating system. It is typically used to store dynamically the bulk of the data being manipulated by the programs. When a program finishes with a block from the heap, it is usually released by that program for other programs to use as necessary.

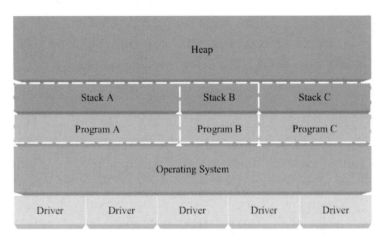

Figure 8—Types of Memory Usage

1.5. Problem Solving

In general terms, solutions to non-trivial problems are found by a two-pronged approach. On the one hand, we consider the original information and ask ourselves what could be done with that information using existing tools. On the other hand, we also consider the objective, and consider different ways in which that objective might be achieved. The

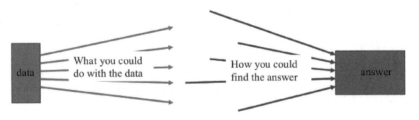

Figure 9—Generalized Problem Solving

process of creative problem solving then becomes a search for a match between states one can achieve from the given data and states from which the answer can be achieved.

For example, you have collected over the years a huge number of baseball cards, and you wish to find the names of the 10 "qualified" players with the highest lifetime batting average. To qualify, the players must have been in the league at least 5 years, had at least 100 plate appearances per year, and made fewer than 10 errors per year.

The cards contain all the relevant information for each player. You just have to organize the cards to solve the problem. Clearly, there are a number of steps between the stack of cards and the solution. In no particular order, these are:

a. Write down the names of the players from some cards,
b. Sort a stack of cards by the lifetime batting average,
c. Select all players from a stack with 5 years or more in the league,
d. Select all players from a stack with less than 10 errors per year,
e. Select all players from a stack with over 100 plate appearances per year, and
f. Keep the first 10 players from a stack.

When you think about it from right to left, a. is probably the last step, and f. is probably the step before that. When you think about it from left to right, this is where the hard work is going to come. Intuitively, when you think about sorting a stack of cards, this seems like a lengthy process that should be done on as few cards as possible. Since the sorting should probably be done on a small number of cards, you should do all the selecting before the sorting. Continuing that line of reasoning, you would reduce the total effort if the first selection pass was the criteria that eliminated most cards. You might even consider combining all 3 selection steps into one.

The final solution would then be the steps in this order: (c, d, e) b, f, a.

1.6. Programming Language Background

To discuss concepts in computer science, we also need some understanding of the background of programming languages. This section discusses five aspects of programming languages: abstraction, the underlying paradigm, the questions of compilation and data typing, and the difference between describing the generic behavior of components and creating instances of these components.

1.6.1. Abstraction

Definition: "Expressing a quality apart from a particular implementation."

We make use of the concept of abstraction in everyday conversation without thinking about it:

"To convert from Centigrade to Kelvin, you add 273 to **the temperature**."
"He **drove home** from the office."

The first is an example of ***data abstraction***. "The temperature" could mean a single reading from the thermometer hanging outside the window, or a table of temperature readings for the month of August. The specifics are unimportant; the phrase captures all you need to know.

The second example is actually much more complex—an example of multiple levels of ***procedural abstraction***. To a businessman taking the same route home every night, "drove home" is all that is required to understand the idea. To a competent driver unfamiliar with the route, the next level of abstraction might be necessary—turn right out of the parking lot, left onto Main Street, etc. To the design of a futuristic robotic commuter vehicle, an incredibly fine-grained level of abstraction is required. Everything taken for granted in the above abstractions must be meticulously spelled out—start the engine, accelerate the vehicle, look out for traffic, keep in lane, find the turn, steer the vehicle, control the speed, observe and obey all signs, etc.

1.6.2. Algorithms

In Section 1.5, we discussed problem solving as the ability to isolate sub-problems that seem simple and appropriate to solve, and then assemble to solutions to these sub-problems. The solutions to each of these sub-problems would be expressed ***an algorithm***, which is a sequence of instructions for solving a problem.

The process of solving each sub-problem and assembling the solutions to form the solution to the whole problem would also be expressed as an algorithm.

The level of abstraction needed to describe an algorithm varies greatly with the mechanism available. For example, if you wished to describe the algorithm for baking cookies, it might take the following forms:

- To your grandmother who has been baking cookies for the last 50 years, all you need is "please bake some cookies."
- To any ordinary person, it might be: "buy a cookie mix, follow the directions."
- To a young person learning to cook from scratch, it might be an intricate series of instructions for measuring, sifting and combining ingredients, setting oven temperature, preheating the oven, baking until . . .

In programming terms, we frequently express algorithms first conceptually at a high level of abstraction, as in Section 1.5. The solutions to each sub-problem would then be expressed at lower and lower levels of abstraction until the description is sufficient to write programs that solve the whole problem.

1.6.3. Programming Paradigms

From the Greek word *paradeigma*—to show alongside—a paradigm can be defined as "a set of assumptions, concepts, values, and practices that constitutes a way of viewing reality for the community that shares them, especially in an intellectual discipline."[2] So a programming paradigm

---

[2] American Heritage Dictionary.

becomes a codified set of practices[3] allowing the community of computing professionals to frame their ideas. We will consider three radically different paradigms: functional programming, procedural programming, and object-oriented programming.

Functional programming is typically associated with languages like Lisp and Forth in which every programming operation is actually implemented as a function call with no side effects[4] permitted or implemented in the language. This has the enormous advantage that without side effects, a programming solution can be mathematically proven to be correct. Except for the discussion of recursion, we will make no further mention of this paradigm.

Procedural programming is typical of languages like FORTRAN, C and MATLAB where the basic programs or subprograms are sequences of operations on global data. Side effects from subprograms are considered poor practice, but not prohibited by the language.

Object-oriented programming (OOP) is typical of languages like C++, Ada and Java, and is a relatively new addition to the world of paradigms. It is characterized by the concept of encapsulating, or packaging, data items together with the methods or functions that manipulate those data items. In this paradigm, side effects are explicitly managed by controlling access to the data and methods in a particular grouping. The major theme in true OOP is that "everything is an object." In this book, we will use MATLAB's version of classes to illustrate the fundamental concepts of OOP.

It is somewhat ironic to note the following:

- While the functional programming paradigm depends on the absence of side effects, the Lisp language for example depends on the function (**define...**) to define the name and body of a function (a side effect, and in fact the only purpose of the function).
- Most OOP languages that would declare that everything is an object actually require a main program to initiate program execution—a procedural concept.
- Furthermore, for understandable reasons of efficiency, some OOP languages that would like to make the claim that "everything is an object" actually permit the existence of primitive data types (integers, floating point numbers and characters) that are not objects.

1.6.4. *Assigning Values to Variables.*

Concept: Assigning values to variables.

The concept of assigning values to variables is the first challenge facing novice programmers. The difficulty arises because many programming languages (including MATLAB) present this simple concept in a syntax that is very similar to conventional algebra, but with significantly different meaning. Consider, for example, the following algebraic expression:

---

[3] We are still "above" the level of programming languages—there are many languages in which one can express solutions in each paradigm.

[4] A side effect is a change in the state of the program environment.

$$z = x + y$$

In normal algebra, this is a two-way relationship that is an identity for the duration of the problem. If you knew the values of z and x, one could derive the value of y with no further analysis. However, to a programmer, this statement has a different meaning. It just means that you want to sum the values given to the variables x and y, and store the result in a variable called z. If either x or y are unknown at the time of executing this statement, an error ensues. In particular, this relationship is true *only for this statement*. The relationship can be revoked in the next instruction, which might be:

$$z = 4*x - y$$

In algebra, this pair of statements collectively constrain the values of x, y and z. In programming, the only significance is that the programmer decided to calculate the current value of z differently. A few languages, sensitive to this dilemma, use a different symbol for assigning values to a variable. In Pasca or Ada, the above would be written as:

$$z := x + y$$

thereby clearly indicating that this is an assignment statement, not an algebraic identity.

In general, variable names may contain any combination of upper and lower case alphabetic letters, numbers and the special characters _ and $ (no spaces), but must not begin with a numeric character. They may be hundreds of characters long, but must be unique within the first 64.

Style Points:
1. Some early versions of the FORTRAN and BASIC languages severely restricted the number of characters you could use for variable names. You should not program as if you were still in the "bad old days." Choose names for variables that fit the meaning of their content.
2. Since the space character is not permitted in variable names, there are two conventions for joining multiple words together to make a single variable name. One uses the underscore character to separate the words (file_size), the other capitalizes the internal words (fileSize). You should choose one convention and be consistent with it.

➤ **If you have not yet installed MATLAB on your computer, follow the manufacturer's directions for performing the installation.**

➤ **Start MATLAB according to directions.** *(Continued)*

Table 3—The MATLAB Command Window

> When MATLAB finishes initialization, you will see three windows on the screen. We will concern ourselves only with the Command Window for the moment. It is the large panel to the right in the default screen configuration.

> You should see a prompt in that window. It might look like ">>" or "EDU>" depending on the nature of your license. This is your invitation to type something. Text that you should type will be shown thus in this book:

```
>> radius = 49
```

> Note that all entries into the MATLAB Command Window terminate with the 'Enter' key. The MATLAB system response will be shown thus:

```
radius =
    49
>>
```

> The above response indicates that MATLAB has stored the value 49 in a variable named 'radius.' To retrieve the value of radius, you just enter its name[5]:

```
>> radius
ans =
    49
```

> This response indicates that you requested the value of the radius and MATLAB retrieved the value 49. Since you did not specify where to put this result, MATLAB stored the result in a default variable named 'ans.'

Table 3—The MATLAB Command Window *(Continued)*

1.6.5. Data Typing

Concept: Specifying the type of data in a variable.

Different languages also take different approaches to declaring the type of a particular variable. In general, interpreted languages tend to let the variable assume the type of the data being stored there. This permits the programmer to take responsibility for the type of each variable. This is

---

[5] Followed by pressing the "Enter" key.

referred to as an ***untyped language***. Each assignment statement is presumed correct: if the variable already existed, its value is reassigned; if it did not exist before, a new variable is created.

➤ **Make the following entries in the MATLAB Command Window:**

```
>> radius = 49
radius =
    49
>> radius + 1
ans =
    50
>> radius = 'radius of a circle'
radius =
    radius of a circle
>> radius + 1
 ans =
    115     98     101     106     118     116      33     112
103     ...
```

➤ By putting 49 into the variable radius, you established its type as numeric, and enabled it to be used in normal arithmetic operations. When you stored a string in the variable radius, adding 1 to it resulted in something entirely different[6].

Table 4—Variable Storage

While this is good for interpreted languages, it has two undesirable consequences that are really hard to unravel as the program runs:

· Typographical errors misspelling variable names in assignment statements cause new variables to be declared unnoticed, and
· Logical errors that assign incompatible data to the same variable can cause obscure run-time errors.

Typed languages require that both the name and type of a variable be defined before a value can be assigned to it. Armed with this information, a compiler can then do a better job of assur-

---

[6] Notice that this did not cause an error in MATLAB as in some other languages, because addition is actually defined for character strings in MATLAB, as we will see in Chapter 10. It just did something radically different.

ing that the programmer is not using a variable in such a way as to accidentally damage the data content.

The use of typed languages falls into two categories: weak typing and strong typing.

If the programmers decide to restrict the type specifications to built-in data types (typically, double, int, char, etc.) and any class names created by the programmers, this is viewed as *weak typing*, and is the normal approach to typing.

In some extreme circumstances, programmers may elect to be more restrictive and define specific data types with a restricted set of permitted interactions. This is called *strong typing*. They might define, for example, the following data types all of which are actually of type **double: Meters**, **Seconds** and **MetersPerSecond**. The compiler would then be provided with a set of rules whereby assignments can only be made to a variable of type **MetersPerSecond** from another variable of the same type, or by dividing a variable of type **Meters** by a variable of type **Second**[7].

1.6.6. Classes and Objects

Concept: Contrasting the type of a variable vs. its value[8].

It is vital that we draw the distinction between the definition of a data type as discussed above and an instance of that type. The type **double** specifies the format, content and expected behavior (i.e. operations it can support) of a particular representation of a number[9]. However, until a variable is declared, for example, by:

```
thisNumber = 42.0
```

there is no actual numerical value upon which mathematical operations can be performed. So the word **double** corresponds to a type definition or **class**, while the variable **thisNumber** is a variable of that type, an instance of that class or in our terms, an **Object**.

1.7. Outline of the Book

This book is designed to facilitate teaching the material in different styles, and at different speeds. This is especially true of MATLAB, which has a number of specialized constructs for operating on arrays of values. There are two schools of thought about the appropriate way to introduce MATLAB concepts. One school would introduce these constructs first and follow up with the

---

[7] Before rushing to judgment on the pickiness of this approach, note that this would have avoided the loss in 1999 of the Mars Climate Orbiter that crashed into Mars because one group used English units while another used metric.

[8] There will be a more formal definition of this concept later.

[9] In most modern languages, the floating point representation conforms to the ANSI/IEEE Standard 754-1985, the Standard for Binary Floating Point Arithmetic.

more "normal" concept of iteration; we would call this the "arrays first" approach. The other school would teach iteration first and deal with the MATLAB specific array operations later—the "arrays last" approach.

1.7.1. Book Content

The remaining chapters in this book are in four parts:

- Part I: Fundamental programming concepts. These concepts include those necessary for Turing completeness[10] (vectors, iteration and conditional behavior) together with some added concepts (procedural abstraction—i.e., functions or methods—recursion, character strings and structures).
- Part II: More advanced procedural concepts.
- Part III: Object-oriented concepts.
- Part IV: Appendices with reference materials and answers to selected exercises.

1.7.2. Teaching Outlines

If you choose not to teach the OO section, you can easily omit Part III.

Whether or not you teach the OO portion, you can teach the "arrays last" approach to MATLAB by using Part I and then Part II, or "arrays first" using Part II before Part I.

1.7.3. A Final Thought Before We Go On

It may have struck you as curious that this book is about implementation in MATLAB, and yet there have already been a number of references to the Java language. MATLAB is already extremely compatible with Java and can actually use Java classes from inside MATLAB's command window, scripts and functions. We currently confine this text to MATLAB syntax and implementation even of the OO concepts. However, as subsequent releases of MATLAB arrive, it is possible that Java will become so accessible to the MATLAB programmer that we will be able to expand the appropriate chapters to include Java implementations.

---

[10] The ability to mimic Alan Turing's originally proposed computing machine that processed data in an infinite strip. (The infinite size requirement is not usually enforced.)

PART I

PROGRAMMING FUNDAMENTALS

*Whom shall he teach knowledge? and whom shall he make to understand doctrine? . . .
For precept must be upon precept, precept upon precept; line upon line, line upon line; here
a little, and there a little . . .*

Isaiah 28:9-10

2. GETTING STARTED WITH MATLAB[1]

MATLAB is one of a number of commercially available, sophisticated mathematical computation tools, such as MAPLE, Mathematica, and MathCad. Despite what their proponents may claim, no single one of these tools is "the best." They all have strengths and weaknesses. Each will allow you to perform basic mathematical computations, but they differ in the ways that they handle symbolic calculations and more complicated mathematical processes. MATLAB excels at computations involving matrices. In fact its name, MATLAB, is short for **Mat**rix **Lab**oratory. At a very basic level, you can think of these programs as sophisticated, computer-based calculators. They can perform the same functions as your scientific calculator, and **many more**. In many engineering classes, performing computations with a mathematical computation program is replacing more traditional computer programming. That doesn't mean you shouldn't learn a high-level language such as C++ or FORTRAN; but programs such as MATLAB have become a standard tool for engineers and scientists.

Today's MATLAB has capabilities far beyond the original MATLAB and is an interactive system and programming language for general scientific and technical computation. Its basic element is a matrix. Because MATLAB commands are similar to the way that we express engineering steps in mathematics, writing computer solutions in MATLAB can be much quicker than writing solutions in a high-level language. It's important to understand when to use a computational program such as MATLAB and when to use a general purpose, high-level programming language. MATLAB excels at numerical calculations, especially matrix calculations, and graphics. However, you wouldn't want to write a word processing program in MATLAB. C++ and FORTRAN are general-purpose programs, and would be the programming tool of choice for large application programs such as operating systems or drafting software. (In fact, MATLAB, which is a large application program, was written in C, a precursor to C++.) Usually, high-level programs do not offer easy access to graphing. The primary area of overlap between MATLAB and high-level programs is in "number crunching"—programs that require repetitive calculations or processing of large quantities of data. Both MATLAB and high-level languages are good at processing numbers. It is usually easier to write a "number crunching" program in MATLAB, but it usually executes faster in C++ or FORTRAN. The one exception to this rule is with matrices. Because MATLAB is optimized for matrices, if a problem can be formulated with a matrix solution, MATLAB executes substantially faster than a similar program in a high-level language.

MATLAB is available in both a professional version and a student version. The professional version is probably installed in your college or university computer laboratory, but you may enjoy having a student version at home.

---

[1] Section 2.1 of Etter, Kuncicki & Moore "Introduction to MATLAB® 7" ISBN 0-13-147492-8.

2.1. Student Edition of MATLAB

In this section, we explain the differences between the professional and student versions of MAT-LAB, and introduce you to the MATLAB environment. A number of examples are presented. We encourage you to type the example problems into MATLAB as you read the book, and observe the results.

Hint: You may think some of the examples are too simple to type in yourself—that just reading the material is sufficient. However, you will remember the material better if you both read it and type it!

The MathWorks provides an inexpensive student version of MATLAB for the Microsoft® Windows, McIntosh, and Linux operating systems. The student version of MATLAB includes the following components of the professional version:

- The basic MATLAB engine and development environment
- The MATLAB notebook
- Simulink
- The symbolic math toolbox functions

You probably won't be able to tell the difference between the student and professional versions. Matrix sizes are unlimited in both; the amount of memory in your computer is the limiting factor: The Simulink toolbox for the student version is limited to 300 modeling blocks, but that is usually more than adequate.

Other toolboxes besides the included symbolic math toolbox must be purchased separately; however, most problems can be solved with the standard software. Not all toolboxes are available for the student version[2].

The only difference you should notice is the command prompt. In the professional version the prompt is > >, but in the student version it is EDU»

2.2. MATLAB Windows

To begin MATLAB, use your mouse to click on the MATLAB icon (which should be located on the desktop) or use the start menu. If you are using a UNIX operating system, type **MATLAB** at the shell prompt. You should see the MATLAB prompt (**>>** or **EDU>>**), which tells you that MATLAB is waiting for you to enter a command. To exit MATLAB, type **quit** or **exit** at the MATLAB prompt, choose EXIT MATLAB from the file menu, or select the close icon (x) from the upper right-hand corner of' the screen. (See Figure 10.)

---

[2] For more information, please see the MATLAB website, www.themathworks.com.

MATLAB uses several display windows. The default view includes a large command window on the right, and stacked on the left are the current directory, workspace, and command history windows. Notice the tabs at the bottom of the windows on the left, which allow you to access the hidden windows. Older versions of MATLAB also included a launch pad window, which has been replaced by the start button in the lower left-hand corner. In addition, document windows, graphics windows, and editing windows will automatically open when needed.

2.2.1. Command Window

You can use MATLAB in two basic modes. The command window offers an environment similar to a scratch pad. Using the command window allows you to save the values you calculate, but not the commands used to generate those values. If you want to save the command sequence, you will need to use the editing window to create an M-file. M-Files are MATLAB files that con-

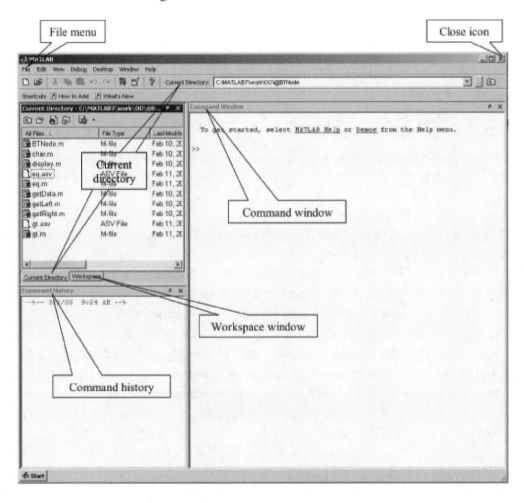

Figure 10—MATLAB Opening Window

tain program code. An M-File is an ASCII text file similar to a C or FORTRAN source code file. (See Chapter 3.) Both approaches are valuable. Here, we will concentrate on using the command window.

You can perform calculations in the command window in a manner very similar to the way you perform calculations on a scientific calculator. Most of the syntax is even the same. For example, to compute the value of 5 squared, type the command

```
>> 5^2
```

The following output will be displayed:

```
ans =
     25
```

Or to find the cos of π, type:

```
>> cos(pi)
```

which results in the following output:

```
ans =
    -1
```

MATLAB uses the standard algebraic rules for order of operation, which becomes important when you chain calculations together.

Hint: You may find it frustrating to discover that when you make a mistake, you can't just overwrite your command after you have executed it. This is because the command window is creating a list of all the commands you've entered. You can't "un-execute" a command, or "un-create" it. What you can do is enter the command correctly, and then execute your new version. MATLAB offers several ways to make this easier for you. One way is to use the arrow keys, usually located on the right hand side of your keyboard. The up arrow, ↑, allows you to move through the list of commands you have executed. Once you find the appropriate command, you can edit it, and then execute your new version. This can be a real time-saver. However, you can also always just retype the command.

2.2.2. Command History

The command history window records the commands you issued in the command window. When you exit MATLAB, or when you issue the **clc** command, the command window is cleared.

However, the command history window retains a list of all of your commands. You may clear the command history using the file menu if you need to. If you work on a public computer, as a security precaution MATLAB's defaults may be set to clear the history when you exit MATLAB. If you entered the example commands above, notice that they are repeated in the command history window. This window is valuable for a number of reasons. It allows you to review previous MATLAB sessions, and it can be used to transfer commands to the command window. For example, in the command window, type

```
>> clc
```

This should clear the command window, but leave the data in the command history window intact. You can transfer any command from the command history window to the command window by double clicking (which also executes the command) or by clicking and dragging the line of code into the command window. Try double clicking

```
cos(pi)
```

which should return:

```
ans =
    -1
```

Click and drag

```
5^2
```

from the command history window into the command window. The command won't execute until you hit enter, and then you'll get the following result:

```
ans =
    25
```

You will find the command history useful as you perform more and more complicated calculations in the command window.

2.2.3. Workspace Window

The workspace window keeps track of the variables you have defined as you execute commands in the command window. As you do the examples, the workspace window should just show one variable, **ans**, and tell us that it has a value of **25** and is a **double** array.

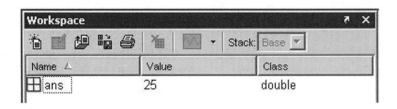

Set the workspace window to show us more about this variable by right-clicking on the bar with the column labels. (This is new to MATLAB 7.) Check size and bytes, in addition to name, value, and class. Your workspace window should now display:

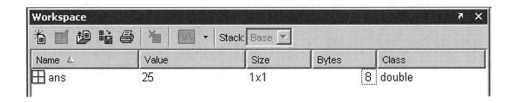

The yellow grid-like symbol indicates the variable **ans** is an array. The size, 1×1, tells us that it is a single value (one row by one column) and therefore a **scalar**. The array uses 8 bytes of memory. MATLAB was written in C, and the class designation tells us that in the C language **ans** is a **double** precision, floating point array. For our needs it is enough to know that the variable **ans** can store a floating point number (one with a decimal point). MATLAB considers every number you enter to be a floating point number, whether you put a decimal in the number or not.

You can define additional variables in the command window and they will be listed in the workspace window. For example, type

>> A = 5

which returns:

A =

    5

Notice that the variable **A** has been added to the workspace window, which lists variables in alphabetical order. Variables beginning with capital letters are listed first, followed by variables starting with lowercase letters:

Entering matrices into MATLAB is not discussed in detail in this section. However, you can enter a simple one-dimensional matrix by typing

```
>> B = [1, 2, 3, 4]
```

which returns:

```
B =
    1    2    3    4
```

The commas are optional. You'd get the same result with

```
>> B = [1 2 3 4]
B =
    1    2    3    4
```

Notice that the variable **B** has been added to the workspace window and that its size is a **1 × 4** array:

You define two-dimensional matrices in a similar fashion. Semicolons are used to separate rows. For example,

```
>> C = [ 1 2 3 4; 10 20 30 40; 5 10 15 20]
```

returns:

```
                 C =

                       1      2      3      4
                      10     20     30     40
                       5     10     15     20
```

Notice that **C** appears in the workspace window as a **3×4** matrix. You can recall the values for any variable by just typing in the variable name. For example, entering

```
        >> A
```

returns:

```
        A =
             5
```

Although we have only introduced variables that are matrices, other types of variables, such as symbolic variables, are possible.

If you prefer to have a less cluttered desktop, you may close any of the windows (except the command window) by selecting the x in the upper right-hand corner of each window. You can also personalize which windows you prefer to keep open by selecting View from the menu bar and checking the appropriate windows. If you suppress the workspace window, you can still find out what variables have been defined by using the command **who**, which just lists their names, or

```
        >> whos
```

which returns:

Name	Size	Bytes	Class
A	1x1	8	double array
B	1x4	32	double array
C	3x4	96	double array
ans	1x1	8	double array

Grand total is 18 elements using 144 bytes

2.2.4. Current Directory Window

When MATLAB either accesses files or saves information onto your computer, it uses the current directory. The default for the current directory varies, depending on your version of the software and how it was installed. However, the current directory is listed at the top of the main window. The current directory can be changed by selecting another directory from the drop-down list located next to the directory listing, or by browsing through your computer files using the browse button located next to the drop-down list (circled on Figure 11).

2.2.5. Document Window

Double clicking on any variable listed in the workspace window automatically launches a document window containing the array editor. Values stored in the variable are displayed in a spreadsheet format. You can change values in the array editor, or you can add new values. For example, if you have not already entered the two-dimensional matrix C, enter the following command in the command window:

$$\text{>> C = [1 2 3 4; 10 20 30 40; 5 10 15 20];}$$

Placing a semicolon at the end of the command suppresses the output so that it is not repeated back in the command window; however, **C** should now be listed in the workspace window. Double click it. A document window will open above the command window, as shown in Figure 12.

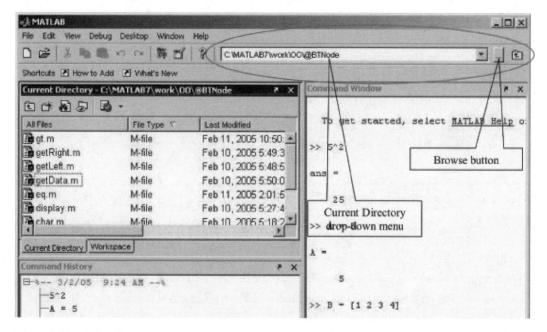

Figure 11—The Current Directory Window Lists All the Files in the Current Directory

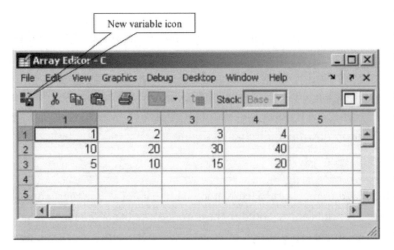

Figure 12—The Document Window Displays the Array Editor

You can now add additional values to the C matrix, or change existing values.

The document window that displays the array editor can also be used in conjunction with the workspace window to create entirely new arrays. Run your mouse slowly over the icons in the shortcut bar at the top of the workspace window. The function of each icon should appear if you are patient.

The new-variable icon looks like a page with a large asterisk behind it. Select the new-variable icon. A new variable called **unnamed** should appear in the variable list. You can change its name by right clicking and selecting rename from the pop-up menu. To add values to this new variable, double click it and add your data from the command window.

2.2.6. Graphics Window

The graphics window(s) launches automatically when you request a graph. To create a simple graph, first create an array of **x** values:

$$>> x = [1\ 2\ 3\ 4\ 5];$$

(Remember, the semicolon suppresses the output from this command; however, a new variable x, appears in the workspace window.) Now create a list of **y** values:

$$>> y = [10\ 20\ 30\ 40\ 50];$$

To create a graph, use the plot command:

$$>> plot(x,y)$$

The graphics window opens automatically. (See Figure 13.) Notice that a new window label also appears on the task bar at the bottom of the windows screen. It will either be titled <Student Version> Figure..., or simply Figure 1, depending on whether you are using the student or professional version of the MATLAB software. Any additional graphs you create will overwrite

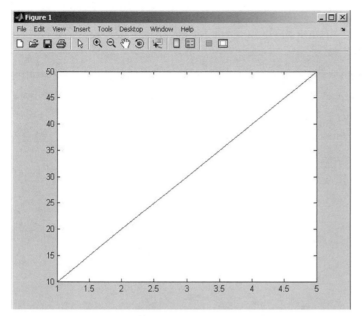

Figure 13—MATLAB Makes It Easy to Create Graphs

Figure 1 unless you specifically command MATLAB to open a new graphics window.

MATLAB makes it easy to modify graphs by adding titles, x and y labels, multiple lines, and more.

2.2.7. Edit Window

The editing window is opened by choosing **File** from the menu bar, then **New**, and finally **m-file** (**File → New → m-file**). This window allows you to type and save a series of commands without executing them. You may also open the edit window by typing edit at the command prompt.

2.2.8. Start Button

The start button is located in the lower left-hand corner of the MATLAB window. It offers alternative access to the MATLAB toolboxes and to the various MATLAB windows, help function, and Internet products. Toolboxes provide additional MATLAB functionality for specific content areas. The start button is new to MATLAB 7 and replaces the launch pad window used in MATLAB 6.

Style Points:

MATLAB naturally presents numerical results in a default format where if the value is an integer, there are no decimal places presented, but if there is a fractional part, four decimal places appear. You can change this presentation by various options of the **format** command. See MATLAB help for details.

2.3. Examples

2-1 In the command window, write the commands that will solve the following problems:
   a. You throw a ball straight up in the air with an initial speed of 25 m/s. [g = 9.8 m/sec2] Compute tp, the time it takes to reach the highest point, and hp, the highest distance the ball rises from the release point.

b. You are constructing a hemispherical dome with an outer radius of 50ft. The walls will be solid concrete 9" thick. Calculate v, the number of cubic yards of concrete that will be needed.

c. A jet aircraft is flying 100ft above a level plain at 600 mph. Suddenly, the ground begins to rise at a 4 deg slope. Calculate tx, the amount of time the pilot has to raise the nose before the aircraft strikes the ground.

3. SCRIPTS

3.1. Concept—Text Files

Whether we realize it or not, we all use text files. Whenever we send e-mail or access a Web site, we are looking at text files in a particular form. MATLAB uses text files as a permanent means of saving scripts (sets of instructions) rather than just entering commands in the Command Window. As we will see more formally later, text files are streams of characters stored sequentially with "markers" to indicate the end of each line of text.

3.2. Implementation—M Files

A MATLAB script consists of a combination of executable instructions that MATLAB interprets, and comment statements to enable readers to understand the script. You create **comments** by putting a percent sign (%) in the text file. The MATLAB machinery will ignore all text from that mark to the end of the current line. The MATLAB editor colors all such comments green[1] to separate them from the executable instructions.

Many application programs that use text files use a specific file name extension (the characters after the '.' in the file name) to identify the use to which the text files will be put. MATLAB uses the extension '.m' and its script files are often referred to as "M files."

3.2.1. Creating M Files

With MATLAB running, you create a new script either from the File menu (File->New->M-File), or by clicking the little white box on the left end of the tool bar. MATLAB will open its internal editor with a blank file. You then enter the commands and comments of your script into the file.

3.2.2. The Current Directory

When you have entered a script into the file, it must be named and saved on a disk directory, and MATLAB will need to find that directory—its working directory—in order to run the script. By default, MATLAB expects scripts to be stored in the directory `c:\MATLAB704`[2]`\work`. If you decide to store your scripts elsewhere, you will need to redirect the attention of the MATLAB system to that working directory. There is a MATLAB window that always shows you the location of the current directory.

---

[1] As we will see later, the editor also colors for other reasons—such as reserved words it recognized.

[2] Or wherever your current MATLAB application is stored.

Once script files are saved in your working directory, you can edit them again by selecting and opening them with the MATLAB editor. This is accomplished either by using the File->Open menu item, or double clicking the file name in the current directory window.

3.2.3. Running Scripts

The reason you build script files is to be able to save and re-use program statements without re-typing them in the command window. When you have built and saved a script, you can run it either:

- By typing the name of the script in the command window,
- By using the Debug->Run menu item in the MATLAB editor window, or
- Pressing the F5 key when the script is visible in the editor.

However you execute the script, the trace output is written to the command window as if you had typed the script instructions there one at a time.

Style Points:
1. When writing scripts, you should invest some time in comments. They make the scripts easier to understand as you are developing them, make it more likely you will be able to re-use the script later, and make it easier to grade your work.
2. Scripts should be written incrementally—build a little, test a little—rather than writing a whole script and then trying to find out where in that pile of code you made the mistake(s).

➢ Open a new script file, and type the following commands:

```
sideA = 3;    % the first side of a triangle
sideB = 4;    % the second side of a triangle
hypSq = sideA^2 + sideB^2;   % the square of the
                             % hypotenuse
hypotenuse = sqrt(hypSq)     % the answer
```

➢ Run the script by one of the methods above. You should see the following in the Command Window.

```
hypotenuse =
5
```

➢ Run the script by the other methods as much as you wish.

Table 5—A Simple Script

3.3. Examples

3-1 You are given a circle with radius 5 centered at x = 1, y = 2. You want to calculate the intersection of some lines with that circle. Write a script to find the x and y coordinates of each point of intersection (if they exist) for the following three lines:

$$y = 2x - 1$$
$$y = -2x - 10$$
$$y = x + 5.9054$$

The equation of a circle is:

$$(x - a)^2 + (y - b)^2 = r^2$$

where *(a, b)* is the center of the circle,
    and *r* is the radius

The equation of a line is:

$$y = m\,x + c$$

where *m* is the slope of the line, and
    c is the intercept on the y axis.

3-2 After a very hard week at work, Kirk is driving to Helen, GA for a tubing trip (to cool off). He drives 200 miles North to Timbuktoo. He then turns right and travels 400 miles east to Helen. Write a script to compute the linear distance, d, from the CoC to Helen.

3-3 Write a script to compute the sum of the cubes of:
a. The first 10 numbers
b. The first 65 numbers
c. The sum of cubes from 100 through 150
Hint: The sum of the cubes of first n numbers is $n^2 * (n+1)^2/4$.

4. VECTORS

4.1. Concept: Data Collections

In Chapter 2, we dealt with the idea of performing mathematical and logical operations on single data items. Here, we consider the concept of grouping data items in general, and then specifically consider one very common way to group data.

4.1.1. Data Abstraction

It is frequently convenient to refer to groups of data collectively—"all the temperature readings for May," or "all the purchases from WalMart." This allows us not only to move these items around as a group, but also to consider mathematical or logical operations on these groups.

For example, we could discuss the average, maximum or minimum temperatures for a month, or that the cost of the WalMart purchases had gone up 3%.

4.1.2. Homogeneous Collection

Later, we will encounter collection implementations that allow items in a collection to be of different data types. This first collection type, however, will be constrained to accept only items of the same data type. We refer to collections with this constraint as "homogeneous collections."

4.2. MATLAB Vectors

A vector is the simplest means of grouping a collection of like data items. Initially, we will consider vectors of numbers or Boolean values. Some languages refer to vectors as "linear arrays" or "linear matrices." As these latter names suggest, an array is a n-dimensional grouping of data and a vector is a 1-dimensional array as illustrated in Figure 14.

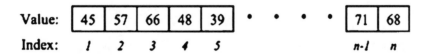

Figure 14—A Vector

4.2.1. Definition of Terms

We usually refer to the individual items in a vector as its **elements**. Vector elements have two separate and distinct attributes that make them unique in a specific vector: their **numerical value**, and their *position* in that vector. For example, we find the individual number 66 in the 3rd position in the vector in Figure 14. Its value is 66, and its index is 3. There may be other items in the vector with value 66, but no other item will be located in this vector at position 3.

4.2.2. Creating a Vector

There are two ways to create vectors that are directly analogous to the techniques for creating individual data items:

- Creating vectors as a series of constant values or
- Producing new vectors by operating on existing vectors.

There are six ways to create vectors from constant values:

- Directly entering the values, e.g. `A = [2, 5, 7, 1, 3]` (actually, the commas are optional, and frequently omitted),
- Entering the values as a range of numbers, e.g. `B = 1:3:20` where the first number is the starting value, the second number is the increment and the third number is the ending value (you may omit the increment if the increment you need is 1),
- Using the linspace function to create a fixed number of values between two limits, e.g. `C = linspace (0, 20, 11)` where the first parameter is the lower limit, the second parameter is the upper limit, and the third parameter is the number of values in the vector, or
- Using the functions `zeros(1,n)` `ones(1,n)` and `rand(1,n)` to create vectors filled with 0, 1, or random values between 0 and 1.

```
    ➤  In the Command Window, enter the following:

>> A = [2 5 7 1 3]
A =
     2   5   7   1   3
>> B = 1:3:20
B =
     1   4   7  10  13  16  19
>> C = linspace(0, 20, 11)
C =
     0   2   4   6   8  10  12  14  16  18  20
>> D = [4]
D =
     4                                            (Continued)
```

Table 6—Constructing Arrays

```
>> E = zeros(1,4)
E =
     0 0 0 0
```

> ➤ Now, open the Workspace tab in the upper left MATLAB window. It gives you three pieces of information about each of the variables you created: the name, value and "class" which for now, we can equate to "data type."
> ➤ Notice that if the size of the vector is small enough, the value field shows its actual contents. Otherwise, you see a description of its attributes:

```
<1 x 11 double>
```

Table 6—Constructing Arrays *(Continued)*

In the exercise above, we deliberately created the vector **D** with only one element, and the effect was perhaps surprising. **D** was presented in both the command window and the workspace window as if it were a scalar quantity. In fact, this is generally true in MATLAB—all scalar quantities are really vectors of unit length.

4.2.3. Size of a Vector

Any vector also has a specific attribute: its length (*n* in Figure 14). In most implementations, this length is fixed when the vector is created. However, as we will see shortly, MATLAB provides the ability to increase or decrease the apparent size of a vector by inserting or deleting elements[1]. MATLAB provides two functions to determine the size of arrays in general, and of vectors in particular. The function `size(V)` when applied to an array returns two quantities: the number of rows in the array (always **1** for a vector) and the number of columns (the length of the vector). The function `length(v)` returns the maximum value in the size of an array—for a vector, a number indicating its length.

4.2.4. Accessing the Elements of a Vector

The elements of a vector may be addressed by enclosing the index of the required element in parentheses. In the above example, **A(3)** would return the third element, **7**. If one were to attempt to read beyond the length of the vector or below index 1, an error would result.

---

[1] While these are very useful tools for operating on vectors, we should understand that what is really happening "under the hood" is that a new vector is being created from the specified elements in the original vector. Such operations are not computationally cheap.

One may also store values to elements of a vector. For example, `A(5) = 42` would result in the answer

$$A =$$

| 2 | 5 | 7 | 1 | 42 |

A feature unique to MATLAB is its behavior when attempting to write beyond the bounds of a vector. While it is still illegal to write below the index 1, MATLAB will automatically extend the vector if you write beyond its current end. If there are missing elements between the current vector elements and the index at which you attempt to store a new value, MATLAB will zero fill the missing elements. For example, `A(8) = 3` would result in the answer

$$A =$$

| 2 | 5 | 7 | 1 | 42 | 0 | 0 | 3 |

This procedure in general is referred to as ***indexing a vector***.

4.2.5. Shortening a Vector

There are times when we need to remove elements from a vector. To accomplish this, we make a rather strange use of the empty vector, `[]`. The empty vector, as its name and symbol suggest, is a vector with no elements in it. When you assign the empty vector to an element in another vector, say **A**, that element is removed from **A**, and **A** is shortened by one. So using the vector **A** above, if we entered `A(4) = []` in the command window, the result would be:

$$A =$$

| 2 | 5 | 7 | 42 | 0 | 0 | 3 |

4.3. Operating on Vectors

The name "MATLAB" is a contraction for "Matrix laboratory," and vectors are merely one-dimensional matrices. It does not surprise us then that the essential core of the language is a rich collection of tools for manipulating matrices. We will first see these tools as they operate on vectors, and then generalize them as they apply to arrays (multi-dimensional vectors) and matrices.

Two of the techniques extend directly from operations on scalar values: arithmetic and logical operations. The latter two techniques, concatenation and slicing, are unique to matrices in general, and to vectors in particular.

4.3.1. Scalar[2] Arithmetic Operations

Scalar arithmetic operations can be performed collectively on the individual components of two vectors as long as both vectors are the same length, or one of the vectors is a scalar (i.e., a vec-

---

[2] As opposed to matrix arithmetic operations, which will be covered in Chapter 16.

tor of length 1). Addition and subtraction have exactly the syntax one would expect, as illustrated in the next exercise. Multiplication, division and exponentiation, however, have a small, syntactic idiosyncrasy related to the fact that these are scalar, not matrix, operations. When the language was designed, the ordinary symbols were allocated to the matrix operations. However, since scalar multiplicative operations are fundamentally different from matrix operations, a new set of symbols was required for scalar operations. They allocated the following symbols: .*, ./ and .^ (the dot is part of the symbol) for scalar multiplication, division and exponentiation. Since matrix and scalar addition and subtraction are identical, these artifacts are not required for + and −. We sometimes refer to the dotted operators as 'point-wise' or 'element-by-element' operators.

➤ In the Command Window, enter the following:

```
>> A = [2 5 7 1 3];
>> A + 5
ans =
     7    10    12     6     8
>> A*2 % OK because 2 is a scalar
ans =
     4    10    14     2     6
>> B = -1:1:3
B =
    -1     0     1     2     3
>> A.*B % scalar multiplication
ans =
    -2     0     7     2     9
>> A*B % matrix multiplication does not work here
??? Error using ==> mtimes
Inner matrix dimensions must agree.
>> C = [1 2 3]
C =
     1     2     3
>> A .* C % A and C must have the same length
??? Error using ==> times
Matrix dimensions must agree.
```

➤ Notice the use of the % sign indicating that the rest of the line is not to be interpreted by MATLAB, but serves as a comment on the line for human understanding.

Table 7—Scalar Matrix Operations

4.3.2. Logical Operations

As with scalar arithmetic, logical operations can be performed collectively on the individual components of two vectors as long as both vectors are the same length, or one of the vectors is a scalar (i.e., a vector of length 1). The result will be a vector of Boolean values with the same length as the original vector(s).

➢ **In the Command Window, enter the following:**

```
>> A = [2 5 7 1 3];
>> B = [0 6 5 3 2];
>> A >= 5
ans =
     0    1    1    0    0
>> A >= B
ans =
     1    0    1    0    1
>> C = [1 2 3]
>> A > C
??? Error using ==> gt
Matrix dimensions must agree.
```

Table 8—Matrix Logical Operations

Logical operators can be assembled into more complex operations using logical and (**&**) and or (**|**) operators. These operators actually come in two flavors: **&/|** and **&& / ||**. The single operators **&** and **|** operate on Boolean arrays of matching size to compute logical combinations of the individual logical values. **&& / ||** combine individual logical results, and are usually associated with conditional statements (see Section 5.2.3).

➢ **In the Command Window, enter the following:**

```
>> A = [true true false false];
>> B = [true false true false];
>> A & B
ans =
     1    0    0    0
>> A | B
ans =
     1    1    1    0
```
(Continued)

Table 9—Bit-wise and and or Operations

```
>> C = [1 0 0]
>> A & C
??? Error using ==> and
Matrix dimensions must agree.
```

Table 9—Bit-wise and and or Operations (*Continued*)

4.3.3. Operator Precedence

As usual with arithmetic or logical operations, the precedence of operators governs the order in which operations are performed according to Table 10. The normal precedence can be overruled by enclosing a preferred operation in parentheses '(...).'

Operators	Description
~	Logical not
^	Exponentiation
* /	Multiplication
+ −	Addition
< <= >= >	Comparison
== ~=	Equality
& |	Bit-wise logic
&& ||	Short-circuit logical test

Table 10—Operator Precedence

4.3.4. Concatenation

In Section 4.2.2 above, we saw that the first technique for creating a vector is to assemble numbers between square brackets:

```
A = [2 5 7 1 3]
```

This is in fact a special case of concatenation. MATLAB permits the programmer to construct a new array by concatenating other arrays:

```
A = [B C D ... X Y Z]
```

where the individual items within the brackets may be any array defined as a constant or variable. The only restriction is that all items within the brackets must have the same number of rows. The result will be an array with that number of rows and a number of columns equaling the sum of the number of columns in each individual item. The simple array constructor in Section 4.2.2

above works because each number is a 1×1 array. The result is therefore a $1 \times N$ array (vector) where N is the number of values on the brackets.

➤ **In the Command Window, enter the following:**

```
>> A = [2 5 7];
>> B = [1 3];
>> [A B]
ans =
2 5 7 1 3
```

Table 11—Concatenating Arrays

4.3.5. Defining Ranges of Indices

As we saw above, the basic operation of reading and writing the elements of a vector is called *indexing*. We will see below that indexing is not confined to single elements in a vector. We can accomplish indexing using *vectors of indices*. These index vectors may either be the values of previously named variables, or they can be created anonymously as they are needed. When we index a single element in a vector (e.g. **A(4)**) we are actually creating an anonymous 1×1 index vector **[4]** and then using it to extract that number of elements from the array **A**.

Creating anonymous index arrays as needed makes available some additional features of the colon (slice) operator. The general form of generating a vector of numbers is as follows:

<start> : <increment> : <end>

We already know that if we omit the **<increment>** portion, the default increment is 1. When used anonymously, the following features are also available:

· The key word **end** is defined as the length of the vector, and
· The operator ':' by itself is short for **1:end.**

Finally, it is legal in MATLAB to index with a vector of Boolean values of the same length as, or shorter than, the vector being indexed. For example, if **A** is defined as:

A = [2 5 7 1 3];

then **A([false true false true])** returns

```
ans =
     5      1
```

This is extremely useful, as we will see below, for indexing items in a vector that match a specific Boolean test.

4.3.6. Slicing

The general form of statements for slicing vectors (moving sections of one vector into sections of another) is as follows:

$$B(<range1>) = A(<range2>)$$

Where **<range1>** and **<range2>** are vectors of indices, **A** is an existing array, and **B** can be an existing array, a new array, or absent altogether (giving **B** the name **ans**). The values in **B** at the indices in **range1** are all assigned the values of **A** from **range2**. The rules for use of this template are as follows:

- The size of **range2** must be equal the size of **range1**.
- If **B** did not exist before this statement was implemented, it is zero filled where assignments were not explicitly made.
- If **B** did exist before this statement, the values not directly assigned in **range1** remain unchanged.

To obtain a grasp of these ideas, you should work carefully through the exercise below and study the explanatory notes that follow:

```
 ➤  Build and execute a script containing the following commands:

clear                          % Note 1
clc
A = [2 5 7 1 3 4];
odds = 1:2:length(A);          % Note 2
                               % Note 3
disp('odd values of A using predefined indices')
A(odds)                        % Note 4
disp('odd values of A using anonymous indices')
A(1:2:end)                     % Note 5
disp('put evens into odd values in a new array')
B(odds) = A(2:2:end)           % Note 6
disp('set the even values in B to 99')
B(2:2:end) = 99                % Note 7
disp('find the small values in A')
small = A < 4                  % Note 8
disp('add 10 to the small values')
A(small) = A(small) + 10       % Note 9
disp('this can be done in one ugly operation')
A(A < 4) = A(A < 4) + 10       % Note 10
```

Table 12—Vector Slicing Script

➤ You should see the following output in the Command Window:

```
odd values of A using predefined indices
ans =
        2       7       3
odd values of A using anonymous indices
ans =
        2       7       3
put even values into odd values in a new array
B =
        5       0       1       0       4
set the even values in B to 99
B =
        5       99      1       99      4
find the small values in A
small =
        1       0       0       1       1       0
add 10 to the small values
A =
        12      5       7       11      13      4
this can be done in one ugly operation
A =
        12      5       7       11      13      4
>>
```

Table 13—Vector Slicing Results

Notes:

1. **clear** and **clc** should be the first two commands in a script (see Style Points below).
2. When predefining an index vector, if you want to refer to its size, you must use the **length(...)** function.
3. The **disp (...)** function shows the contents of its parameter in the Command window to explain what is seen there. Comments are only visible in the script.
4. Using a predefined index vector to access elements in the vector **A**. Since no assignment is made, the variable **ans** takes on the value of a 3 element vector containing the odd-numbered elements of **A**. Notice that these are the odd-numbered elements as opposed to the elements with odd values.
5. The anonymous version of the previous command. Notice that we can use the word **end** within the vector.

6. Since **B** did not previously exist (a good reason the have **clear** at the beginning of the script to be sure this is true) a new vector is created with 5 elements (the largest index assigned in **B**). Elements in **B** with indices less that 5 that were not assigned are zero filled.

7. If you assign a scalar quantity to a range of indices in a vector, all values at those indices are assigned the scalar value.

8. Logical operations on a vector produce a vector of Boolean results. This is not the same as the line **small = [1 0 0 1 1 0]**. If you want to create a Boolean vector, you must use **true** and **false**, e.g.:

```
small = [true false false true true false]
```

9. This is actually performing the scalar arithmetic operation '**+ 10**' on an anonymous vector of 3 elements, and then assigning those values to the range of elements in **A**.

10. Not only is this unnecessarily complex, but it is also less efficient because it is applying the logical operator to **A** twice.

Style Points:

1. It is a very good habit to begin all scripts with the two lines **clear** and **clc**.
   a. **clear** empties the current workspace of all variables and prevents the values of old variables from causing strange behavior in this script, and
   b. **clc** clears the command window to prevent confusion about whether an output line was caused by this script, or some earlier activity.

2. A wise student would enter a few lines at a time and run each version of the script incrementally, rather than editing one huge script and running the whole thing for the first time.

3. It is very tempting to build large, complex vector operation expressions that solve messy problems "in one line of code." While this might be an interesting mental exercise, the code is much more maintainable if the solution is expressed a step at a time using intermediate variables.

4.4. Examples

4-1 Vector manipulation is an integral part of MATLAB. Do the following exercises to practice your skill.

Notes:

—Do not hard code any of the answers for this problem.

—You cannot use iteration for any of the parts of this problem.

```
vec = [4 5 2 8 4 7 2 64 2 57 2 45 7 43 2 5 7 3 3 6523 3 ...
        4 3 0 -65 -343];
```

a. Create a new vector, **vecA**, that is the same as the vector **vec** except that all of the 2's have been deleted.

b. Create a new vector, **vecR**, that is the reverse of **vec**.

c. Create a new vector, **vecB**, that swaps the first and second halves of **vec**. So **vecB** will contain the second half of **vec** followed by the first half of **vec**.

d. Create a new vector, **vecS**, that contains all of the elements in **vec** that are smaller than 45. The numbers should be in the same order as they were in **vec**.

e. Create a new vector, **vecT**, that contains true wherever **vec** is greater than 10 and false everywhere else.

f. Create a new vector, **vec2**, that contains every other element of **vec** starting with the second element.

g. Create a new vector, **vec3R**, that contains every third element of **vec** starting from the last element and going towards the first element in **vec**.

h. Create a new vector, **vecF**, that contains the indices of every element in **vec** that is equal to 2.

i. Create a new vector, **vecN**, that contains the indices of every element in **vec** that is equal to 2 or 4.Create a new vector, **vecG**, that is the same as **vec** but with every 2 or 4 at odd indices deleted.

4-2 The two lines below are entered at the command prompt:

```
>> x = [ 9 3 0 6 3]
>> y = mod((sqrt(length(((x+5).*[1 2 3 4 5]))*5)),3)
```

What is the value of y?

4-3 Consider the following vector in MATLAB:

```
vec = [1 0 0 0 0];
```

Which of the following will produce an error?

a) `vec(6) = 1;`
b) `vec(4) = [];`
c) `vec(0) = 1;`
d) `vec([4 5]) = 1;`
e) `vec = [[6 [5] vec]];`

4-4 The following commands are executed in MATLAB:

```
a = [3, 7, 2, 7, 9, 3, 4, 1, 6];
```

```
b = [7];
a(4) = [];
vec1 = a==b;
vec2 = mod(a,2)==0;
c = sum(vec1);
vec3 = vec1+vec2;
d = vec3.*a;
vec4 = find(a > 5);
e = a(vec4) + 5;
vec5 = find(a < 5);
f = vec5.^2;
```

Find the values of **c**, **d**, **e** and **f**.

4-5 Which of the following statements are false?

    a) `[a, b] = max([1 2 3;7 8 9])` will return:

               `a = [7 8 9]` and `b = [2 2 2]`.

    b) `max([1 2 3 4 5])` will return 5.

    c) Typing "`max(1)`" at the command prompt will produce an error.

4-6 You are given the following 3 vectors:

```
nums1 = [7 1 3 5 32 12 1 99 10 24];
nums2 = [54 1 456 9 20 45 48 72 61 32 10 94 11];
nums3 = [44 11 25 41 84 77 998 85 2 3 15];
```

Write a script to create the corresponding vectors **newNums1**, **newNums2**, and **newNums3** containing every other element of the original vectors, starting with the first element.

Example
```
numsEx = [6 3 56 7 8 9 445 6 7 437 357 5 4 3]
newNumsEx => [6 56 8 445 7 357 4]
```

Note: You cannot type the numbers directly into your answer; i.e., if you typed:

```
>> newNumsEx = [6 56 8 445 7 357 4]
```

at the command prompt you would receive no credit.

Hint: The solution should look identical for each of the three vectors, with only the names of the vectors changed.

4-7 Write a *single* MATLAB statement that does each of the following:

    a. Creates a plot of the square root of all the odd numbers from 1 to 99. The values on the *y*-axis should line up with the appropriate places on the *x*-axis.

    b. Multiply all the even columns of all the odd rows of a 10×10 array called **A** by 2.

    c. Given a vector **x**, return the number of positive elements in **x**.

4-8 Write the commands that take a vector of numbers, a, and return a new vector b, containing the cubes of the positive numbers in a. If a particular number is negative, then 0 is put in its place.

Example:

`[1 2 -1 5 6 7 -4 3 -2 0]` will produce `[1 8 0 125 216 343 0 27 0 0]`

Hints:

    1. It might be helpful as an intermediate step to create another vector consisting of only 1's and 0's, corresponding to the positive and negative values of a, respectively.

    2. Familiarize yourself with the "pointwise" or "element-by-element" operator in MATLAB.

4-9 You have just been selected to appear on the show Jeopardy this spring. You decide that it might be to your advantage to use MATLAB to generate a matrix representing the values of the questions on the board.

    a. Generate the matrix *jeopardy* that consists of 6 columns and 5 rows. The columns are all identical but the values of the rows range from 200 to 1000 in equal increments.

    b. Next, generate the matrix ***doubleJeopardy***, that has the same dimensions as *jeopardy* but whose values range from 400 to 2000.

Hint: You can use the matrix "jeopardy" to help arrive at your answer.

    c. You've decided to go even one step further and practice for a round that doesn't even exist yet. Generate the matrix ***squaredJeopardy*** that contains each entry of the original jeopardy matrix squared.

4-10 The Taylor Polynomial is a powerful mathematical tool, which helps approximate the value of various functions within a reasonable range of approximation. For example, it helps in the calculation of an irrational number like 'e'.

The Taylor Polynomial of degree n for e^x, for any x, is given by:

$$e^x = 1 + \frac{x}{1!} + \frac{x^2}{2!} + \frac{x^3}{3!} + \frac{x^4}{4!} + \ldots + \frac{x^n}{n!}$$

Using n = 10, write the MATLAB commands below to calculate the value of e^2 (x = 2, in the formula). Your final answer should be stored in the variable *e2approx*. You MAY NOT use iteration.

4-11 You are given a vector **excalibur** of undeterminable length. However, you do know that it has an odd number of elements. **excalibur** is said to be magical if its middle element is a prime number. Write a MATLAB script that will create the variable **sword** that holds the value 'magical' if **excalibur** is magical or the phrase 'just a plain sword' if it is not.

You may use the following functions:

a. `isprime(...)` e.g.: `isprime(3)=1`
b. `floor(...)` e.g.: `floor(3.999999)=3`

5. CONDITIONAL STATEMENTS

5.1. Concepts

To this point, with the exception of the use of logical expressions to select portions of a vector, our program statements have been sequentially executed. However, it is frequently necessary to make choices on how to process a set of data based on some characteristic of that data. We have seen logical expressions that result in a Boolean result—true or false. This chapter will discuss the code that implements the idea shown in Figure 15. In this flow chart form, a set of statements to be executed is shown as a rectangle, a decision point is shown as a diamond, and the flow of program control is indicated by arrows. When decision points are drawn, there will be at least two arrows leaving that shape, each labeled with the reason one would take that path.

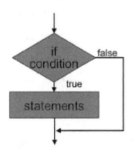

Figure 15—A Simple if Construct

The intention of this concept is to make the execution of a set of statements (frequently referred to as a ***code block***) conditional upon some test. If the result of the test is true, the code block will be executed. Otherwise, the instruction(s) after the end of that code block will be executed next.

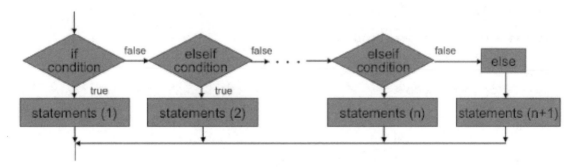

Figure 16—Generalized if Statement

An important generalization of this concept is illustrated in Figure 16. Here, the solution is generalized to permit the first set of statements to be implemented under the first condition as before. Now, however, if that first logical test returns false, a second test is performed to determine whether the second set of statements should be executed. If that test returns false, as many further tests as necessary may be performed, each with the appropriate code block to be implemented when the result is true. Finally, if none of these tests returns true, the last code block—(n+1) in the illustration—is executed. As the diagram shows, as soon as one of the code blocks is executed, the next instruction to execute is that which follows the conditional code.

In particular, if there is no **else** test, it is possible that no code at all is executed in this conditional statement.

There are two common styles in which to implement this conditional behavior. The most general form, the **if** statement, will be discussed first, then the more restrictive, but tidier, **switch** statement. Both implementations are found in most modern languages, albeit with slightly different syntax. In each case, the code block to be implemented is all those statements between the introductory test statement and the next test statement or the end of the conditional.

5.2. If Statements

We consider first the general, language-independent template for the **if** statement, and then its MATLAB implementation.

5.2.1. General Template

Table 14 shows the general template for the **if** statement.

```
if <logical expression 1>
      <code body 1>
elseif <logical expression 2>
      <code body  2>

          .

elseif <logical expression n>
      <code body n>
else
      <default code body>
end
```

Table 14—Template for the if Statement

Notes:
1. The only essential ingredients are the **if** statement, one code body and the end statement. All other features may be added as the logic requires.
2. The code bodies may contain any sequence of legal MATLAB statements including other **if** statements (nested **ifs**), **switch** statements, or iterations (Chapter 6).
3. Nested **if** statements with a code body is an alternative implementation of a logical AND statement.

4. Recall that logical operations can be applied to a vector resulting in a vector of Boolean values. This vector may be used as a logical expression. The **if** statement will accept this expression as **true** if *all of* the elements are **true**.

5.2.2. MATLAB Implementation

Table 15 shows the MATLAB implementation of a typical logical problem: determining whether a day is a weekday or a weekend day. In this case, since each test refers to the same variable, it could also have been implemented as a **switch** statement (see below).

```
if day == 7      % Saturday
      state = 'weekend'
elseif day == 1  % Sunday
      state = 'weekend'
else
      state = 'weekday'
end
```

Table 15—Typical MATLAB Implementation

5.2.3. Logical Expressions

The **if** statement requires a logical expression for its condition. A logical expression is any collection of constants, variables and operators whose result is a Boolean value **true** or **false**[1]. Logical expressions can be created in the following ways:

- The value of a Boolean constant—e.g. **true** or **false**
- The value of a variable containing a Boolean result—e.g. **found**
- The result of a logical operation on two scalar quantities—e.g. **A > 5**
- The result of logically negating a Boolean quantity—e.g. **~found**
- The result of combining multiple scalar logical expressions with the operators **&&** or **||**— e.g. **A && B** or **A || B**
- The results of the MATLAB functions that are the logical equivalent of the **&&**, **||** and **~** operators: e.g. **and(A, B)**, **or(A, B)** and **not(A)**[2]

---

[1] Unfortunately, the MATLAB command window echoes Boolean results as **1** (**true**) or **0** (**false**). In fact, MATLAB will in many ways treat an array of logical results as if they were numerical values.

[2] Beware, however, that whereas you can concatenate the operators—**A && B && C && D**—**and(...)** and **or(...)** only accept two parameters. Concatenation must be achieved by nesting calls—**and(and(A, B), and(C, D))**

• The results of other MATLAB functions that operate on Boolean vectors: `any(...)` and `all(...)`. The result from `any(...)` will be true if any logical value in the vector is **true**. The result from `all(...)` will only be true if all logical values in the vector are **true**. The function `all(...)` is implicitly called by MATLAB if you accidentally supply a vector of boolean values to the **if** statement, as illustrated in Table 16.

```
A = [true true false]
if A
     % will not execute
end
A(3) = true;
if A
     % will execute
end
```

Table 16—Implicit Call to all(...) from the if Statement

5.2.4. Short-circuit Evaluation

When evaluating `&&` or `and(...)`, MATLAB will stop processing the parameters when it finds the first false result (since no other contributions can affect the outcome). Similarly, when evaluating `||` or `or(...)`, MATLAB will stop processing the parameters when it finds the first true result. So it is safe to give the following line of code to the command window:

```
>> if (n ~= 0) && (x/n > 20)
```

One would normally fear that the division would cause a divide by zero error. However, since the test for zero occurs first, if this test returns false (n is zero), short-circuit evaluation does not attempt the remaining condition.

5.3. Switch Statements

We consider first the general, language-independent template for **switch** statements, and then its MATLAB implementation.

5.3.1. General Template

Table 17 shows the general template for the **switch** statement.

```
switch <parameter>
   case <case specification 1>
      <code body 1>
   case <case specification 2>
      <code body 2>
 .

 .

   case <case specification n>
      <code body n>
   otherwise
      <default code body>
end
```

Table 17—Generalized `switch` Template

Notes:

1. All tests refer to the value of the same parameter.
2. **case** specifications may be either a single value or a set of parameters enclosed in braces { .. }[3].
3. **otherwise** specifies the code block to be executed when none of the case values apply.
4. The code bodies may contain any sequence of legal MATLAB statements including other **if** statements (nested **ifs**), **switch** statements, or iterations.

5.3.2. MATLAB Implementation

Table 18 shows the MATLAB implementation of a typical logical problem: determining the number of days in a month. It assumes the value of **month** is 1 .. 12, and **leapYear** is a Boolean variable identifying the current year as a leap year.

```
switch month            % Note 1
   case {9, 4, 6, 11}    % Note 2
      % Sept, Apr, June, Nov
      days = 30;         % Note 3
   case 2                % Feb
      if leapYear        % Note 4
            days = 29;
```

Table 18—Typical MATLAB `switch` implementation *(Continued)*

---

[3] This is actually in the form of a cell array (see Chapter 8).

```
        else
                days = 28;
        end
    otherwise
        days = 31;
end
```

Table 18—Typical MATLAB `switch` Implementation *(Continued)*

Notes:
1. All tests refer to the value of the variable `month`.
2. This `case` specification is a cell array of the months with 30 days.
3. The code bodies extend from the `case` statement to the next control statement (`case`, `otherwise` or `end`).
4. This code body contains an `if` statement to deal with the February case.

Style Points:
1. The use of indentation is not required in MATLAB, and has no significance whatsoever with regard to syntax. However, the appropriate use of indentation greatly improves the legibility of code, and we strongly encourage it. You have probably already noted that in addition to colorizing control statements, the MATLAB text editor automatically places the control statements in the indented positions illustrated above.
2. It is good practice to include `otherwise` in a `switch` statement to trap illegal values entering the switch. The `otherwise` clause should not be used in the main thread of your program unless you are confident that it is safe to use for all incoming values.
3. As noted above, MATLAB will treat an array **A** containing Boolean values as if it contained numbers. It is good practice, however, if this is your intention, to cast **A** to the number type you expect to use (e.g. `double(A)`) to remind you of this logical transition.

5.4. Examples

5-1 Considering the following script

```
a = 1;
b = 2;
c = 3;
if ( ( b * c ) == a )
        a = 5;
else
        a = b + c;
end
b = a + (c^2);
```

What is the value of b after this is run?

5-2 Which of the following evaluates to a Boolean **true**?

a. `( 5 > 4 ) & ( ( 8 + 4 ) < 11 )`
b. `~( ( ( 6 + 4 * 3 ) > 20 ) )`
c. `~( ( 4 ~= 4 ) | (~( 6 < ( 4 * 2 / 8 + 4 ) ) ) )`

5-3 You are given the following information: `A = true`, `B = false`.
Evaluate:

a. `(A && B) || (A && B)`
b. `(A || B) && (A || B)`
c. `(~(A || B)) || (A && B)`

5-4 You have two Booleans, X and Y. You do not know their values (yet).
What you DO know is the following :

a.   `X && X = false`
b.   `X || Y = true`

What are the values of X and Y?

5-5 Rewrite the following MATLAB expression using if statements in place of the or(`|`) and and(`&`) operators.

```
ans = ((a > b) & (b > 100) ) | ( ~((a < b) & (b <100)));
```

5-6 Write a script that calculates the variable mode, the mode of transport used to travel a certain distance according to the following definition. You are given a variable called distance that represents the distance to be covered in feet. (1 mile = 5280 feet)

```
distance <= 2 miles: 'Walk'
2 miles < distance <= 10 miles: 'Bicycle'
10 miles < distance <= 30 miles: 'MARTA'
distance > 30 miles: 'Delta Airlines'
```

5-7 Rewrite the following MATLAB script using only one if/else statement.
Hint: Use the Boolean operators `&` and `|`.

```
if (b > 30)
      if (a > b)
            ans = 1;
      end
elseif (b < 30)
      if (b > a)
            ans = 1;
```

```
        end
else
        ans = 0;
end
```

5-8 Consider a client who wants you to write a simple script to calculate a GPA. Given a value between **0.0** and **4.0** as input, your script is expected to set the value of the variable **letterGrade** to a string according to this:

$$\begin{aligned}
\text{'A'} \text{ for } 3.5 &\le \text{value} \le 4.0 \\
\text{'B'} \text{ for } 2.5 &\le \text{value} < 3.5 \\
\text{'C'} \text{ for } 1.5 &\le \text{value} < 2.5 \\
\text{'D'} \text{ for } 0.5 &\le \text{value} < 1.5 \\
\text{'F'} \text{ for } 0.0 &\le \text{value} < 0.5
\end{aligned}$$

If the input is not valid, your script should set **letterGrade** to **'NA'**.

5-9 Fill in the blank with one of the choices to make this script evaluate so that b = 6;

```
a = 1;
b = 0;
if _____
   b = 6;
else
   b = 2;
end
```

a. **b && a**
b. **b || ~a**
c. **~b**
d. **~a**
e. **a == b**

5-10 You are given a variable named **sideCount** specifying the number of sides on a geometric figure. You need a string containing the name of the shape according to the value of **sideCount**. Write the instructions to calculate the variable ans using the following table:

Value of sideCount	Value of ans
Less than 3	'Not a shape'
3	'Triangle'
4	'Quadrilateral'
5	'Pentagon'
Greater than 5	'Other'

5-11 You have a friend who has too many clothes to store in a tiny wardrobe. Being a good friend, you offer to help this person decide whether each piece of clothing is worth saving. You decide to write a script that will compute the value of each piece of clothing.

Each piece of clothing has five attributes that can be used to determine its value. The attributes are:

condition, color, price, number of matches, and comfort.

Each attribute will be rated on a scale of 1-5.

Your script will analyze a vector V of length 5 containing the ratings for each attribute. The order of attributes in the vector is:

```
[condition color price matches comfort]
```

The script should calculate a variable value between 0 and 100; 100 represents a good piece of clothing while 0 represents a bad piece of clothing.

The points that should be given for each attribute are:

```
Condition:  1 => 0, 2 => 5, 3 => 10, 4 => 15, 5 => 20
Color:      1 => blue => 12
            2 => red (UGA Colors) => 2
            3 => pink => 15
            4 => yellow (GT Colors) => 20
            5 => white => 12
Price:      1 => 8, 2-3 => 16, 4-5 => 20
Matches:    1-2 => 8, 3-5 => 19
Comfort:    1 => 6, 2-3 => 13, 4-5 =>18
```

Note: If a number other than 1-5 is assigned for one of the attributes, then no points should be given.

5-12 We need a script to compute a normalized class average by the following steps:
   a. Given a vector of test scores, **tests**, we first compute a new vector, **normTests**, which will contain the test scores on a linear scale from 0 to 100. A zero still corresponds to a zero, and the highest test score will correspond to a 100.
      Hint: see the built-in function **max()**
   b. Test this script with:
      tests = [90 45 76 21 85 97 91 84 79 67 76 72 89 95 55];
   c. Add to this script the calculation of the letter grade of the class average:

```
     average>90 => A
  80<=average<90 => B
```

```
70<=average<80 => C
60<=average<70 => D
    average<60 => F
```

d. Test your script with the following grade vectors:

```
[70 87 95 80 80 78 85 90 66 89 89 100] -> 'B'
[50 90 61 82 75 92 81 76 87 41 31 98] -> 'C'
[10 10 11 32 53 12 34 54 31 30 26 22] -> 'F
```

6. ITERATION

We now turn to another means of changing the flow of control in a program. The `if` and `switch` statements of Chapter 5 allowed us to decide to skip sets of instructions. The `for` and `while` constructs discussed in this chapter allow us to repeat sets of instructions. Note, however, that the MATLAB language is designed to avoid iteration. Under most circumstances, the array and matrix processing operations built into the language make do-it-yourself loop constructs unnecessary.

6.1. Concepts

Concept: *Iteration* allows controlled repetition of a code block. Control statements at the beginning of the code block specify the manner and extent of the repetition. In principle, there are three styles in which a block of code is repeated. These are commonly referred to as "*test first*," "*test last*" and "*loop-and-a-half*." As the names suggest, test first and test last specify whether you decide to repeat the code block before executing it for the first time or after. Loop-and-a-half refers to the common situation where you are halfway into the execution of a code block before you can really decide whether to repeat the code another time.

Concept: *Traversal* refers to the idea of visiting each element in turn in a collection. The collection we have seen this far is the vector, and iteration is the usual means of traversing arrays in general, and vectors in particular. Later, we will encounter data collections that require different traversal techniques.

6.2. MATLAB Constructs

While there are, in principle, three styles of iteration, MATLAB provides two constructs from which to construct these iterative styles.

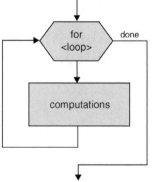

- The `for` loop is generally used to implement "test last" scenarios. It will repeat the computations a fixed number of times, and largely automates the process of managing the iteration.
- The `while` is more flexible in character. The loop can be repeated a variable number of times depending on the values of data being processed. It is much more of a "do-it-yourself" iteration kit, and can be adapted to implement test first and loop-and-a-half scenarios.

Figure 17—Simple for Loop

6.3. For Loops

A simple **for** loop is illustrated in Figure 17. The rhombic shape illustrates the control of repetition. Typically, a variable—the loop control variable—has its value set to each of a range of values in turn. The computations are performed using the current value of that variable. When one set of computations is finished, the variable is automatically changed to the next value. When the range of values specified for the loop control variable is finished, the loop is done and calculations resume at the instructions after the end of the **for** loop.

6.3.1. General for Loop Template

The general template for implementing for loops is illustrated in Table 19.

```
for <variable specification>
    <code body>
end
```

Table 19—General for Loop Template

All of the mechanics of iteration control are handled automatically in the variable specification section. In some languages—especially those with their origins in C—the variable specification is a formidable collection of statements that provide great generality of loop management. The designers of MATLAB, with its origins in array processing, chose a much simpler approach for specifying the variable range, as will be seen below.

6.3.2. MATLAB Implementation

The core concept in the MATLAB for loop implementation is in the style of the variable specification. This is accomplished as follows:

$$\texttt{<variable> = <vector>}$$

where **<variable>** is the name of the loop control variable (e.g. **x**), and **<vector>** is the general specification of a vector (e.g., **A**) by any of the techniques discussed in Section 4.2.2. MATLAB will then proceed as follows:

1. Set the value of **x** to **A(1)**,
2. Execute the code body with that value of **x**,
3. Advance **x** to the next value in **A**, and
4. Repeat steps 2 and 3 until **x** exceeds the range of **A**.

In order to keep the concept simple, the code in Table 20 solves a simple problem that should be done in a single MATLAB instruction: **max(A)** where **A** is a vector of integers between 0 and 100.

However, by expanding this into a **for** loop, we see the basic structure of the **for** loop at work. See the explanatory notes below.

```
A = floor(rand(1,10)*100)  % Notes 1, 2
theMax = A(1);             % Note 3
for x = A                  % Note 4
    if x > theMax          % Note 5
        theMax = x;
    end
end
fprintf('the maximum value in A is %d\n', theMax);
                           % Note 6
%% When executed:
A =
  6 12 6 91 13 61 26 22 71 54
the maximum value in A is 91
>>
```

Table 20—A MATLAB for Loop

Notes:

1. **rand(...)** is a useful means of generating random test data. It produces an array of the specified size containing random numbers between 0 and 1.
2. Since we wanted integers between 0 and 100, we multiplied this whole vector by 100, and then used the function **floor(...)** to remove the fractional part.
3. The tidiest way to find limits of a collection of numbers is to seed the result with the first number. This avoids the problem of seeding the result with a value that is already outside the range of the vector. For example, we might think that **theMax = 0;** would be a satisfactory seed. However, this would not do well if all the elements of **A** were negative.
4. The loop control mechanism as described above.
5. The code body extends from the **for** statement to the associated **end** statement. The code will be executed the same number of times as the length of **A** *even if you change the value of* **x** *within the code body*[1]. At each iteration, the value of **x** will be set to the appropriate element from the array **A**.
6. The **fprintf(...)** function is a very flexible means of formatting output to the command window. See Section 12.2.5 for a full description.

---

[1] This sets the MATLAB for loop apart from the C based for loop implementations where the loop control variable is treated more like an actual local variable.

6.3.3. Indexing Implementation

The above for loop implementation may seem very strange to those with a C based language background in which the loop control variable is usually an index into the array being traversed rather than an element from that array. In order to illustrate the difference, we will adapt the code from Table 20 to solve a slightly different problem that actually approximates more precisely the behavior of **max(A)**. This time, we need to know not only the maximum value in the array, but also its index. This requires that we resort to indexing the array in a more conventional style. See the explanatory notes below.

```
A = floor(rand(1,10)*100)
theMax = A(1);
theIndex = 1;              % Note 1
for index = 1:length(A)    % Note 2
    x = A(index);          % Note 3
    if x > theMax
        theMax = x;
        theIndex = index;  % Note 4
    end
end
fprintf('the max value in A is %d at %d\n', ...
            theMax, theIndex);
                           % Note 5
%% When executed:
A =
  6 12 6 91 13 61 26 22 71 54
the max value in A is 91 at 4
>>
```

Notes:

1. We initialize the index result in case **A(1)** is the largest value.
2. We create an anonymous vector of indices with the same length as **A** and then traverse that vector.
3. We then extract the appropriate element from **A** to operate with it as before.
4. In addition to saving the new max value, we also save the index where it occurs.
5. This is the first occurrence of an example where a logical line of code extends beyond the physical limitations of a single line. Since MATLAB uses the end of the line to indicate the end of an operation, we need the ellipses (. . .) to specify that the logic is continued onto the next line.

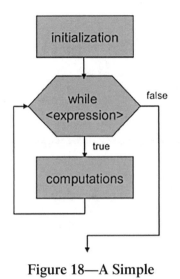

Figure 18—A Simple while Loop

6.4. While Loops

We use while in general for more control over the number of times the iteration is repeated. Figure 18 illustrates the control flow for a while loop. Since the test is performed before the loop is entered, the loop control expression must be initialized to a state that will normally permit loop entry. Exceptions to this might occur if, for example, there were no data at all to process.

6.4.1. General while Template

The general template for implementing while loops is illustrated in Table 21. Since the logical expression controlling the iteration is testing some state of the workspace, two things that were automatic in the **for** loop must be manually accomplished with the **while** loop: initializing the test, and updating the workspace so that the test will eventually fail and the iteration will stop.

```
<initialization>
while <logical expression>
        <code body>    % must make some changes
                % to enable the loop to terminate
end
```

Table 21—General while Template

6.4.2. MATLAB while Loop Implementation

For the sake of consistency, we will again solve the same problem, this time using the **while** syntax.

```
A = floor(rand(1,10)*100)
theMax = A(1);
theIndex = 1;
index = 1;                % Note 1
while index <= length(A)  % Note 2
    x = A(index);
```
(Continued)

Table 22—MATLAB while Loop Code

```
    if x > theMax
        theMax = x;
        theIndex = index;
    end
    index = index + 1;      % Note 3
end
fprintf('the max value in A is %d at %d\n', ...
            theMax, theIndex);
```

➤ `%% When executed:`

```
A =
  6 12 6 91 13 61 26 22 71 54
the max value in A is 91 at 4
>>
```

Table 22—MATLAB `while` Loop Code *(Continued)*

Notes:
1. We initialize the index value since this is manually updated.
2. This test will fail immediately if the vector A is empty.
3. We manually update the index to move the loop closer to finishing.

6.4.3. MATLAB loop-and-a-half Implementation

Here, we turn to a different problem to illustrate the implementation of the loop-and-a-half iteration style. We will continually ask the user for the radius of a circle until he enters a zero radius, which will be our cue to terminate the iteration. For each radius entered, we want to display the area and circumference of the circle.

```
R = 1;                                  % Note 1
while R > 0                             % Note 2
    R = input('Enter a radius: '); % Note 3
    if R > 0                            % Note 4
        area = pi * R^2;
        circum = 2 * pi * R;
        fprintf('area = %f; circum = %f\n', ...
            area, circum);
    end
end                                             (Continued)
```

```
➢   %% When executed:
```

```
Enter a radius: 4
area = 50.265482; circum = 25.132741
Enter a radius: 3
area = 28.274334; circum = 18.849556
Enter a radius: 100
area = 31415.926536; circum = 628.318531
Enter a radius: 0
>>
```

Notes:

1. Initialize the radius value since this is manually updated.
2. This test will never fail so you can ask the user at least once.
3. The **input(...)** function shows the user the text string, translates what is typed and stores the result in the variable provided.
4. You only want to present the area and circumference if the radius is positive.

Style Points:

1. The use of indentation is not required in MATLAB, and has no significance whatsoever with regard to syntax[2]. However, the appropriate use of indentation greatly improves the legibility of code, and we strongly encourage it. You have probably already noted that in addition to colorizing control statements, the MATLAB text editor automatically places the control statements in the indented positions illustrated above.
2. We wrote the for loop examples in two styles: the direct access style and the indexing style. Many people code in the indexing style even when the index value is not explicitly required. To do so is only slightly tacky, demonstrating some ignorance of the full power of the MATLAB language.

6.5. Examples

6-1 Fill in the blanks with **for** or **while**:

A _____ loop can loop forever if the loop variable is not updated. A _____ loop always has an index variable.

---

[2] This is not true of a language like Python where the indentation level actually defines the code bodies.

6-2 What is the value of **k** at the end of the following code fragment?

```
k = 1;
for i = 1:50
    k = k + mod(i,2);
end
```

6-3 How many times will the following loop be executed? Choose the best answer.

```
c =0
i=10;
while i ~= 0
    c=c+i;
    i=i-3;
end
```

6-4 Given below is a code fragment:

```
x = zeros(2*n-1,n);
if mod(n,2) == 0
    for i = 1:n
        x((n - (i - 1)) : (n + ( i - 1)),i) = i;
    end
else
    for i = 1:n
        x(n - (i - 1) : n + ( i - 1), (n - i + 1)) = i;
    end
end
```

What are the results for the following values of **n**?

```
n = 1:
n = 2:
n = 3:
n = 4:
```

6-5 What will be the value of **a** when this script is executed?

```
a = 0;
b = [1 1 0 1 0];
for i = b(1:end-1)
  a = a + ~i;
end
```

6-6 Assume you have the following code block in a script:

```
B = eye(6,6);
for counter = B
```

```
        disp(counter);
    end
```

How many lines are printed when the code is run?

6-7 What is printed when the following code block is run?

```
A = [1 2 3; 4 5 6; 7 8 9];
B = ones(3,3) * 2;
sizeA = size(A);
for pacific = 1:sizeA(1)
    for atlantic = 1:sizeA(2)
        arctic = A(pacific,atlantic);
        while arctic > 1
            B(pacific,atlantic) = B(pacific,atlantic) * 2;
            arctic = arctic - 1;
            if(B(pacific, atlantic) > 100)
                break;
            end
        end
    end
end
disp(B);
```

6-8 Complete the following exercises in iteration. Although you will probably see ways to solve these problems without iteration, you must use it for all these solutions.

a. Iterate through the following vector, **a**, using a *for* loop and create a new vector, **b**, of the same size containing Boolean values. The item in **b** should be **true** if the corresponding item in **a** is positive, and **false** for all other values.

$$a = [-300\ 2\ 5\ -63\ 4\ 0\ 5\ -23\ 46\ 0\ 896\ -230\ .23\ -.01\ 22]$$

b. Iterate through the vector, **a**, using a *while* loop and create a new vector, **c**, containing Boolean values by the same criteria as in section a.

c. Iterate through the following string array, **d**, using a *for* loop and create a new vector, **f**. The item in f should be the character 'A' wherever the corresponding item in **d** is 'G', and 'T' wherever the item in **d** is 'B'. All other characters should not be changed.

d = 'GBBBBBGGBGBGBABGBFBBGGGTGBGBGGBBGGJGGBGKGBLGBGTGGGB'

d. Iterate through the string array, **d**, using a *while* loop and create a new vector, **g**, under the same rules as part c.

e. Iterate through the following logical array, **n**, using a *for* loop and create a new vector, **m**, whose item should be 2 wherever the corresponding item in **n** is true and −1 otherwise.

```
n = [true false false true true true false true...
    false true false false false false true false...
    true false false true true false true true false]
```

f. Iterate through the following array, **z**, using a *while* loop. Replace every element with the number 3 until you reach a number larger than 50. Leave the rest unchanged.

$$z = [1 \ 3 \ 4 \ 5 \ 45 \ 7 \ 3 \ 6 \ 7 \ 8 \ 50 \ 4 \ 64 \ 34 \ 32 \ 56 \ 43]$$

6-9 Now that you are comfortable with iteration, you are going to have to solve an interesting problem. It seems that UGA once again dropped the ball, and forgot the value of pi. You are to write a script that repeatedly asks the user for a number (more on what this number is later) and computes an approximation to the value of pi. The script will stop when the user enters a number less than or equal to 0.

You are going to use the following algorithm based on geometric probability. You have a quarter circle inside of a unit square (the quarter circle has area pi/4). You pick a random point inside the square. If it is in the quarter circle, you get a "hit" and if not, you get a "miss." The approximate area of the quarter circle will be given by the number of hits divided by the number of points you chose.

The number entered by the user is the number of points chosen, and the script computes the approximate value of pi. Try using 1000, then 10000, then 100000 points and see how much closer you get to the value of pi.

Hint: Use the function **rand(...)** in this problem.

6-10 Write a script that transforms a vector **v** by raising each element in the vector to the power of its index and then reversing the order of the elements.

Examples:

```
V = [4 3 -6 5 2] -> [32 625 -216 9 4]
```

7. FUNCTIONS

Functions are an implementation of procedural abstraction and encapsulation. Functions can also be viewed as providing the ability to map its input parameters onto its output values. While we have already made use of some built-in functions by calling them, this chapter will deal with creating and using your own functions.

7.1. Concepts

Procedural abstraction is the concept that permits a collection of instructions that solve a particular sub-problem to be packaged together and referred to collectively rather than individually. This is exactly analogous to the concept of data abstraction in Section 4.1.1 where individual data items are collected together to form a group. We have already used a number of built-in procedural abstractions. All the mathematical functions that compute, for example, the sine of a collection of angles or the max of a vector are procedural abstractions. They allow us to express the need for a computation without knowing or caring about its details.

Encapsulation is the concept of putting a wrapper around a collection that you wish to protect from outside influence. Functions encapsulate the code they contain in two ways. The variables declared within the function are not visible from elsewhere, and its ability to change the values of variables (otherwise known as causing side effects) is restricted to its own code body.[1]

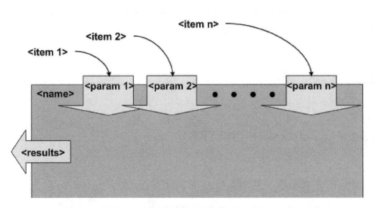

Figure 19—Abstract View of a Function

Mapping is the concept of establishing a relationship between input parameters and output results. For example, a mathematical function like the **sine** function provides a mapping between an angle in radians and the sine of that angle. In this particular case, we refer to the mapping as "one-to-many" because there are many angles that can provide the same sine, but only one sine for a given angle. Other functions like x^N provide a "one-to-one" mapping because each result is achieved by a unique input value. There are rare occasions upon which

---

[1] There are occasions where this restriction is undesirable for some particular variables. MATLAB's global mechanism allows global access to certain variables when they are correctly identified both inside and outside the function.

a function is called upon to produce different results from the same input value—"many-to-one" or "many-to-many" mappings. The various random number generators in MATLAB would be an example of these mappings.

7.2. Black Box View of a Function

The most abstract view of a function can be seen in Figure 19. A function definition consists of the following components:

- A name that has the same syntactic description as a variable name
- A set of 0 or more parameters provided to the function[2], and
- Zero or more results to be returned to the caller of the function[3].

The basic operation of a function begins before execution of the function actually starts. If the function definition requires N parameters, the calling instructions first prepare N items of data from its workspace to be provided to the function. These items may be constants, variables that have been defined, the result of some mathematical operation(s) or the result returned from other functions. When these items have been identified and computed, copies of the values these items are made and assigned to the names of the N parameters the function is expecting[4]. Values are assigned to parameters by position in the calling statement and function definition.

Once the parameter names have been bound[5] in the function's workspace, the function's code body is executed, beginning with the first instruction. If results have been defined for the function, every exit from the code body must return valid values for the results.

7.3. Implementation

7.3.1. General Template

The general layout of a function definition is shown in Table 23.

---

[2] Although the number of parameters is usually fixed, most languages including MATLAB provide the ability to deal with a variable number of parameters.

[3] MATLAB is unique among languages in providing the ability to return more than one result from a function.

[4] This is referred to as "passing by value"—the only technique provided in MATLAB for passing in parameters. Some languages provide an alternative technique: "passing by reference" wherein the storage location for the parameters remains in the caller's workspace. This is usually a bad thing, allowing deliberate or accidental assignments to the name of a function parameter to "reach back" into the scope of the calling function and thereby cause implicit side effects.

[5] i.e., have received a value assignment.

```
<function> <return info> (<parameters>)
<documentation>
      <code body>    % must return the results
```

Table 23—Generic Function Template

7.3.2. MATLAB Function Definition

Table 24 illustrates a typical MATLAB function called **cylinder** that consumes two parameters, the height and radius of a cylinder, and produces the cylinder volume.

```
function volume = cylinder(height, radius) % Note 1
% function to compute the volume of a cylinder
                                           % Note 2
    base = pi * radius^2;                  % Note 3
    volume = base * height;                % Note 4
                                           % Note 5
```

➤   %% When executed:

```
>> help cylinder
  function to compute the volume of a cylinder
>> cylinder(1, 1)
ans =
    3.1416
>>
```

Table 24—Normal MATLAB Function Implementation

Notes:

1. The MATLAB function definition is introduced by the key word **function** followed by the name of the return variable (if any) and the = sign.
2. Comments written immediately after the function header are available to the command window when you enter 'help <function name>'.
3. Although variable scoping forbids access to the caller's scope, the code body still has access to all built-in MATLAB names, e.g. **pi** as used here.
4. You must make at least one assignment to the result variable.
5. The function definition needs no **end** statement. The code body terminates either as the end of the file or at the next function definition in the same file (see below).

7.3.3. Storing and Using MATLAB Functions

All MATLAB functions must be created like scripts in an m-file. When the file is first edited, it must be saved in an m-file with the same file name as the function. The function in the illustration above named `cylinder` must be saved in a file named `cylinder.m`.

Once the file has been saved, you may invoke the function by entering its name and parameters of the right type and number either in the command window, in a script or in other function definitions. If you do not specify an assignment for the function call, it will be assigned to the variable `ans`.

7.3.4. Returning Multiple Results

MATLAB is unique in providing the ability to return more than one result from a function. The multiple results are specified as a vector of variable names: `[area, volume]` as illustrated in Table 25. Assignments must be made to each of the result variables. However, the calling program is not required to make use of all the return values. See the examples below.

```
function [area, volume] = cylinder(height, radius)
                                    % Note 1
% function to compute the area and volume
%                                   of a cylinder
    base = pi * radius^2;
    volume = base * height;
        area = 2 * pi * radius * height;
```

```
    %% When executed:
```

```
>> [a, v] = cylinder(1, 1)          % Note 2
a =
    6.2832
v =
    3.1416
>> cylinder(1, 1)                   % Note 3
ans =
    6.2832
>> a = cylinder(1, 1)               % Note 3
a =
    6.2832
>> v = cylinder(1, 1)               % Note 4
v =
    6.2832
>>
```

Table 25—Returning Multiple Results

Notes:

1. Multiple results are specified as a vector of variable names, each of which must be assigned from the code body.
2. Normal use of the multiple answers is to put the names of the variable to receive the results in a vector. The names may be any legal variable name, and the values are returned in the order of the results defined.
3. If you choose less than the full number of results (or none at all), the answers that are specified are allocated from left to right from the available results.
4. The results are allocated by position and not name recognition. Although we called this variable **v**, it still receives the value of the first result, **area**. If you only wanted the second value, you should make the call something like this:

```
[junk, v] = cylinder(1, 1);
```

7.3.5. Auxiliary (Local) Functions

Since MATLAB uses the name of the file to identify a function, every function should normally be saved in its own m-file. However, there are times when auxiliary functions are needed to implement the algorithm contained in the main function in a file. If this auxiliary function is used in no code body other than one main function, it can be saved in the same file as its calling function after the definition of the main function. By convention, many people append the word **local_** to the name of local functions.

7.3.6. Encapsulation in MATLAB

Encapsulation is accomplished in most modern languages including MATLAB by implementing the concept of variable scoping.

Variable scoping defines the locations within your command window, MATLAB system and m-files to which variables have access. It is related to the current workspace window. When using the command window or running a script m-file, as when you access the value of a variable, the system will reach into your current workspace and then into the MATLAB system libraries to find its current value. This is referred to as *global scope*. When you write a function, its local variables including the internal names of its parameters are not included in your current workspace, and it does not look into your current workspace for values of variables it needs. This is referred to as *local scope* wherein the variables within the function are not visible in global scope, and they are unable to cause side effects by making assignments to variables in global scope.

Style Points:

1. Before you include a function in a complex algorithm, you should always test its behavior in isolation in a script. This test script should validate not only the normal operation of the function, but also its response to erroneous input data it might receive.

2. While any legal MATLAB instruction is permitted within the code body of a function, it is considered bad form (except temporarily for debugging purposes) to display values in the command window.

3. We also actively discourage the use of the `input(...)` function within the code body. If you need to input some values to test a function, do so from the command window or a test script.

7.4. Examples

7-1 Write a function called ***myMin4*** that will take in 4 numbers and return the minimum. You may not use the built-in `min()` function.

Examples:
```
myMin4(1,3,5,7) -> 1
myMin4(8,9,3,4) -> 3
```

7-2 Write the function ***meansAndMedian*** which takes in a vector of numbers, **v**, and returns the arithmetic and geometric means, as well as the median. You can assume that the numbers in **v** are sorted in ascending order.

You may not use the built-in functions `mean()` or `median()`. The geometric mean of **N** numbers is their product raised to the power of **1/N**.

7-3 Write an iterative function called ***factorial*** which consumes a number and returns the factorial of the given number. The factorial of a number can be found using the equation:

$$F(x) = x*(x-1)*(x-2)...*2*1$$

Remember the factorial of 0 is equal to 1, and you must protect yourself from negative numbers. Call the function `error(...)` if this occurs.

Examples:
```
factorial(5) -> 120
factorial(0) -> 1
factorial(10) -> 3628800
```

7-4 This example will lead you through the steps to writing and using a function to find the roots of a quadratic equation. The question involves a ball thrown upwards with an initial velocity V. We need to know the times at which it will pass an altitude h.

   a. Set up the problem by writing a script to determine the parameters of the problem.

   b. Write a function ***roots*** that consumes the three coefficients A, B and C that calculates the standard solution for the two roots of a quadratic equation:

$$x = (-B \pm \sqrt{(B2-4\ A\ C)}) / 2\ A$$

   c.   Run and test the script with various values of the velocity and distance.

   d.   Should you do anything special if the roots are complex?

7-5 Your uncle Rico insists that at one time, he could throw a football a quarter mile (1 mile = 5280 ft). Write a MATLAB function called ***howFast*** that consumes an angle in degrees and returns the velocity in meters per second (m/s) that Uncle Rico would need to throw the ball a quarter mile.

    The distance that the ball travels is computed by the formula:

$$d = \left(\frac{v^2}{g}\right)\sin(2\vartheta)$$

where v is the speed the ball is initially thrown, ϑ is the angle consumed by the function, and g is 9.8 m/s2. (1 m = 3.28 ft).

7-6 The United States Postal Service has given you the task of calculating the "check digit" of its zip codes. The check digit is calculated by adding up the digits of the five-digit zip code and seeing what would have to be added to the sum to get a multiple of 10. For example, the check digit for the zip code 51220 would be 0 (as $5 + 1 + 2 + 2 + 0 = 10$), while the check digit for 82125 would be 2 (as $8 + 2 + 1 + 2 + 5 = 18$).

    Write a MATLAB function called ***checkDigit*** that takes in a vector of zip code digits that range from 0 to 9 and returns the check digit.

    You also need to check that the zip code provided is a valid zip code—i.e., that it is of length 5. If it is not a valid zip code, return -1.

    Examples: `checkDigit([9 8 0 3 4])` should return `6`.

                      `checkDigit([7 2 1 4])` should return `-1`.

7-7 The code for the function ***magicCarpetRide*** is shown below.

```
function answer = magicCarpetRide(x,y,z)
if x && z
    if (x || ~y)
        answer = 'Last night I held Aladdins lamp';
    elseif ~y
        answer = 'Let the sound take you away';
    else
        answer = 'Any place it goes is right';
    end
elseif y||z
    if z
        answer = 'You dont know';
```

```
        else
            answer = 'Right between the sound machine';
        end
    else
        answer = 'Why dont you tell your dreams to me?';
    end
```

What are the values of **A**, **B**, **C**, and **D**?

```
A = magicCarpetRide(1,0,0)
B = magicCarpetRide(1,0,1)
C = magicCarpetRide(0,0,1)
D = magicCarpetRide(0,1,0)
```

7-8 Write a function called *crazyVector* that takes in a vector and two integers (v, m, n) respectively. This function returns a vector containing the mth, $2m^{th}$, $3m^{th}$, etc. elements from the original vector, each raised to the power n.

Examples:
```
crazyVector([2 3 5 6 7 8 3 5 6 7], 2, 3)
                          -> [27   216   512   125   343]
crazyVector ([2 3 5 6 7 8 3 5 6 7], 3, 2) -> [25   64   36]
```

7-9 You are given an array of numbers representing the rainfall amounts for a certain period of time. As an example, consider this array:

```
A = [3   6   -1   11   4   1.2   7   -1.7   5   1.3   -0.001]
```

a. Write a **script** that uses a **for** loop to display each rainfall amount contained in the array **A** on a different line in the Command Window. You may assume that the array **A** already exists in the Workspace, and you may use the **disp(...)** function.

b. You realize there are some negative values in the rainfall data that don't make sense, so you decide to exclude these erroneous values from your calculations. Write a **function** that will compute the average of all the *non-negative* values in the rainfall data array. You must allow for the fact that that there may not be any non-negative values in the array.

c. Add the instructions to test this function in your script.

7-10 A ternary logic system consists of three states: true (1), false (−1), and possibly true or false (0). Ternary expressions can be applied to values in the ternary system in the same manner as Boolean expressions in the binary system. The implementation of the ternary and and or expressions in this system is as follows:

X	Y	tand(x,y)	tor(x,y)
-1	-1	-1	-1
-1	0	-1	0
-1	1	-1	1
0	-1	0	0
0	0	0	0
0	1	0	1
1	-1	-1	1
1	0	0	1
1	1	1	1

   a. Write the function **tand(x,y)** according to the above specification.

   b. Write the function **tor(x,y)** according to the above specification.

   c. Write a test script that thoroughly evaluates the capabilities of these two functions by iterating across all possible values of x and y.

7-11 You work for a chopstick company, and have been appointed to take an overall inventory of chopsticks at every store location. Write a function called **chopsticks** that takes in an array of positive integers representing the number of *individual* chopsticks at each store. Unfortunately, one chopstick isn't very useful, so unpaired chopsticks do not count in the overall inventory. Your function **chopsticks** must return the total number of *complete pairs* of chopsticks in inventory.

Hint: The built-in MATLAB function **mod(x, y)** might be useful.

7-12 Write a function called **replace** that takes in a vector V and returns a modified vector of the same size. The function will replace all values in V greater than 60 with a -1 and all numbers in V perfectly divisible by 10 with the number 10. All other numbers in the vector should be changed into zeros.

Hint: **mod(30,10)** gives the remainder of **30/10**.

Example:
```
replace([0 12 30 50 42 81 10] -> [0 0 10 10 0 -1 10]
```

7-13 You're playing a game where you roll a die 10 times. If you roll a 5 or 6 seven or more times, you win 2 dollars; four or more times, you win 1 dollar; and if you roll a 5 or 6 three or less times, you win no money.

Write a function called **diceGame** that takes in a vector representing the dice values and returns the amount of money won.

Examples:

    diceGame([5 1 4 6 5 5 6 6 5 2]) should return 2
    diceGame([2 4 1 3 6 6 6 4 5 3]) should return 1
    diceGame([1 4 3 2 5 3 4 2 6 5]) should return 0

Note: This function should work for any length vector.

7-14 Write a function called **checkFactor** that takes in two numbers **a** and **b**, and checks if **a** is divisible by **b**. Your function should return **true** if this is true, and **false** if it's not. You may not assume that both numbers are positive.

Examples:

checkFactor(25, -6) should return **false**.
checkFactor (-9, 3) should return **true**.
checkFactor (3, 9) should return **false**.

7-15 We need to generate a strange series of numbers. Here are the steps involved:
   a. Write the function **squares** that consumes a positive integer n, and returns a vector that is the squares of the numbers from 1 to n inclusive.
   b. Write the code for the function **mysteryFunction** that consumes a vector and produces a vector of the same length. Each item in the new vector will be the sum of the corresponding item and its predecessor in the old vector.

Examples:

mysteryFunction(1:5) -> [1 3 5 7 9]
mysteryFunction(squares(12)) ->
                    [1 5 13 25 41 61 85 113 145 181 221 265]

7-16 Coming off a respectable 7-6 record last year, the Georgia Tech football team is looking to improve on that this season. They want you to write a function called **teamRecord** that takes in two parameters—**wins**, and **losses**—and returns two values—**season**, and **wPercentage**.

❑ **wins** = numbers of wins for the season

❑ **losses** = number of losses for the season

❑ **season** = 1 for a winning season, ie. there are more wins than losses

        = 0 otherwise

❑ **wPercentage** = the percentage of games won (ranging from 0 to 100)

Example:
```
[season,wPercentage] = teamRecord(3,9)
season =
   0
 wPercentage =
    25
```

7-17 Write and test a function called ***myFactor*** that consumes a positive integer and returns the prime factors of that integer in a vector. If a factor is repeated then it should be in the vector for each time this factor appears. You may not use the built-in functions **primes()** or **factor()**, but you may use **isprime()**.

Note: The number 1 is not prime, but **myFactor(1)** should return **1**.

Example:
```
myFactor(70) -> [2 5 7]
myFactor(24) -> [2 2 2 3]
```

8. GENERIC ARRAYS

So far, we have used arrays (vectors) containing only numbers. However, we have also had occasion to need collections of a more general nature—to collect multiple values in the switch/case statement for example.

8.1. Concept

Heterogeneous collections permit data of different data types to be stored in a collection. They allow data abstraction to apply to a much broader class of element. The implementation language usually restricts their contents to being any item (object) that can claim to be an instance of some class[1]. The fact that the contents of these collections are generic severely restricts the operations that can be performed on them. However, their utility does emerge in a number of applications.

8.2. Implementation

There are a number of mechanisms for implementing generic collections, as will be seen when we consider dynamic data structures. At this point, we will restrict ourselves to considering generic arrays.

8.2.1. MATLAB Cell Array Creation and Access

In MATLAB, generic arrays are called cell arrays. They are distinguished from numerical arrays by the use of braces—{ ... }—rather than parentheses for index references. Cell arrays are actually arrays of containers. They may be constructed in two ways:

 • By putting a comma separated list of data items between braces:

```
>> A = { 3, [1,2,3], 'abcde'}
A =
    [3]    [1x3 double]    'abcde'
```

 • By assigning values individually to a variable indexed with braces. Consider the following exercises, and study the notes below carefully. They achieve exactly the same result as the example above.

---

[1] In MATLAB, this is no restriction at all since every data item in MATLAB is an object. Some languages like Java do not consider the primitive data types (numbers, Booleans, characters) to be objects, and therefore exclude them from generic collections.

```
>> A{1} = 3                              % Note 1
A =
     [3]                                 % Note 2
>> A{2} = [1 2 3]                        % Note 3
A =
     [3]    [1x3 double]                 % Note 4
>> A{3} = 'abcde'                        % Note 5
A =
     [3]    [1x3 double]    'abcde'      % Note 6
>> A{3}                                  % Note 7
ans =
abcde
>> A(3)                                  % Note 8
ans =
     'abcde'
>>
```

Table 26—Cell Arrays

Notes:
1. Just as we do with number arrays, cell arrays are created "on the fly" by assigning values to an indexed variable.
2. When the values from **A** are displayed, their appearance is different from that of the contents of a number array. Here, the symbology **[3]** indicates that this is a 1×1 array containing the value **3**.
3. A cell array can contain any legal MATLAB object—like a number array.
4. Again, the display shows that the cell array entry is the whole object.
5. Here, we put a character string at index **3**.
6. The display of the character string entry includes the quote marks as a reminder that this is a character string object.
7. You can "reach into" the container of a cell array by using the braces as the index. This is referred to as ***content indexing***. Notice that the result here is the contents of the character string (without the quote marks).
8. It is legal to index a character array with parentheses to retrieve the container and its contents. This is referred to as ***cell indexing***. Notice that the quote marks are back.

8.2.2. Uses for Cell Arrays

There are a number of uses for cell arrays in MATLAB, some of which will become evident in later chapters. For now, these examples will suffice:

· Containing lists of possible values for **switch/case** statements.

```
switch month
   case {9, 4, 6, 11}
        % Sept, Apr, June, Nov
    days = 30;
   case 2                  % Feb
    if leapYear
      days = 29;
    else
      days = 28;
    end
   otherwise
    days = 31;
end
```

Table 27—A switch Clause

· Substituting for parameter lists in function calls. Suppose you have a function **largest(a, b, c)** that consumes three variables and produces the largest of the three values provided. It can be used in the following styles:

```
A = 4;
B = 6;
C = 5;
N = largest(A, B, C)
  N =
       6
cells = { 4, 6, 5 };
N = largest(cells{1:3})
  N =
       6
>>
```

Table 28—Passing Cell Arrays as Parameters

8.2.3. Operations on Cell Arrays

Because cell arrays are permitted to contain objects of any data type, general cell array operations provided by MATLAB are severely limited. The only legal operations on a general cell array are indexing, iteration and slicing. However, if you choose to restrict the contents of a particular cell array, you may perform some interesting operations. For example,

```
>> A = { 3, [1,2,3], 'abcde'}
A =
    [3]    [1x3 double]    'abcde'              % Note 1
>> B = A{1:2}                                   % Note 2
??? Illegal right hand side in assignment.
           Too many elements.
>> A{1:2}                                       % Note 3
ans =
     3
ans =
     1     2     3
>> [a, b, c] = deal²(A{:}))                     % Note 4
a =
     3
b =
     1     2     3
c =
abcde
>> [a, b] = deal(A)                             % Note 5
a =
    [3]    [1x3 double]    'abcde'
b =
    [3]    [1x3 double]    'abcde'
>> B = A(1:2)                                   % Note 6
B =
    [3]    [1x3 double]
>> for i = 1:2                                  % Note 7
s(i) = sum(A{i})
end
s =
     3
s =
     3     6
>>
```

Table 29—Exercising Cell Arrays

---

[2] In general, the **deal(...)** function consumes any number of parameters and makes as many assignments as there are outputs assigned. Check the MATLAB help files for **varargin**, **nargin**, **varargout** and **nargout** to think about the implementation of the **deal(...)** function.

Notes:

1. The same cell array we used above.
2. Slices and content addressing produce some interesting results! Recall that the contents of a cell array are actually considered by MATLAB to be a comma separated list of variables, useful in being passed to a function call (see above).
3. Reinforcing Note 2. Evaluating two comma separated variables results in two separate evaluations.
4. The `deal(...)` function accomplishes what could not be accomplished by simple assignment of cell contents to a single variable (Notes 2 and 3 above). You must provide the cell array contents to the `deal(...)` function.
5. A surprising result of providing the whole array, the equivalent of using cell indexing instead of content indexing.
6. You can slice with cell addressing.
7. Iteration works with content addressing as long as you restrict the contents of the cell array items to objects for which the operation you intend to perform are legal[3].

8.3. Examples

8-1 Given the following code:

```
a{1} = 'My favorite class';
a{2} = 'is CS';
a{3} = 1371;
x = a{1};
y = a{2}(2);
z = a(3);
```

what are the data types of **x**, **y**, and **z** respectively?

8-2 Consider the following code blocks. Decide which will run correctly, and what the output would be.

```
a. a = {3 3 3};
   a(2)*3
```

---

[3] I would like to have claimed here that extending this to look for the third element in A would produce an error. However, when we come to character arrays, we will find that mathematical operations on character arrays are legal—they just produce some very strange results!

b. `x = {4 5 6 7};`
   `y = x{3}*7`
c. `d = 0:3:21;`
   `e = 4234;`
   `f = d(0)*e`
d. `g = 0:6:23;`
   `g`
e. `m = [1 2 ; 2 3]`
   `m(2,2)*ones(4)`

8-3 We need to be able to transform numerical vectors into cell arrays, and cell arrays to vectors.

  a. Write a function called *vecToCells* that converts a vector of numbers into a cell array of strings. Each item in the string will be the value of the cell array as generated by `sprintf(...)` using the format string `'%g'`.

  b. To test this function, build a vector with random length (between 20 and 100) of random numbers in the range (0 .. 1,000,000), and pass this vector to your *vecToCells* function, displaying the results in the Command Window.

  c. Now, write and test a function that accepts a cell array of strings and builds a vector of numbers of the same length. Each item in the output vector will be the length of the strings in each cell array.

8-4 In this exercise, we will use a somewhat artificial cell array to build some fundamental cell array operations. We will use a cell array containing vectors with random sizes and contents, and then process it with a number of standard operations.

  a. Write a function *randomVector* that first generates a random size (between 1 and 5) and then fills a vector of that size with random integers in the range (0:100).

  b. Generate another random number between 5 and 25 that is the size of the cell array, and build a cell array *randVCells* of that size by calling *randomVector* that many times.

  c. Write a function *traverse* that iterates across *randVCells* displaying each vector on a separate line in the Command Window.

  d. Write a function *map* that consumes rvca, a random vector cell array, and produces a new cell array of the same size with each of the vectors in rcva reversed. Test this new cell array with *traverse*.

  e. Write a function *filter* that consumes rvca, a random vector cell array, and produces a new, shorter cell array containing only those cells from the original array whose lengths are greater than 3.

  f. Write a function *fold* that consumes rvca, a random vector cell array, and produces a number that is the total value of all the items in all the vectors in the cell array.

g. Write a function *largest* that consumes rvca, a random vector cell array, and produces the largest vector. The largest vector is that with the greatest length. If two are of equal length, the vector with the greatest sum will be returned.

h. Write a function *search* that consumes rvca, a random vector cell array, and finds the first vector of length 1 (a scalar).

9. STRUCTURES

Structures provide an implementation of data abstraction that is different from arrays. Whereas arrays provide access to the data by index, structures provide access to the data by field name. Structures also have much in common with generic arrays in that they implement heterogeneous collections that may contain different entries of any legal data type. In fact, it is not uncommon for a structure to contain other structures in one or more of its elements.

9.1. The Concept of Structures

Most modern languages implement the concept of a structure in the same way. Structures, like arrays, are collections of data objects. Like the generic arrays of the previous chapter, structures implement the concept of heterogeneous collections—they may contain objects of any data type[1]. Unlike arrays or generic arrays, components in a structure are accessed by field name rather than by numerical index.

9.2. Basic MATLAB Structures

Structures in MATLAB have many uses that we will discuss in later chapters. At the moment, we will consider merely the application where it is useful to store data items by name rather than by numerical index. We first consider a single structure, and then the extension of this idea to an array of structures.

9.2.1. Constructing and Accessing One Structure

An individual structure can be created by assigning values to its individual elements as in the exercise below:

```
   ➤  In the Command Window, enter the following commands:

>> entry.first = 'Fred'                          % Note 1
entry =
    first: 'Fred'
>> entry.last = 'Jones';                         % Note 2
                                                 (Continued)
```

Table 30—Building a Structure

---

[1] We noted that Java does not permit its primitive data types—numbers, characters and Booleans—to be stored in generic collections. However, these data types, together with all Java objects, are permitted in Java structures.

```
>> entry.age = 37;                              % Note 3
>> entry.phone = '(123) 555-1212'              % Note 4
entry =
    first: 'Fred'
     last: 'Jones'
      age: 37
    phone: '(123) 555-1212'
>> entry.phone                                  % Note 5
ans =
  (123) 555-1212
```

Table 30—Building a Structure *(Continued)*

Notes:
1. Storing a string in a structure object named **'entry'** in the field named **'first'**. Note that when the variable entry is displayed, we see each of the fields defined for that structure.
2. Adding a new field name to the same object, also containing a string, but suppressing the variable display.
3. Adding the field **'age'** containing a number.
4. Since phone numbers usually contain punctuation, we could store them as strings. We will see a better way below.
5. We access the value of an individual field with the same dot operator used to store the data.

It is frequently useful to write a function that will assign its parameters to the fields of a structure and then return that structure. Table 31 shows the code for a function that consumes parameters that describe a CD, and assembles a structure containing those attributes by name. Table 32 illustrates the ability to retrieve from a structure a cell array containing its field names, and then how to access the structure indirectly by way of those field names[2].

```
function ans = makeCD(gn, ar, ti, yr, st, pr)
% integrate CD data into a structure
    ans.genre = gn;
    ans.artist = ar;
    ans.title = ti;
    ans.year = yr;
    ans.stars = st;
    ans.price = pr;
```

Table 31—The makeCD Function

---

[2] Essentially, this restores the ability to index items in a structure by indexing the cell array of field names.

```
   >> CD = makeCD( 'Blues', 'Charles, Ray', ...
   'Genius Loves Company', 2004, 4.5, 15.35 )
CD =
     genre: 'Blues'
    artist: 'Charles, Ray'
     title: 'Genius Loves Company'
      year: 2004
     stars: 4.5000
     price: 15.3500
>> flds = fieldnames(CD)                         % Note 1
flds =
     'genre'
     'artist'
     'title'
     'year'
     'stars'
     'price'
>> field = flds{2}
field =
artist
>> CD.(field)                                    % Note 2
ans =
Charles, Ray
>>
```

Table 32—Operating on a Structure

Notes:
   1. The **fieldnames(...)** function consumes a structure and returns a cell array of strings which are the names of the fields in that structure.
   2. You can then access the structure contents indirectly by way of a variable containing the name of the field by putting the variable in parentheses after the field selector character, "."

9.3. Structure Arrays

Very frequently, it is useful to form a collection of data items, each of which contains the same fields of information. MATLAB implements the concept of structure arrays with some interesting properties:

- Like normal arrays or cell arrays, items can be stored and retrieved by their index in the array.
- As structures are added to the array, MATLAB forces all elements in the structure array to implement the same field names. Note: This is a little hazardous when making manual additions to a structure array. A typographical error while entering a field name results in all the structures having that bad field name added. If this happens, you can use the **fieldnames(...)** function to determine the situation, and then the **rmfield(...)** function will remove the offending entry.
- You would normally use iteration to process specific fields in a structure array.

9.3.1. Constructing Structure Arrays

Structure arrays can be created in the following ways:

- Creating values for individual fields, as illustrated in Table 33,
- Using a function to create each individual structure (Table 34 illustrates these concepts by implementing a collection of CDs as a structure array using the function **makeCD(...)** from Table 31), or
- Using MATLAB's **struct(...)** function to build the whole structure array as in Table 36.

Table 35 illustrates the tools for manipulating a CD collection.

9.3.2. Manipulating Structures

Structures and structure arrays can be manipulated in any of three ways:

- using the '.' notation directly with a field name:
- using the '.' notation indirectly with a variable containing the field name:
- using MATLAB's equivalent built-in functions:
  - **nms = fieldnames(str)** returns a cell array containing the names of the fields in a structure or structure array.

```
>> flds = fieldnames(collection)
```

  - **tf = isfield(str, <fldname>)** determines whether the given name is a field in this structure or structure array.

```
>> if isfield(collection, 'price') ...
```

  - **str = setfield(str, <fldname>, <value>)** returns a new structure with the specified field set to the specified value.

```
>> collection(1) = setfield(collection(1),...
         'price', 19.95);
```

- `val = getfield(str, <fldname>)` returns the value of the specified field.

```
>> disp(getfield(collection(1),'price') );
```

- `str = rmfield(str, <fldname>)` returns a new structure with the specified field removed.

```
>> noprice = rmfield(collection,'price');
```

```
>> entry(1).first = 'Fred';
>> entry(1).last = 'Jones';
>> entry(1).age = 37;
>> entry(1).phone = '(123) 555-1212';
>> entry(2).first = 'Sally';
>> entry(2).last = 'Smith';
>> entry(2).age = 29;
>> entry(2).phone = '(000) 555-1212'
entry =
1x2 structure array with fields:
     first
     last
     age
     phone
```

Table 33—Building a Structure Array "By Hand"

```
% extracts from http://www.cduniverse.com/  12/30/04
collection(1) = makeCD( 'Blues', 'Clapton, Eric',...
 'Sessions For Robert J', 2004, 2, 18.95 )
collection(2) = makeCD( 'Classical', ...
 'Bocelli, Andrea', 'Andrea', 2004, 4.6, 14.89 )
collection(3) = makeCD( 'Country', 'Twain, Shania',...
 'Greatest Hits', 2004, 3.9, 13.49 )
collection(4) = makeCD( 'Latin', 'Trevi, Gloria',...
 'Como Nace El Universo', 2004, 5, 12.15 )
collection(5) = makeCD( 'Rock/Pop', 'Ludacris',...
 'The Red Light District', 2004, 4, 13.49 )
collection(6) = makeCD( 'R & B', '2Pac',...
 'Loyal To The Game', 2004, 3.9, 13.49 )
collection(7) = makeCD( 'Rap', 'Eminem',...
 'Encore', 2004, 3.5, 15.75 )
collection(8) = makeCD( 'Heavy Metal', 'Rammstein',...
 'Reise, Reise', 2004, 4.2, 12.65 )
```

Table 34—Building a Structure Array—One Structure at a Time

```
>> collection(5)
ans =
     genre: 'Rock/Pop'
    artist: 'Ludacris'
     title: 'The Red Light District'
      year: 2004
     stars: 4
     price: 13.4900
>> flds = fieldnames(collection)
flds =
    'genre'
    'artist'
    'title'
    'year'
    'stars'
    'price'
collection(5).strs = 0.5;
>> collection(5)
ans =
     genre: 'Rock/Pop'
    artist: 'Ludacris'
     title: 'The Red Light District'
      year: 2004
     stars: 4
     price: 13.4900
      strs: 0.5
>> collection(1)
ans =
     genre: 'Blues'
    artist: 'Clapton, Eric'
     title: 'Sessions For Robert J'
      year: 2004
     stars: 2
     price: 18.9500
      strs: []
>> collection = rmfield(collection, 'strs');
>> collection(1)
ans =
     genre: 'Blues'
    artist: 'Clapton, Eric'
     title: 'Sessions For Robert J'
      year: 2004
     stars: 2
     price: 18.9500
```

Table 35—Using a Structure Array

```
% illustrate the use of the struct(...) function
genres = {'Blues', 'Classical', 'Country' };
artists = {'Clapton, Eric', 'Bocelli, Andrea',...
 'Twain, Shania' };
years = { 2004, 2004, 2004 };
stars = { 2, 4.6, 3.9 };
prices = { 18.95, 14.89, 13.49 };
collection = struct( 'genre',  genres, ...
                     'artist', artists, ...
                     'year', years, ...
                     'stars', stars, ...
                     'price', prices)
collection =
1x2 structure array with fields:
    genre
   artist
     year
    stars
    price
```

Table 36—Building a Structure Array Using the Function struct(...)

9.4. Examples

9-1 The following script is run in MATLAB:

```
team1 = ...
    struct('name', 'Falcons', 'sport', 'Football');
team1.city = 'Atlanta';
team2 = ...
    struct('name', 'Fire', 'sport', 'Football', ...
                                'city', 'Chicago');
team2.record = '2-2';
team2.sport = 'Soccer';
team1 = setfield(team1,'city', 'ATL');
team3 = rmfield(team2, 'record');
team4 = team2;
teams = [team1, team2, team3, team4];
A = isstruct(team2)
B = team(1).sport
C = isfield(team4,'record')
D = team(3).name
E = getfield(team3, 'sport')
```

What are the values of **A**, **B**, **C**, **D**, and **E**?

9-2 The following script is run in MATLAB:

```
GT.Offense = 60;
GT.Defense = 45;
GT.QB = 'Ball';
NC.Offense = 85;
NC.Defense = 65;
NC.QB = 'Durant';
UGA.Offense = 3;
UGA.Defense = 4;
UGA.QB = 'Greene';
football = [GT NC UGA];
football(1).Factor = 2;
football(2).Factor = 4;
football(3).Rank = 5;
[m n o] = football(:).Offense;
[val, posn] = max([m n o]);
c = [];
for i = [3 1 2]
        c = [c football(i).Defense];
        d(i) = (football(i).Offense);
end
a = football(posn).Rank;
b = football(posn).QB;
```

What are the values of **a**, **b**, **c** and **d**?

9-3 You are given an array of structures named **Stats**. Each structure contains the following fields:

Name, BA, HomeRuns, Errors

Write a function named ***MVP*** that takes in that array and returns the most valuable player of the season. The MVP is defined as the player with the highest batting average (**BA**) given he has at least 25 home runs and at most 5 errors.

For example, if the array were constructed thusly:

```
Stats(1).Name = 'Sleepy';
Stats(1).BA = 0.27;
Stats(1).HomeRuns = 19;
Stats(1).Errors = 4;
Stats(2).Name = 'Dopey';
Stats(2).BA = 0.03;
Stats(2).HomeRuns = 2;
Stats(2).Errors = 4;
Stats(3).Name = 'Grumpy';
```

```
Stats(3).BA = 0.46;
Stats(3).HomeRuns = 32;
Stats(3).Errors = 12;
Stats(4).Name = 'Doc';
Stats(4).BA = 0.29;
Stats(4).HomeRuns = 46;
Stats(4).Errors = 0;
Stats(5).Name = 'Happy';
Stats(5).BA = 0.31;
Stats(5).HomeRuns = 27;
Stats(5).Errors = 4;
```

MVP(Stats) should return 'Happy'.

9-4 Suppose we have a **car** structure that has the following fields:

> **basePrice** → a number representing the starting price of the car
>
> **trim** → the style of the car, represented as a string
>
> **cc** → a Boolean variable indicating that the car has cruise control
>
> **dualAB** → a Boolean variable indicating that the car has dual air bags

a. Write a function called **carOptions** that takes in a car structure and returns its final price from the base price and options:

> The standard trim of the car is '**S**'.
>
> If the trim is '**LS**', add $600.
>
> If the trim is '**LE**', add $1200.
>
> If the car has cruise control, add $150.
>
> If the car has dual air bags, add $300.

b. Now, write a function inventory that consumes an array of **car** structures, and calculates the total value of the vehicles.

9-5 You have a structure array of friends. Each structure contains a Name, Age, Gender, Birthplace, and Zip code. An example of this structure might be:

```
techFriend.Name = 'George P. Burdell';
techFriend.Age = 100;
techFriend.Gender = 'Male';
techFriend.Birthplace = 'Atlanta';
techFriend.ZipCode = 30332;
```

Write a **function** named *older* that will take in an array of the above structure type and an age. Your function should return a new structure array containing every friend whose age is higher than the provided age. If none of the friends contained in the structure array meets the age criteria, return the empty vector, **[]**.

9-6 We wish to create a "library" as an array of structures. Each structure has the following fields:
- Title
- Author
- ISBN
    a. Using MATLAB structures, create the first two entries for the "library" structure array, using data of your choosing.
    b. Write a script that will display the titles of all the books in a library structure array. (You should be able to deal with libraries of all different sizes).

9-7 In terms of atomic physics, every electron has four numbers associated with it, called the quantum numbers. These are 'principal' (energy), 'azimuthal' (angular momentum), 'magnetic' (orientation of angular momentum) and 'spin' (particle spin) quantum numbers. Wolfgang Pauli hypothesized (correctly) that no two electrons in an atom can have the same set of four quantum numbers; i.e., if the principal, azimuthal and magnetic numbers are the same for two electrons, then it is necessary that the electrons to have different spin numbers.

Scientists from UGA have come to you to get some assistance with some research they are doing. They ask you to write a function called 'UGAhelper' that takes in two structures. Each structure represents an electron in a hydrogen atom and has the following fields:

❏ prinicipal (this is always > 0)
❏ azimuthal
❏ magnetic
❏ spin

The first three fields are numbers while the spin field is a string with either the value 'up' or 'down'. Your function compares the values in the two structures and checks if they all have the same values for the four fields. If true, you are required to switch the spin of one of the structures (it doesn't matter which one).

You also have to add a field called 'energy' to both structures. The value stored in this field must be $-2.18*10^{18}/n^2$, where n is the value of the principal quantum number for that electron. You have to return both the structures with the energy field added to both, so that the one with the higher energy is first. If the energies are equal, return the one with the 'up' spin first. If both have the same spin and the same energy, the order does not matter.

9-8 It turns out that since you've become experts on rating clothing, Acme Clothing Company has hired you to rate their clothes. Clothes are now structures instead of vectors with the fields (all of which are numbers between 0 and 5):

❏ Condition
❏ Color
❏ Price

❑ Matches

❑ Comfort

a. We first have to convert your old clothing rating system to their model. Write a function *convertGarment* that consumes a vector of clothing values and produces a structure according to the Acme model.

b. Now, write a function *convertClothes* that consumes an array (think of it as a vector of vectors) of clothing assessments and produces an array of Acme clothing structures. Your original data is:

```
clothes = [3 2 1 4 5; 1 5 4 3 2; 5 5 5 5 5; 4 1 3 4 3;
           0 1 0 0 1; 2 2 1 2 ; 2 0 1 4 3; 5 4 3 2 1]
```

c. Acme has a much simpler way of rating their clothes than you used before:

5 * Condition + 3 * Color + 2 * Price +   Matches + 9 * Comfort

Write a script called rateClothes that will add a Rating field and a Quality field to each of the structures in the acmeClothes array. The Rating field in each structure should contain the rating of that particular article of clothing. The Quality field is a string that is 'premium' if the Rating is over 80, 'good' over 60, 'poor' over 20, and 'liquidated' for anything else.

Notes:

You MUST use iteration to solve this problem.

9-9 One requirement for all freshman classes is an issue of a 'Standing' during the middle of the term. The results are either a Satisfactory (S) or Unsatisfactory (U). Since you are the office employee in charge of issuing these grades, you decide to write a function called *standing* to help you. You pull the grade file and discover that the grades are organized like this:

Each student is a single element of a structure array, and each student has two fields: 'name' and 'classes'. 'classes' is a struct itself that contains the letter grade for five classes: 'math', 'science', 'english', 'history' and 'cs'. Grades can be 'A', 'B', 'C', 'D', 'F', or 'W.'

Your function should add two more tier-one fields for each student: 'standings' and 'status'.

· 'standings' should be a string of S's (if grade is A, B or C) and U's (if grade is anything else) for each of the five classes in alphabetical order;

· 'status' should be either 'GOOD' if there are more S's than U's in the standings field, or 'BAD' otherwise.

Your function should take in a structure array and return the same structure array with the two added fields.

9-10 Georgia Tech has added a new award for students that were "almost there" last semester and just missed getting into the Dean's List.

   a. Write a function called ***almost*** that iterates through an array of student structures that it takes in, and returns a cell array of names of those that have a semester GPA between 2.9 and 2.99 (inclusive). The student structure has the following three fields:

   ❑ Name—string (eg.: 'George P. Burdell')
   ❑ Semester_GPA—decimal number (eg.: 2.97)
   ❑ Cumulative_GPA—decimal number (eg.: 3.01)

   b. Write a test script that populates an array of student structures and verifies that ***almost*** is working correctly.

10. PRINCIPLES OF PROBLEM SOLVING

Programming is really all about applying the computer as a tool to solve problems. As we gain more experience with the language, we have more computing tools to apply, and can attack larger, more complex problems. We now have sufficient tools available to consider a more principled approach to data manipulation and problem solving.

To this point, we have explored a few different ways to collect data, and a number of operations that can be performed on those collections. By applying an operation to a data collection, we can take a step towards solving a larger problem. While each solution step can be adapted to solve a range of relatively small problems, more powerful problem solving can be accomplished by assembling solution steps in a logical sequence.

We will first consider the nature of solution steps, and then a technique for assembling those steps to solve larger problems.

10.1. The Character of Solution Steps

First, we document a taxonomy of the operations we expect to be able to perform on collections. Table 37 lists the generic operations, a brief description of each and a discussion of the consequences.

Operations	Description	Consequence
Build **Insert**	Creating a collection from a data source (external file or traversing another collection) usually accomplished by inserting one item at a time	New collection of data
Traverse	Touch each item of data in the collection	Collection is unchanged—frequently used to display a collection, write it to a file or build a collection in a different form
Map	Change the content of some or all of the items in the collection	A new collection of the same length, but the content of some or all items changed
Filter	Removing some items from the collection	A new collection with reduced length, but the content of the items remains unchanged
Fold	Touch the entire collection summarizing the contents with a single result	A single result summarizing the collection in some way (e.g. sum, max or mean)

(Continued)

Table 37—Taxonomy of Solution Steps

Operations	Description	Consequence
Search	Traverse the collection until an item matches a given search criterion and then stop, returning a result	A single result or the indication that the result was not achieved
Sort	Put the collection in order by some specific criterion	A new collection of the same length in order

Table 37—Taxonomy of Solution Steps *(Continued)*

10.2. Summary of Operations

The following paragraphs explain the fundamental operations, using operations on the array of structures used in Section 9.3 as examples. While it is conceivable—in fact, commonly practiced—to combine multiple operations into one computing module, it is poor abstraction, and leads to code that is hard to understand and/or debug. We will discuss below the proper methods for assembling operational steps into larger solutions.

10.2.1. Building

Building a collection is the process of beginning with an empty collection and assembling data elements by inserting them one at a time into the new collection. The size of the collection increases continually until the process is finished. For example, we built the CD collection initially by repeated calls to the **makeCD** method as shown in Table 34. The collection can also be built by applying a custom read function to a text file containing the CD information with the following command:

```
>> collection = readCDs('myCDs.txt');
```

The data file was originally written by traversing a CD collection (see below). The custom function to read the file is illustrated in Table 38.

```
Function CDs = readCDs(filename)
% read a text file describing the CD collection.
% The first line specifies the number of CDs and
% attributes
% The second line lists the attributes
% The third line lists the class of each attribute
% Subsequent lines list the data for each CD,
%   one line per CD
```

Table 38—the Custom CD read Function

10.2.2. Traversal

Traversal involves moving across all elements of a collection and performing some step (not necessarily the same step) on each element. The elements of the collection are not affected. Table 39 illustrates the basic outline for traversing a collection in template form. It assumes that you are doing something with the traversal like writing a file that needs to be initialized and finalized. These two steps may not always be required.

```
<initialize the output>
for item <across the whole collection>
   <operate on the item>
<end of the loop>
<finalize the output>
```

Table 39—Traversal Template

Table 40 illustrates a function to print a selected attribute for all the CDs in a collection to a text file. This function could be invoked with the line

```
>> printCDs (collection, 'artists.txt', 'artist', 's');
```

```
function printCDs(CDs, filename, attrib, type)
% usage: printCDs(CDs, attrib, type)
% print the specified attribute of all the CDs
%    attrib must be one of the attributes as
%                        a character string
%    type specifies the print form to be used
%                        by fprintf
fh = fopen(filename, 'w');
for CD = CDs
    fprintf( fh, ['%s: %' type '\n'], ...
            attrib, CD.(attrib))
end
fclose(fh);
```

Table 40—Printing a Selected CD Attribute

Notes:

1. Since some CD attributes are strings, and some numbers, we have to specify how to display them with a third parameter. This forced us to assemble the format string dynamically to incorporate the data type specifier.

2. Attributes can be accessed indirectly via a variable by putting the variable in parentheses when selecting the structure attribute (`CD.(attrib)`).

For a second traversal example, consider the need to save a collection to a text file after making modifications to the original collection. The function in Table 41 accomplishes this. It is called by the line:

```
>> writeCDs(collection, 'myCDs.txt');
```

Since this function is a little messy, see the following notes for a detailed explanation.

```
function writeCDs(CDs, fileName)
% write a text file with sufficient information to be
% able to retrieve a structure file from it

fh = fopen(fileName, 'w');
attribs = fieldnames(CDs);                      % Note 1
fprintf(fh,'%d\t%d\n',length(CDs),length(attribs) );
for index = 1:length(attribs)                   % Note 2
    fprintf(fh, '%s\t', attribs{index} );
end
fprintf(fh,'\n');                               % Note 3
for index = 1:length(attribs)
    att = attribs{index};
    type{index} = class(CDs(1).(att));          % Note 4
    fprintf(fh, '%s\t', type{index} );
end
fprintf(fh,'\n');
for CD = CDs                                     % Note 5
    for index = 1:length(attribs)
        switch class(CD.(attribs{index}))
          case 'char'
            str = ['"' CD.(attribs{index}) '"'];
          case 'double'
            str=sprintf('%g', CD.(attribs{index}) );
        end
        fprintf(fh, '%s\t', str );              % Note 6
    end
    fprintf(fh,'\n');                           % Note 7
end
fclose(fh);
```

Table 41—Writing to a Text File

Notes:

1. **fh** is called the file handle. When the file is opened successfully by **fopen(...)**, this handle is passed to any **fprintf(...)** call whose output should be directed to that file rather than the command window. Also, recall that **fieldnames(...)** produces a cell array of strings. The first line in the text file will contain the number of CDs and the number of attributes for each CD.

2. The second line in the file will be a tab separated list of the attribute names.

3. The third line will be a tab separated list of strings showing the data type of each attribute.

4. We find the type of any data item from the function **class(...)**.

5. The remaining lines in the file contain the contents of each CD structure. The outer **for** loop traverses the CD structures. The inner **for** loop traverses all the attributes of each structure. The **switch** within the inner loop determines the type of each attribute and how to save that as text[1]. If the type is **char** (a text string that might include spaces), the string is enclosed in quotes ("") so that we can subsequently recover it by using the **%q** format specifier. If the type is **double**, we use the **%g** format conversion to preserve its magnitude as well as possible and produce a string.

6. Each attribute is written as a tab separated string.

7. The new line character terminates the structure.

For a third example, we frequently combine traversal of one collection with building another to transform one collection into the form of another. This is left as an exercise for the students.

10.2.3. Mapping

The purpose of mapping is to transform a collection by changing each of its elements according to some functional description without changing its length. It is distinct from traversal because its intent is to change the data elements. While many languages permit collections to be modified in place, MATLAB always forces you to create a new collection. However, this is still considered mapping. The scalar mathematical and logical operations on vectors are good examples of mapping. Table 42 illustrates the basic outline for mapping.

---

[1] Java programmers will recognize the dilemma of presenting numerical values uniformly. In this section, as we struggle with representing different data types appropriately, we start to wonder whether there should be a way to treat all data types uniformly without caring exactly what they contain. There is: it's called polymorphism. It requires us to use objects instead of raw data, and we will see this in Part III of this text.

```
<initialize the new collection>
for item <across the whole collection>
   <extract the item>
   <modify the item>
   <insert modified item in new collection>
<end of the loop>
<finalize the new collection>
```

Table 42—Template for Mapping

Table 43 shows a function that will add an attribute to all the CDs reflecting the value of each CD as the ratio of the number of stars to the price. Note the use of **eps** to guard against free CDs in the collection. Note also the use of the indexed form of the for loop in order to be able to store the new CD in the new collection. This function would be invoked by:

>> addedCDs = addValue(collection);

```
function newCDs = addValue( CDs )
%   newCDs = addValue( CDs )
% add the value attribute
for index = 1:length(CDs)
    CD = CDs(index);
    CD.value = CD.stars / (CD.price + eps);
    newCDs(index) = CD;
end
```

Table 43—Mapping a CD Collection

10.2.4. Filtering

Filtering involves removing items from a collection according to specified selection criteria. The remaining items in the collection should not be changed, and the collection will usually be shorter than before. Typically, we filter vectors by applying built-in logical operations and then indexing with the results to produce new shorter arrays. Table 44 illustrates the general template for filtering a collection.

```
<initialize the new collection>
for item <across the whole collection>
   <extract the item>
   if <keep the item>
       <insert item in new collection>
   <end if>
<end for>
<finalize the new collection>
```

Table 44—Template for Filtering

Table 45 is the code for a generic function to filter CDs by a given attribute and value. It needs the auxiliary function illustrated in Table 46 to compare two values in a uniform way. It could be invoked by this call:

```
>> noRayCharles = filterCDs(collection,'artist','Charles, Ray');
```

```
function newCDs = filterCDs( CDs, attrib, value )
%   newCDs = filterCDs( CDs, attrib, value )
% get rid of all CDs with the attribute
%                     equalling the given value
index = 1;
for CD = CDs
    if ~valueEq( CD.(attrib), value )
        newCDs(index) = CD;
        index = index + 1;
    end
end
if index == 1
    newCDs = [];
end
```

Table 45—Filtering CDs

```
function ans = valueEq( A, B )
% are A and B equal, regardless of data type?
switch class(A)
    case 'char'
        ans = strcmp(A, B);
    otherwise
        ans = (A == B);
end
```

Table 46—Auxiliary Function to Test for Equality

10.2.5. Folding

Folding is a special case of traversal where all of the items in the collection are touched and summarized as a single result. The collection is not altered in size or value by the operation. Totaling, averaging or finding the largest element in a vector are typical examples of folding. In this case, having gone to the trouble of adding a value attribute, we might want to find the CD with the best value. Table 47 is the generic template for folding a collection. The general form of a fold should be to initialize the summary value and then traverse the whole collection updating the summary.

```
<initialize the summary value>
for item <across the whole collection>
   <extract the item>
   <update the summary value>
<end for>
<finalize the summary value>
```

Table 47—Template for Folding

The function in Table 48 accomplishes this[2]. When the summary involves calculating the maximum or minimum of something, it can be traumatic to choose the right starting value. This function illustrates a neat solution to this dilemma: picking the value of the first item, then comparing that to all the rest. The function would be called by:

$$\text{>> bestCD = bestValue(collection);}$$

```
function theCD = bestValue(CDs)
% find the best value
theCD = CDs(1);
bestVal = theCD.value;
for index = 2:length(CDs)
    CD = CDs(index);
    if CD.value > bestVal
        theCD = CD;
        bestVal = CD.value;
    end
end
```

Table 48—Finding the Best CD

10.2.6. Searching

Searching is the process of traversing the collection and applying a specified test to each element in turn, terminating the process as soon as the test is satisfied. This is superficially similar to folding except that it is not necessary to touch all the elements of the collection—the search stops as soon as an element of the collection matches the search criteria. If the criteria are extremely complex, it is sometimes advisable to perform a mapping or folding before the search is performed. Table 49 is the general template for code to search a collection. There are almost always two exit criteria—finding what you seek, or failing to find it. The while loop therefore needs two logical conditions to continue—you have not found the answer, and have not yet failed to find it.

---

[2] Note that we carefully avoided generality here by not letting the user specify the attribute. Had we permitted this, we would need another type-independent auxiliary function to determine which of two values was greater.

```
<initialize not succeeded>
<initialize traversal>
while <not succeeded and not failed>
   <extract the item>
   if <found criteria>
       <set found true>
       <return result>
   else
       <move on down the collection>
   <end if>
<end while>
<check for failure>
```

Table 49—Template for Searching

Table 50 illustrates the search for a particular CD, using the auxiliary equality test created above. It could be invoked by:

```
>> joshCD = findCD(addedCDs, 'artist', 'Groban, Josh')
```

```
function theCD = findCD(CDs, attrib, value)
% find the specific CD
index = 1;
found = false;
while (index <= length(CDs)) && ~found
    CD = CDs(index);
    if valueEq(CD.(attrib), value)
        found = true;
        theCD = CD;
    else
        index = index + 1;
    end
end
if ~found
    theCD = [];
end
```

Table 50—Searching for a CD

Notes:

1. The use of a **while** loop because we intend to terminate the search at success.
2. There are two possible exits from the **while** loop—when the index passes the end of the collection, indicating failure, or when the CD has been found.

3. If we should exit the **while** loop without finding the CD, we need to return something to the user—null, the empty vector, is usually a good choice. The user can check for this by calling **isempty(...)**.

10.2.7. Sorting

Sorting involves re-ordering the elements in a collection according to a specified ranking function that defined which item "comes before" another. Sorting is computationally expensive. However, if a large collection of data is stable—items are added or removed infrequently—but is frequently searched for specific items, keeping the data sorted can greatly improve the efficiency of the searches. We will devote a later chapter to the details of sorting.

10.3. Assembling Solution Steps

Solution steps are combined in one of two ways—sequentially, or nested. When considering the overall strategy for solving a problem, one might identify steps A and B as contributing to the solution. Your logical statement might say either "do A and then B"—sequential steps—or "for each part of A, do B"—nested steps.

For example, consider the kaleidoscope problem in Section 19.4.1 below. One could generalize the problem and then reconstruct the solution along the following lines:

- A – Build a collection of sub-pictures as follows:
  - ❑ B – For each sub-picture, construct the sub-picture by filtering portions of the overall picture.
- C – Then, traverse the sub-pictures:
  - ❑ D – Map the sub-picture by rotating some number of clicks.
  - ❑ E – Then map the sub-picture by diagonally mirroring.
  - ❑ F – Then map the sub-picture by rotating back.
- G – Then, fold the sub-picture collection back into a single picture.

Diagrammatically, this might look like Figure 20 where the major intermediate steps are collections of sub-pictures before and after the mirroring process.

Figure 20—Assembling Kaleidoscope Steps

11. ARRAYS

In Chapter 4, we saw that a vector is the simplest means of grouping a collection of like data items. We now extend these ideas to include arrays of multiple dimensions, typically confined to two dimensions. Each row will have the same number of columns, and each column will have the same number of rows.

At this point, we will refer to these collections as "arrays" to distinguish them from the "matrices" we will discuss in a later chapter. While arrays and matrices are stored in the same way, they differ radically in the operations one performs on them. Figure 21 illustrates a typical 2-dimensional array A with m rows and n columns, commonly referred to as an m-by-n array.

$$A_{(m\times n)} = \begin{bmatrix} a_{11} & a_{12} & \cdots & a_{1n} \\ a_{21} & a_{22} & \cdots & a_{2n} \\ \vdots & & \ddots & \\ a_{m1} & a_{m2} & \cdots & a_{mn} \end{bmatrix}$$

Figure 21—A 2-D Array

11.1. Properties of an Array

As with vectors, we refer to the individual items in an array as its ***elements.*** These also have the unique attributes combining their value and their position that, in an n-dimensional array, will be a vector of n index values.

When applied to an array **A** with **n** dimensions, the function `size(...)` will return the information in one of two forms.

- If called with a single return value like `sz = size(A)`, it will return a vector of length n containing the size of each dimension of the array.
- If called with multiple return values like `[rows, cols] = size(A)`, it returns the individual array dimension up to the number of values requested. There may be more dimensions than you provide variable storage for.

The `length(...)` function returns the maximum dimension of the array.

The transpose of an m×n array, indicated by the apostrophe character ('), returns an n×m array with the values in the rows and columns interchanged. See Figure 22.

$$
A'_{(n \times m)} = \begin{bmatrix} a_{11} & a_{21} & \ldots & a_{m1} \\ a_{12} & a_{22} & \ldots & a_{m2} \\ \vdots & & \ddots & \\ a_{1n} & a_{2n} & \ldots & a_{mn} \end{bmatrix}
$$

Figure 22—The Transpose of an Array

A number of special cases arise that are worthy of note:

· When a 2-D matrix has the same number of rows and columns, it is called "square."
· When the only non-zero values in an array occur when the row index and column index are the same, the array is "diagonal."
· When there is only one row, the array is a "row vector," or just a "vector" as we saw earlier.
· When there is only one column, the array is a "column vector." Clearly, a column vector is the transpose of a row vector.

11.2. Creating an Array

Arrays can be created from either by entering values directly, or by using one of a number of built-in MATLAB functions that create arrays with specific characteristics.

· As with vectors, you can directly entering the values in an array, using either a semicolon (;) or new line to indicate the end of a row, e.g. `A = [2, 5, 7; 1, 3, 42]`.
· The functions `zeros(m, n)` and `ones(m, n)` create arrays with m rows and m vectors filled with zeros and ones respectively.
· The function `rand(m, n)` fills an array with random numbers in the range .. `1`.
· The function `diag(...)` takes several forms, the most useful of which are `diag(A)` where `A` is an array that returns its diagonal as a vector, and `diag(V)` where `V` is a vector that returns a square matrix with that diagonal.
· Finally, MATLAB provides the function `magic(m)` [1] that fills a square matrix with the numbers `1 to m`^{2} organized in such a way that its rows, columns and diagonals all add up to the same value.

See the examples below.

------

[1] The magic square is an important entity in test design, allowing a designer to optimize tests of linearly related data.

➢ In the Command Window, enter the following:

```
>> A = [2, 5, 7; 1, 3, 42]
A =
    2      5      7
    1      3     42
>> z = zeros(3,2)
z =
    0      0
    0      0
    0      0
>> [z ones(3, 4)]   % concatenating vectors
ans =
    0      0      1      1      1      1
    0      0      1      1      1      1
    0      0      1      1      1      1
>> rand(3,4)
ans =
    0.9501    0.4860    0.4565    0.4447
    0.2311    0.8913    0.0185    0.6154
    0.6068    0.7621    0.8214    0.7919
>> rand(size(A))
ans =
    0.9218    0.1763    0.9355
    0.7382    0.4057    0.9169
>> diag(A)
ans =
    2
    3
>> diag(diag(A))
ans =
    2      0
    0      3
```

(Continued)

Table 51—Constructing Arrays

```
>> magic(4)
ans =
     16     2     3    13
      5    11    10     8
      9     7     6    12
      4    14    15     1
>>
```

Table 51—Constructing Arrays *(Continued)*

11.3. Accessing the Elements of an Array

The elements of an array may be addressed by enclosing the index of the required element in parentheses. In the above example, `A(2, 3)` would return the lower right element, **42**. If one were to attempt to read outside the length of the rows or columns, an error would result.

One may also store values to elements of a vector. For example, `A(2, 3) = 0` would result in the answer

```
        A =
            2     5     7
            1     3     0
```

As with vectors, MATLAB will automatically extend the array if you write beyond its boundaries. If there are missing elements between the current vector elements and the index at which you attempt to store a new value, MATLAB will zero fill the missing elements. For example, `A(4, 1) = 3` would result in the answer

```
        A =
            2     5     7
            1     3     0
            0     0     0
            3     0     0
```

11.4. Removing Elements of an Array

In the same way that we removed elements from a vector, elements can be removed from arrays. However, since the arrays must remain rectangular, elements have to be removed as complete rows or columns. So for example, referring to the array **A** above, if we did `A(3, :) = [ ]`, we would be removing all elements from the third row, and the result would be:

```
        A =
            2     5     7
            1     3     0
            3     0     0
```

Similarly, if we then did **A(:, 3)** = **[ ]**, the result would be:

```
A =

     2     5
     1     3
     3     0
```

11.5. Operating on Arrays

Array operations extend directly from vector operations: arithmetic and logical operations, concatenation and slicing.

11.5.1. Scalar[2] Arithmetic Operations

Scalar arithmetic operations can be performed collectively on the individual components of two arrays as long as both arrays have the same dimensions, or one of them is a scalar (i.e., a vector of length 1). Addition and subtraction have exactly the syntax one would expect, as illustrated in the next exercise. Multiplication, division and exponentiation, however, use the "dot operator" symbols—**.***, **./** and **.^** (the dot is part of the symbol)—for scalar multiplication, division and exponentiation.

➤ **In the Command Window, enter the following:**

```
>> A = [2 5 7
   1 3 2]
A =

     2     5     7
     1     3     2
>> A + 5
ans =

     7    10    12
     6     8     7
B = ones(2, 3)
B =

     1     1     1
     1     1     1
>> B = B * 2
```

(Continued)

Table 52—Scalar Matrix Operations

---

[2] As opposed to matrix arithmetic operations, which will be covered in Chapter 15.

```
B =
     2      2      2
     2      2      2
>> A.*B % scalar multiplication
ans =
     4     10     14
     2      6      4
>> A*B % matrix multiplication does not work here
??? Error using ==> mtimes
Inner matrix dimensions must agree..
```

Table 52—Scalar Matrix Operations *(Continued)*

11.5.2. *Array Logical Operations*

As with vectors, logical array operations can be performed collectively on the individual components of two arrays as long as both arrays have the same dimensions, or one of the arrays is a scalar (i.e., a vector of length 1). The result will be an array of Boolean values with the same size as the original array(s).

```
  ➤   In the Command Window, enter the following:

>> A = [2 5; 1 3]
A =
     2      5
     1      3
>> B = [0 6; 3 2];
>> A >= 4
ans =
     0      1
     0      0
>> A >= B
ans =
     1      0
     0      1
>> C = [1 2 3 4]
>> A > C
??? Error using ==> gt
Matrix dimensions must agree.
```

Table 53—Array Logical Operations

11.5.3. Concatenation

MATLAB permits the programmer to construct a new array by concatenating other arrays as long as each component has the same number of rows:

$$A = [B \ C \ D \ \ldots \ X \ Y \ Z]$$

The result will be an array with that number of rows and a number of columns equaling the sum of the number of columns in each individual item.

```
➤  In the Command Window, enter the following:

>> A = [2 5; 1 7];
>> B = [1 3]';  % the transpose makes a column vector
>> [A B]
ans =
2 5 1
1 7 3
```

Table 54—Concatenating Arrays

11.5.4. Defining Ranges of Indices

As we saw with vectors, indexing is not confined to single elements in an array. We can accomplish indexing using *vectors of indices* in each dimension of the array. These index vectors may either be the values of previously named variables, or they can be created anonymously as they are needed.

We can use the general form of generating a vector of numbers is as follows:

$$\texttt{<start> : <increment> : <end>}$$

including the following:

- The key word **end** that refers to the end of the specific dimension in which it is included,
- the operator ` : ` , that includes all values on that dimension, and
- recall also that a vector of Boolean values can be used.

11.5.5. Linearizing Arrays

We cannot complete a discussion of arrays without revealing one of MATLAB's ugliest secrets. Multi-dimensional arrays are not stored in some nice, rectangular chunk of memory somewhere. Like all other blocks of memory, the block allocated for an array is sequential, and the array is stored in that space in column order. Normally, if MATLAB behaved as we "have a right to expect," we wouldn't care how an array is stored. However, there are circumstances under which the authors of MATLAB needed to expose this ugly secret.

The way this ugliness manifests itself is shown in the following example. One would expect a loud complaint from MATLAB when trying to reference the 11th row of an array with only 3 rows. In fact MATLAB "unwound" the storage of the array, counted down to the 11th entry—3 for column 1, 3 for column 2, 3 for column 3—and then extracted the second element of column 4[3].

➤ **Enter the following in the Command Window:**

```
>> A = [2 5 7 3
        8 0 9 42
        1 3 4 2]
A =
        2       5       7       3
        8       0       9      42
        1       3       4       2
>> A(11)
ans =
       42                        % (sigh!)
```

Table 55—Linearizing Arrays

Style Point:

1. Do not ever—not ever!—make use of this abomination as part of your program logic. It makes the code hideous to look at and/or understand, and is never the "only way to do" anything.

11.5.6. Slicing

The general form of statements for moving sections of one array into sections of another is as follows:

$$\text{B(<rangex1>, <rangey1>) = A(<rangex2>,<rangey2>)}$$

Where each **<range..>** is an index vector as defined above, **A** is an existing array, and **B** can be an existing array, a new array, or absent altogether (giving **B** the name **ans**). The values in **B** at the specified indices are all assigned the corresponding values sliced from **A**. The rules for use of this template are as follows:

---

[3] There is actually a good, practical reason for including this behavior, as illustrated below with the **find(...)** function.

- The sizes of each sliced array must be equal.
- If **B** did not exist before this statement was implemented, it is zero filled where assignments were not explicitly made.
- If **B** did exist before this statement, the values not directly assigned remain unchanged.

To obtain a grasp of these ideas, you should work carefully through the exercise below and study the explanatory notes that follow:

➤ **Build and execute a script containing the following commands:**

```
A = [2 5 7 3
     1 3 4 2];
[rows, cols] = size(A);
odds = 1:2:cols;
disp('odd columns of A using predefined indices')
A(:, odds)                    % Note 1
disp('odd columns of A using anonymous indices')
A(end, 1:2:end)               % Note 2
disp('put evens into odd values in a new array')
B(:, odds) = A(:, 2:2:end)    % Note 3
disp('set the even values in B to 99')
B(1, 2:2:end) = 99            % Note 4
disp('find the small values in A')
small = A < 4                 % Note 5
disp('add 10 to the small values')
A(small) = A(small) + 10
disp('this can be done in one ugly operation')
A(A < 4) = A(A < 4) + 10      % Note 6
small_index = find(small)     % Note 7
A(small_index) = A(small_index) + 100
```

Table 56—Slicing Arrays

Notes:

1. Using a predefined index vector to access the columns in **A**. The `:` specifies that we are using all the rows.
2. The anonymous version of the previous command. Notice that we can use the word **end** within any dimension of the array.
3. Since **B** did not previously exist (a good reason the have **clear** at the beginning of the script to be sure this is true) a new array is created. Elements in **B** that were not assigned are zero filled.

4. Putting **99** into some number of locations in **B**.

5. Logical operations on an array produce an array of Boolean results.

6. Not only is this unnecessarily complex, but it is also less efficient because it is applying the logical operator to **A** twice.

7. The function **find(...)** is occasionally useful for extracting from an array of Boolean data the indices of the true values. However, it cannot produce indices into n-dimensional arrays. In this example, it would somehow have to return {[1,1], [1,4], [2,1],[2,2],[2,4]} in some useable form. So rather than struggle with this, **find(...)** returns a column vector of the index values in the linearized version of the original array, as shown below.

```
   ➢  You should see the following output:
```

```
odds =
     1     3
odd columns of A using predefined indices
ans =
     2     7
     1     4
odd columns of A using anonymous indices
ans =
     1     4
put evens into odd values in a new array
B =
     5     0     3
     3     0     2
set the even values in B to 99
B =
     5    99     3
     3     0     2
find the small values in A
small =
     1     0     0     1
     1     1     0     1
add 10 to the small values
A =
    12     5     7    13
    11    13     4    12
```

(Continued)

Table 57—Array Slicing Results

```
this can be done in one ugly operation
A =
    12     5     7    13
    11    13     4    12
do the same thing with indices
small_index =
     1
     2
     4
     7
     8
A =
   112     5     7   113
   111   113     4   112
```

Table 57—Array Slicing Results *(Continued)*

11.6. Examples

11-1. Given the array A defined as:

$$A = [1 \ 3 \ 2; \ 2 \ 1 \ 1; \ 3 \ 2 \ 3];$$

which of the following commands will produce the matrix below?

$$B = \begin{bmatrix} 3 & 2 \\ 2 & 1 \end{bmatrix}$$

a.   B = [A(3,2:3) ; A(2,1:2)];
b.   B = [A(3,1:2) ; A(2,1:2)];
c.   B = [A(1,2:3) ; A(1:2,3)'];
d.   B = [A(3,3:-1:2) ; A(2,2:-1:1)];

11-2   Write a function named *fiddle* that consumes a 2-dimensional array A and doubles the size of the array by replicating each item horizontally, vertically and diagonally.

   You should not need iteration to solve this problem.

Example:
```
>> A = [1 4 7; 8 9 3]
A =
     1 4 7
     8 5 3
>> fiddle(A)
```

```
ans =
     1 1 4 4 7 7
     1 1 4 4 7 7
     8 8 5 5 3 3
     8 8 5 5 3 3
```

11-3 Write a function called *machoNumbers* that takes in one array and returns another of the same size. The first number in each row of the array is the "macho" number; it cannot stand to have any larger numbers following it on the row.

It might be helpful to write a function that will compare the first number of each row to all the others and set anything on that row larger than the first number to zero.

Example:
```
>> a = [1 2 3; 5 4 3; 9 10 8]
a =
     1   2   3
     5   4   3
     9  10   8
>> machoNumbers(a)
ans =
     1   0   0
     5   4   3
     9   0   8
```

11-4 Write a function named *rowProduct* that will take in one parameter: a two-dimensional array named **A**. This function will calculate the product of the even values in each row and store that product in a vector. If a row has one even value, the product will be simply that value. If there are no even values, the product is one.

Example:
```
rowProduct([1 2 4; 3 6 9; 0 6 8; 5 7 9])
```
should return: **[8 6 0 1]**

11-5 Write a function called *createMatrix* that does the following:
   a. Takes in a positive integer N that is divisible by *either* two or three.
   b. Create a matrix filled with all the numbers from one to N.
   c. If N is divisible by two, returns a two-column matrix;
   d. Otherwise, returns a three-column matrix.
   e. Returns the filled matrix.

Note: You can use the MATLAB function **rem(x,y)** to check if the remainder of dividing x by y is equal to zero. Also, it doesn't matter if your matrix is in ascending or descending order.

Examples:
```
>> createMatrix(8)
ans =
        8       7
        6       5
        4       3
        2       1
>> createMatrix(9)
ans =
        9       8       7
        6       5       4
        3       2       1
```

11-6 Write a function called **multiples** that takes in an array (of any dimensionality) called **numbers** and a number called **divisor**, and then returns a vector called **multiplesVec** that contains only those elements of **numbers** that are multiples of **divisor**. If there are no elements in the array **numbers** or the resulting vector, your function should return an empty vector.

   Hint: You should not need iteration to solve this problem.

11-7 Write a script to create a multiplication table. This should be a 10-by-10 array where the product of 1*1 is in the upper left square and the product of 10*10 is in the bottom right. See example below.

1	2	3	4	...
2	4	6	8	...
3	6	9	12	...
4	8	12	16	...
...	...	...	...	...

11-8 Write a function called **getMMM** that will take in a matrix of any size, iterate through the entire matrix and return the min, max and mean of all the elements of the matrix.

   Note: Do not use the built-in functions for min, max or mean.

11-9 Write a function *pyramid* that consumes a positive, odd integer **n** and produces a **n** by **(2*n-1)** array containing a pyramid of numbers.

Example:

`pyramid(5)` should produce:

```
[0 0 0 0 1 0 0 0 0
 0 0 0 2 1 2 0 0 0
 0 0 3 2 1 2 3 0 0
 0 4 3 2 1 2 3 4 0
 5 4 3 2 1 2 3 4 5]
```

12. CHARACTER STRINGS

To this point in the text, we have seen the use of character strings that we can store in variables and display in the command window. In reality, we have already seen a significant amount of character manipulation that we have taken for granted. The M files we use to store scripts and functions consist of lines of legible characters separated by an invisible "new-line" character.

For example, a variable containing a numerical value uses an internal representation for efficient numerical computation[1]. However, whenever we need to see the value of that number in the command window, that internal representation is automatically converted into a character string representing its value in a form we can read. Similarly, when we use the `input(...)` function, the set of characters that we enter is automatically translated back to the internal number representation.

This chapter presents the underlying concept of character storage and the tools MATLAB provides for converting data values, for operating on character strings, and for manipulating subsets of the strings.

12.1. Character String Concepts

Concept: Recall that one of the concepts related to the definition of a function in Section 7.1 is the concept of mapping. Here, we will apply that concept to the process of translating a character (like this 'A') from its graphical form to a numerical internal code. *Character mapping* allows each individual graphic character to be uniquely represented by a numerical value[2].

Concept: Character strings can be viewed as a collection of characters that takes two forms:

- An external representation for the human reader consisting of a set of characters surrounded by delimiting symbols such as '**Fred Jones**', and
- An internal representation as a collection of numerical character equivalent values.

Concept: Casting is the process of changing the way a language views a piece of data. To this point, we have dealt exclusively with numbers, and have therefore been unconcerned about languages treating data types differently. MATLAB implements casting as a function with the name of the data type expected. In essence, these functions implement the mapping from one character representation to another. See the following examples.

---

[1] See Appendix Chapter 33 for details.
[2] These values are discussed in Appendix Chapter 32.

```
>> int8('A')
ans =
    65
>> char(100)
ans =
d
>> char([97 98 99 100 101])
ans =
abcde
>> double('fred')
ans =
   102   114   101   100
>>
```

12.2. MATLAB Implementation

MATLAB's external specification of character strings uses the single quote mark (') to delimit character strings, and its editor colorized the resulting string as we have seen, e.g. 'genre'. This satisfies all the requirements except the question of how to include the delimiting quote mark within a string. This is accomplished by doubling the quote mark if it is intended to be included thus: 'don''t do that!'[3].

Internally, character strings are represented as vectors of numbers. Conversion between the internal and external representations is illustrated in Table 58 and the accompanying notes.

➤ Enter the following in the Command Window

```
>> fred = 'Fred'                          % Note 1
fred =
Fred                                      % Note 2
>> a = int8(fred)                         % Note 3
a =
    70   114   101   100                  % Note 4
>> name = char(a + 1)                     % Note 5
name =
Gsfe
>> next = fred + 1                        % Note 6
next =
    71   115   102   101                  % Note 7
```

Table 58—Converting Characters

---

[3] The '' in this illustration is a pair of ' marks, not the ordinary quotation mark ''.

Notes:

1. Single quotes delimit a string to be assigned to the variable **fred**.
2. When a string is presented as a result, the delimiters are omitted.
3. **int8(...)** casts a string to a numerical data type.
4. Results in a vector of the same length as the string containing the numerical mapping of each letter.
5. You can perform any mathematical operation on the vector and use **char(...)** to cast it back to a string.
6. When you apply arithmetic operations to a string, an implicit mapping to the numerical equivalent occurs.

12.2.1. *Slicing and Concatenating Strings*

Since strings are internally represented as vectors, we can perform all the usual vector operations on strings, as illustrated in Table 59.

```
  ➢   Enter the following in the Command Window

>> first = 'Fred'
first =
Fred
>> last = 'Jones'
last =
Jones
>> name = [first, ' ', last]
name =
Fred Jones
>> name(1:2:end)
ans =
Fe oe
>> name(end:-1:1)
ans =
senoJ derF
>>
```

Table 59—Slicing and Concatenating Strings

12.2.2. *Arithmetic and Logical Operations*

As we saw in Table 58, mathematical operations can be performed on the numerical mapping of a character string. If you do not explicitly perform that casting first, MATLAB will do the cast for you, and create a result of type double (not usually suitable for character values). Note that the fact that **char('a' + 1)** returns **'b'** is an accident of the character type mapping.

Logical operations on character strings are also exactly equivalent to logical operations on vectors, with the same automatic casting.

```
   ➤  Enter the following in the Command Window

>> n = 'fred'
n =
fred
>> n > 'g'
ans =
     0     1     0     0
>>
```

Table 60—Logical Operations on Strings

12.2.3. Simple Data Output: The disp(...) Function

We have already seen the use of the **disp(...)** function to present data in readable form in the Command Window. As the illustrations below indicate, it can present the values of any variable regardless of type, or of strings constructed by concatenation. Note, however, that an explicit number conversion is required to concatenate variables with strings.

```
   ➤  Enter the following in the Command Window

>> a = 4;
>> disp(a)
     4
>> disp(['the answer is ', a])
the answer is
>> disp(['the answer is ', int2str(a)])
the answer is 4
>>
```

12.2.4. Simple Data Input: The input(_) Function

There is an equivalent simple function that allows a script to request data values from the user. The function **input(...)** consumes a string, presents that string in the command window and waits for the user to type some data followed by the Enter key. MATLAB then attempts to interpret the data typed in the same way it interprets data typed directly to the Command Window. It uses the first character entered to determine the type of data:

- A numeric character suggests a number.
- A alphabetic character suggests a variable.
- The string delimiter, ', denotes a string.

The remainder of the input is then parsed[4] according to the rules for that data type.

```
         ➤   Enter the following into the Command Window:

>> n = input('Enter a number: ')          % Note 1
Enter a number: 5
n =
     5
>> n = input('Enter a number: ')
Enter a number: fred                      % Note 2
n =
Fred
>> n = input('Enter a number: ')
Enter a number: 1sdf                      % Note 3
??? 1sdf
Error: Missing MATLAB operator.
Enter a number: s1df                      % Note 4
??? Error using ==> input
Undefined function or variable 's1df'.
Enter a number: char(fred - 2)            % Note 5
n =
Dpcb
>> n = input('Enter a number: ')          % Note 6
Enter a number: 'ABCD'
n =
ABCD
>>
```

Table 61—MATLAB String Representations

Notes:

1. MATLAB attempts to interpret the result as a number, or as the name of an existing variable.
2. Although we asked for a number, MATLAB is quite happy to return the contents of the variable **fred** that happens to be a string.

---

[4] 'Parse' is a $5 word meaning "take a character string and extract the information from it based on a certain set of rules."

3. MATLAB distinguishes between a variable and a number by the first digit. Here, the information entered was an illegal variable name beginning with a number. When `input(...)` detects an error parsing the text entered, it automatically resets[5] and requests a new entry.

4. Although this is a correctly formed variable, its value is not known.

5. The `input(...)` function actually treats the string entered as an expression to be evaluated by the same process as MATLAB parses the Command Window entries.

6. If you actually want a string literal entered, it must be enclosed in the string delimiters.

12.2.5. *Complex Input and Output*

MATLAB inherited from the C based languages a powerful set of conversion functions that construct strings from the values of variables, and extract data from strings. They are briefly discussed below. Consult the MATLAB help desk for complete information.

Caution: `fprintf(...)` and `sprintf(...)` are functionally identical to the functions of the same name in C or C++. However, while `sscanf(...)` has the same name as its C equivalent, its MATLAB functionality is very different.

- `count = fprintf(<file>,<format>,<values>)` takes the values provided, formats them as specified in the format string and writes them to the file specified (see Chapter 17) or to the Command Window if that parameter is omitted. It returns the number of characters actually generated. The format specification is a string containing two types of special entry. The `%` character introduces the conversion specification for one of the value parameters, the most common of which are `%d` (integer), `%f` (real) and `%s` (string). The '`\`' character introduces format control information, the most common of which are `\n` (new line) and `\t` (tab).
- `str = sprintf(<format>,<values>)` has the same functionality, but returns a character string in stead of writing to the screen or a file.
- `A = sscanf(<string>, <format>)` takes the given string, decodes it according to the format string and populates a matrix with the resulting data. If the string contains more data than the format command specifies, the format command is repeated.

➢ **Enter the following into the Command Window:**

```
>> a = 42;
>> b = 'fried okra';
>> n = fprintf('the answer is %d\n cooking %s',...
                          a,              b);        (Continued)
```

Table 62—C Based I/O Functions

---
[5] We will see the MATLAB mechanism for achieving this in Chapter 14.

```
 the answer is 42
  cooking fried okra
 n =
      37
 >> s = sprintf('the answer is %d\n cooking %s\n', ...
                              a,              b)
 s =
 the answer is 42
  cooking fried Okra
 >> A = sscanf('42 3.14159 -1','%f')
 A =
    42.0000
     3.1416
    -1.0000
 >>
```

Table 62—C Based I/O Functions *(Continued)*

12.2.6. *Comparing Strings*

Since strings are readily translated into vectors of numbers, they may be compared in the obvious way using the logical operators we used on numbers. However, there is the obvious restriction that the strings must either be of the same length, or one of them must be of length 1, before it is legal to compare them with these operators. To avoid this restriction, MATLAB provides the C style function **strcmp(<s1>, <s2>)** that returns **true** if the strings are identical and **false** if they are not[6].

```
    ➤  Enter the following into the Command Window:
```

```
>> 'abcd' == 'abcd'
      1    1    1    1
>> 'abcd' == 'abcde'
??? Error using ==> eq
Array dimensions must match for binary array op.
>> strcmp('abcd', 'abcde')
ans =
    0                                                    (Continued)
```

Table 63—String Comparison

---

[6] Note this is another digression from the normal behavior of the strcmp function in C that returns –1, 0 or 1 depending on the ASCII alphabet comparison of the two strings.

```
>> strcmp('abcd', 'abcd')
ans =
     1
>> 'abc' == 'a'
ans =
     1     0     0
>>
```

Table 63—String Comparison *(Continued)*

Notes:

1. Whenever a comparison produces a logical vector as a result, you need to use the logical summary functions **all(...)** or **any(...)** to extract the expected single result. If you experiment a little, you will see this is different from **and(...)** and **or(...)**.

2. **strcmp(...)** deals gracefully with strings of unequal length.

12.2.7. Arrays of Strings

Since a single character string is stored as a vector, it seems natural to consider storing a collection of strings as an array. The most obvious way to do this, as in previous examples, has some limitations, for which there are nice, tidy cures built into MATLAB. Consider the example in Table 64. Character arrays can be constructed either

- As a vertical vector of strings all of which must be the same length, or
- Using a special version of the char cast function that accepts a variable number of strings with different lengths, pads them with blanks to make all rows the same length and stores them in an array of character codes.

```
    ➤  Enter the following into the Command Window:

>> v = ['Character strings having more than'
        'one row must have the same number '
        'of columns just like arrays!      ']
v =
Character strings having more than
one row must have the same number
of columns just like arrays!
```
(Continued)

Table 64—Arrays of Characters *(Continued)*

```
>> v = ['MATLAB gets upset'
        'when rows have'
        'different lengths']
??? Error using ==> vertcat
All rows in the bracketed expression must have the
same number of columns.
>>eng=char('Timoshenko','Maxwell','Mach','von Braun')
eng =
Timoshenko
Maxwell
Mach
von Braun
>> size(eng)
ans =
     4    10
```

Table 64—Arrays of Characters *(Continued)*

12.3. Examples

12-1 Write the function **myStrcmp(s1, s2)** according to the specification given by the MATLAB **help strcmp** command.

12-2 Write the function **nthWord(sentence, n)** that consumes a character string containing words separated by blanks and produces the nth word from that sentence.

   Hint: **find(str == ' ')** produces the indices of the spaces in the sentence that separate all the words except the first and the last.

12-3 Write and test a function called ***DNAComplement*** that consumes a set of letters as a character array that form a DNA sequence such as **'gattaca'**. The function will produce the complement of the sequence as follows:

   a <-> t and **g <-> c** (a's become t's, g's become c's, and vice versa)

   so that 'gattaca' would become **'ctaatgt'**.

   Assume all the letters in the sequence will be lowercase and that they will all be either **a, t, g,** or **c.**

   Note: You may be tempted to use iteration for this problem, but you don't need it.

12-4 Write a function called ***firstLetters*** that consumes a string of words and returns an array containing the first letter of each word.

Examples:

```
>> firstLetters('Maybe this thing works as it is supposed to')
>>    ans = 'Mttwaiist'
>> firstLetters('OK')
>>    ans = 'O'
```

You can assume there are no punctuation marks in the input string.

12-5 We need a function called ***anagram*** that consumes 2 character strings and returns **true** if the two are anagrams of each other and **false** otherwise.

An anagram is a word or group of words whose letters can be rearranged to spell another word or group of words.

    a. Write the function ***removeSpaces*** that consumes a character string and returns that same string with any spaces removed.

    b. Write the function ***anagram***.

You can assume all the characters will be lowercase, but you cannot assume there will be only one word.

Examples:

```
>> a1 = anagram('dormitory', 'dirty room') -> true
>> a2 = anagram('yes', 'no') -> false
>> a3 = anagram('cat', 'dog') -> false
>> a4 = anagram('conversation', 'conservation') -> true
```

Hint: Characters each have a numerical value, and you can also make use of the **sort(...)** function.

12-6 Write a function called ***myContains*** that takes in 2 strings. This function checks to see if the second string is a located inside the first string and returns the starting point of that substring. If the substring is not located inside the primary string, the function returns zero.

```
myContains('George Burdell', 'dell') -> 11
myContains('CS1371','131') -> 0
myContains('GaTech', 'GaTech') -> 1
```

Note: Spaces count as a character.

12-7 Write a function called ***tripFlip*** that takes in a string and switches each even-indexed character with the odd-indexed character immediately preceding it.

You must use iteration to complete this problem.

Examples:

```
tripFlip('orange') -> 'ronaeg'
tripFlip('Matlab is cool') -> 'aMltbai soclo'
```

Notes:

    a. Spaces count as characters as well. If the string has an odd numbered length, then the function ignores the last letter.

    b. You may assume that the string length is always greater than one.

12-8   Write a function called *gibberish* that takes in a string of the lowercase characters `'a'` – `'z'` and produces a gibberish word. You get the gibberish word by moving every letter in the word forward six spaces in the alphabet. Also, the alphabet must wrap around so that:

    `a->g, b->h,  ... t->z, u->a, v-> b, w->c, x->d, y->e, z->f`

Hint: You may find the `mod(x,y)` function useful.

Example: `gibberish('buzz') -> 'haff'`

12-9   We need to count the vowels in a character string. Follow these directions:

    a. Write a function called *isConsonant* that takes in a letter of the alphabet. It returns **true** if the letter is a consonant, and **false** if it is a vowel. You can assume that only lowercase letters will be passed into the function, but you should not need to write out all the consonants!

    b. Write an iterative function called *countVowels* that takes in a character string and returns the number of vowels in the array. You MUST use *isConsonant* in this function.

12-10   Write a function called *middler* that consumes a character string that is a complete name and returns a numerical value of 1 or 0 depending on whether there is a middle name or not in the string. If there is a middle name or middle initial in the string, middler should return **true**; otherwise, the function should return **false**.

Examples:

    `middler('George Burdell')` should return **false**,
    `middler('Madonna')` should return **false**, and
    `middler('Pamela Lee Anderson')` should return **true**.

12-11   You have a big problem. In one of your CS courses, your professor decides that the only way you will pass the class is if you write a function for him. All the grades in his class have been stored into one long string of characters like

    `'ACFCABDFACAFBCDAFCBAWCBCBAWDDABWDDCCCFAAB'`

    a. Your job is to write a function called *CrazyGrade* that will take in the long string and flip the grades according to the following specifications:

      ❑ A becomes F

      ❑ B becomes D

❑ C remains unchanged

❑ D becomes B

❑ F becomes A

❑ And for kicks, W becomes Y

Your function should take in a string and return an inverted string. You may assume that the string will only consist of valid letter grades.

Examples:

1. `CrazyGrade('BADDAD')` should return `'DFBBFB'`
2. `CrazyGrade('BAWBAW')` should return `'DFYDFY'`

b. To make matters worse, he wants you to organize this modified grade set (see part a). Write a function called *GradeDist* to bunch together all the similar grades (put all the A's next to each other, B's next to each other, etc.) Then calculate and return the professor's grade distribution. Your function should take in a string and return a string with all similar grades grouped together, along with an array containing percentage values from A's all the way to F's.

Examples:

If there are 15% A's, 16% B's, 33% C's, 16% D's, 16% F's and 4% Y's, GradeDist should return [15 16 33 16 16 4].

Hint: Your header would be: function [anstring dist] = gradeDist(str).

13. RECURSION

Recursion is another technique by which a body of code can be repeated in a controlled manner. In Chapter 6, we saw repetition achieved by inserting control statements in the code (either **for** or **while**) to determine how many times a code block would be repeated. Recursion uses the basic mechanism for invoking functions (methods) to manage the repetition of a block of code. While some problems are naturally solved by iterative solutions, there is a significant number of problems for which a recursive solution is elegant and easily understood.

13.1. Concepts

The implementation of recursion depends on a special kind of stack built into the architecture of the central processing unit (CPU). This is called an ***activation stack***. It enables the CPU to determine which functions are active or suspended awaiting the completion of other function calls. To understand the activation stack, we first consider the basic concept of a stack.

13.1.1. A Stack

A stack is one of the fundamental data structures of computer science. It is best modeled by considering the trays at the front of the cafeteria line. You can't see how many trays there are on the stack, and the only access you have to them is to take a tray off the stack or put one on. So a stack is a collection of objects of arbitrary size with a restricted number of operations we are allowed to perform on that collection. Unlike a vector where it is permissible to read, add or remove items anywhere in the collection, with a stack we are only allowed the following operations:

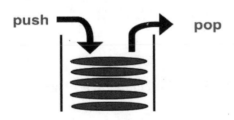

· Push an object onto the stack,
· Pop an object off the stack,
· Peek at the top object without removing it, or
· Check if the stack is empty.

Figure 23—Behavior of a Stack

13.1.2. Activation Stack

The core concept that enables recursive programs to function is the concept of an activation stack. The activation stack is the means by which the operating system allocates memory to functions in an application for local storage. Typically, local storage is required by a function for four reasons:

· Storing the location of the function to be evaluated,
· Storing the location in memory to return to when the function execution completes,

- Storing copies of the function parameter values, and
- Space for the values of any local variables defined within the function.

When the user requests a specific application program, the operating system allocates enough memory to load the executable code, and a block of memory to contain its activation stack (see Section 1.4). When an application calls a function, the above information specific to that function call is assembled into an object called a "stack frame" and pushed onto the activation stack. The calling program is then suspended and control passed to the function specified in the frame on the top of the stack. When that function completes, its activation stack is popped off the stack and destroyed, and control is returned to the frame beneath which is now the top of the stack. If an active function calls another function, this process is repeated. The calling function is suspended, a stack frame is pushed onto the activation stack for the new function call and the new function runs to completion.

13.2. Recursion Defined

Following the logic above, there is no reason in principle why a function could not in fact call itself, and this is the logical basis for recursive programming. Of course, as with iterative programming, if there is no mechanism to stop the recursion, the process would repeat endlessly. In the case of endless recursion, since space is being consumed on the activation stack, the operating system will usually terminate the process when the memory allocated for the activation stack is exhausted.

The canonical illustration of recursion is the computation of a factorial. We could view the calculation of 5! In two ways:

```
5! = 5 * 4 * 3 * 2 * 1
5! = 5 * 4!
```

The second representation is the recursive view that we should examine more closely. In general,

```
n! = n * (n-1)!
```

This definition would not be complete, however, without realizing that this definition must stop somewhere. This is easy with the factorial function because 0! is defined mathematically as 1.

In this example, we see the three necessary characteristics of a recursive function:

1. There must be a terminating condition to stop the process.
2. The function must call a clone of itself.
3. The parameters to that call must move the function towards the terminating condition.

13.3. Recursion Implementation

13.3.1. General Template

Table 65 shows the general template for recursive functions. The words formatted like **`<function>`** are generic constructs that must be replaced by language specific implementations.

```
<function> <return info> <name> (<parameters>)
<documentation>
    if <terminating condition>
            <return> <seed value>
        <else>
            <return> <operation> <name> (<new params>)
        <end>
```

Table 65—General Recursive Template

13.3.2. MATLAB Implementation

In MATLAB, the following general guidelines indicate how the recursive template is implemented:

- The **`<function>`** key word is implemented as the word **`function`**.
- The **`<return info>`** is implemented as "**`result = `**", where the variable **`result`** may be any legal variable name or a vector of variable names.
- The **`<return>`** is implemented as "**`result =`**", where the variable used must match one of the variable names in the **`<return info>`**, and all variables specified must receive a value before completing the function.
- The **`<seed value>`** key word is the value at the terminating condition.
- The **`<operation>`** key word is any mathematical operation that should be performed on the result of the recursive call.
- The **`<new params>`** key word indicates how the parameters to the recursive call change to reflect motion towards the terminating condition.

The MATLAB implementation of the factorial function is shown in Table 66.

```
function result = fact(N)
% recursive computation of N!
    fprintf('fact( %d )\n', N);  % testing only
    if N == 0
        result = 1;
    else
        result = N * fact(N - 1);
    end
%% When executed:
>> fact(4)
fact( 4 )
fact( 3 )
fact( 2 )
fact( 1 )
fact( 0 )
ans =
    24
```

Table 66—MATLAB Listing for Factorial

13.4. Wrapper Functions

Consider the factorial function again for a moment—specifically, ask how you would deal with a user who accidentally called for the factorial either of a negative number, or of a number containing a fractional part. MATLAB is not protected from this programmer error. There are three possible strategies for dealing with this situation.

1. *The legalist approach*, which ignores the negative values, lets the user's program die and the responds to user complaints by pointing out that the documentation clearly indicates that you should not call for the factorial of a negative number. This is not usually the best approach either from the customer relations view, or the technical support effort view, especially since recursive code that hangs up usually crashes with a stack overflow—not the easiest symptom to diagnose!

2. *In-line coding*, where you build into the code a test for N less than zero (or fractional), and exit with a meaningful error message. While this is an improvement over the first choice because it does exit gracefully, the test is in a bad place. Since the function is recursive, the code for that test is repeated as many times as the function is called. While modern computers are fast enough that one would probably not notice the difference, this is in general a poor implementation of a good idea.

3. *A wrapper function,* which is the best solution. You write a function that performs any tests or setup that the recursion requires, and then call the recursive function as a helper to the main function call. Table 67 illustrates this idea as a template, and Table 68 is the MATLAB implementation. The process of announcing an error will be presented in a later chapter. While there is a small computational cost to using a wrapper, it is only executed once rather than each time the recursive function is called.

```
<function> <return info> <name> (<parameters>)
<documentation>
    if <bad condition>
            <announce error>
      <else>
            <return> <local name> (<parameters>)
      <end>
<function> <return info> <local name> (<parameters>)
<documentation>
    if <terminating condition>
            <return> <seed value>
      <else>
            <return> <operation> ...
                        <local name> (new params>)
      <end>
```

Table 67—Template for a Wrapper Function

```
function result = fact(N)
% computation of N!
    if (N < 0) || ((N - floor(N)) > 0)
        error('bad parameter for fact');
    else
        result = local_fact(N);
    end
function result = local_fact(N)
% recursive computation of N!
    fprintf('fact( %d )\n', N);
    if N == 0
        result = 1;
    else
        result = N * local_fact(N - 1);
    end
```
(Continued)

Table 68—MATLAB Implementation of a Factorial Wrapper

```
%% When executed:
>> fact(-1)
??? Error using ==> fact
bad parameter for fact
>> fact(.5)
??? Error using ==> fact
bad parameter for fact
>> fact(4)
fact( 4 )
fact( 3 )
fact( 2 )
fact( 1 )
fact( 0 )
ans =
    24
```

Table 68—MATLAB Implementation of a Factorial Wrapper *(Continued)*

13.5. Tail Recursion

While "normal" recursion is an effective way of using the function call mechanism to manage repetition, it can consume significant amounts of the activation stack. Tail recursion is a technique for accomplishing recursive behavior without consuming activation stack resources. It requires a wrapper function to initialize the recursion, and uses an extra parameter in the function call to carry the emerging result of the recursion.

The driving characteristic of a tail recursive solution is that every exit from the recursive helper function must either return a result, or be a stand-alone call to the recursive helper with no operations to be performed on it. All mathematical and logical operations must occur in computing the new parameters for the recursive call(s). When tail recursion is detected, almost all modern language compilers recognize this situation and construct the executable code to operate in place in the existing stack frame. This avoids pushing unnecessary duplicate stack frames onto the activation stack.

Table 69 is the template for tail recursive processing, and Table 70 is the MATLAB code for a tail recursive version of the factorial function.

```
<function> <return info> <name> (<parameters>)
<documentation>
    <return> <local name> (<parameters>, <init>)
<end>
```
(Continued)

Table 69—Tail Recursion Template

```
<function> <return info> ...
            <local name> (<parameters>, <result>)
   if <terminating condition>
      <return> <result>
   <else>
      <return> <local name> (<new params>, <new res>)
   <end>
```

Table 69—Tail Recursion Template *(Continued)*

```
function ans = fact(N)
% computation of N!
   ans = local_fact(N, 1);
   end

function ans = local_fact(N, res)
   fprintf('local_fact( %d, %d )\n', N, res);
   if N == 0
      ans = res;
   else
      ans = local_fact(N-1, N * res);
   end
%% When executed:
>> fact(4)
local_fact( 4, 1 )
local_fact( 3, 4 )
local_fact( 2, 12 )
local_fact( 1, 24 )
local_fact( 0, 24 )
ans =
    24
```

Table 70—Tail Recursive Factorial in MATLAB

13.6. Mutual Recursion

Recursion is not always accomplished by a function directly calling itself. On rare occasions, the logic of a solution calls for function A to call function B, and then function B calls function A. Of course, at least one of the functions must be seeking the terminating condition.

The canonical example of this situation is a pair of odd/even functions, although there are more direct ways to determine odd and even using the remainder when the number is divided by 2. The function **odd(N)** can test for 0 and 1 to terminate, and then call **even(N-1)**. Similarly, the function **even(N)** can test for 0 and 1 to terminate, and then call **odd(N-1)**.

13.7. Generative Recursion

A discussion of recursion would not be complete without mentioning, but not elaborating on, the concept of generative recursion. Consider a program that models the behavior of a billiard ball rolling on a billiard table and bouncing off the cushions. Does it represent the three basic characteristics of recursion?

- There is definitely a terminating condition in which the ball reaches one of the pockets.
- One could certainly represent the repetitive process of updating the position of the ball as a recursive, even tail recursive function.
- However, is this process always moving towards the terminating condition? In one sense, obviously not, because the ball is sometimes moving away from a pocket and sometimes towards it. In fact, if friction is suitably represented in the model, the ball may roll to a stop without ever reaching a pocket.

In a broader sense, however, I would argue that the ball is approaching the terminating condition to the degree that falling into a pocket is in the future, and as long as time is elapsing in the model, the ball is moving towards the time when it is in a pocket. The fact that physics may intervene and prevent that future event from actually occurring does not detract from the ball's hopeful search for a resting place. There would be two terminating conditions: one with the ball in the pocket, the other with the ball stationary.

So generative recursion is a recursive process in which there is a terminating condition, but the model of the process permits an unsuccessful attempt to achieve that condition.

13.8. Examples of Recursion

13.8.1. Fibonacci Series

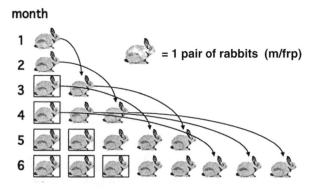

Figure 24—Fibonacci Rabbit Population

The Fibonacci series was originally named for the Italian mathematician Leonardo Pisano Fibonacci who was studying the growth of rabbit populations in the 11th century. He hypothesized that rabbits mature one month after birth, after which time, each pair would produce a new pair of rabbits each month. Starting with a pair of newborn rabbits free in a field, he wanted to calculate the rabbit population after a year. Figure 24 illustrates the calculation for the first 6 months, counting rabbit pairs. It soon becomes clear that the number of rabbits in month **N** comprises the number in month **N-1** (since in this ideal example, none of them die) plus the new rabbits born to the mature pairs (shown in boxes in the figure). Since the rabbits mature after a month, the number of mature pairs that produce a new pair is the number of rabbits in the month before, **N-2**. So the algorithm for computing the population of pairs after **N** months, **fib(N)**, is recursive:

- There is a terminating condition: when **N = 1** or **N = 2**, the answer is **1**.
- The recursive condition is: **fib(N) = fib(N-1) + fib(N-2)**.
- The solution is moving towards the terminating condition since as long as **N** is a positive integer, computing **N-1** and **N-2** will move towards **1** or **2**.

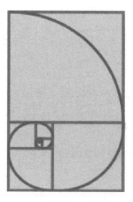 

Figure 25—Fibonacci in Nature

The algorithm produces the Fibonacci series:

1, 1, 2, 3, 5, 8, 13, 21, 34, 55, 89, 144, 233, ... [1]

giving a population after a year of 144.[2]

To the surprise of naturalists, this series of numbers occurs in nature in a remarkable number of circumstances. Consider, for example, Figure 25 where a set of squares placed side by side in a rotating sequence is drawn using the Fibonacci series for the size of each square. The resulting geometric figure is a close approximation to the logarithmic spiral so frequently found in nature, such as the nautilus shell pictured here.

13.8.2. Detecting Palindromes

We might want to determine whether a word or phrase received as a string is a palindrome, i.e. if it is spelled the same forwards and backwards. One could design a recursive function named **isPalindrome(<string>)** as follows:

---

[1] A closely related phenomenon is the golden ratio or golden number computed as the limit of the ratio of successive Fibonacci series values—approximately 1.618034—that has been found to occur in nature wherever articles are packed tidily together. Flower petals and seeds in pods are good examples. Search the Web for Fibonacci for more information on this topic.

[2] Truth in lending laws require me to point out that while computing the Fibonacci series recursively is a very nice, conceptually simple approach, it is a nightmare as far as the computational load on your processor. Do not try to compute beyond about 27 numbers in the series. An iterative solution, while less elegant, runs in linear time rather than exponential.

- The function `isPalindrome(<string>)` terminates if the `<string>` has zero or one character, returning **true**.
- It also terminates if the first and last characters are not equal, returning **false**.
- Otherwise (first and last are equal), the function returns `isPalindrome(<shorter string>)` where the shorter string is obtained by removing the first and last characters of the original string.
- Clearly, since the string is always being shortened, the recursive solution is approaching the terminating condition.

13.8.3. Other Recursive Examples

In future chapters, we will discuss fundamental concepts in numerical analysis, sorting and manipulating trees and graphs where recursive processing is frequently the best, and often the only practical, way to generate the solution.

13.9. Examples

13-1 We will write the recursive function *oddTotal* to solve the following problem: The user will input a positive integer **N**, and your function is expected to add up all the *odd integers* between **1** and **N**.

    a. Identify specifically the three aspects of recursion as they apply to this problem.

    b. Write this function in recursive style.

    c. Write a script to repeatedly ask the user for a number, compute oddTotal of that number if it is positive, or otherwise stop the iteration.

13-2 You know that 'Σ' refers to the function "summation of." For example,

$$\sum_{x=2}^{6} x(x-1) = (2*1) + (3*2) + (4*3) + (5*4) = 40$$

Similarly the symbol 'Π' is used to represent "product of." For example

$$\prod_{x=2}^{5} x(x-1) = (2*1)*(3*2)*(4*3)*(5*4) = 2280$$

    a. Identify specifically the three aspects of recursion as they apply to this problem.

    b. Write a recursive function called **myMultiOf** which takes in **n** and returns **y** evaluated as the following:

$$y = \prod_{x=2}^{n} x(x-1)$$

You may assume that **n** is an integer that is greater than 1.

13-3 Ackermann's Function is "a function to end all functions." The work done by the function ack grows much faster than polynomials or exponentials.

Given the following recursive method:

```
ans = ack(x, y)
      if x == 0
            ans = y + 1;
      elseif y == 0
            ans = ack(x - 1, 1);
      else
            ans = ack(x - 1, ack(x, y - 1));
      end
```

What is the result of **ack(1, 4)**?

Hint: Tracing this on the activation stack simplifies things.

13-4 Starting with the first line below, write a recursive function that takes in a positive integer **N** and displays the following message **N** times without returning anything:

'I love Computer Science!'

Your function *must* utilize numerical recursion for you to receive credit for this problem.

function myRecursive (N)

13-5 Write a function called **GCD** to find the greatest common divisor of two numbers. You must use recursion and no iteration of any kind to solve this problem. Recall that the GCD of m and n is the largest integer that divides both m and n with no remainder. You may assume both m and n will be positive.

Hint: you may need to call a recursive helper function and pass it m, n and a third parameter that is initially the smaller of m and n.

13-6 For this problem you will be required to write three recursive functions—*recurSum*, *recurProd* and *recurFact*.

    a. *recurSum* will take in a vector and compute the sum of the elements of the vector, with the following header:

function ans = recurSum(arr)

    b. *recurProd* will take in a vector and compute the product of the elements of the vector with the following header:

function ans = recurProd(arr)

    c. *recurFact* will take in a number and return the factorial of the number with the following function header:

```
function ans = recurFact(num)
```

13-7   Write a function called **tracker** that takes in a structure and returns the number of levels at which it has a field called **Inner**. Each field named **Inner** can also be structures having a field called **Inner**, but at each level there can be only one field called **Inner**. The innermost structure will not contain a field called **Inner**. You must use recursion. Your function header should be:

```
function num = tracker(astruct)
```

Hint: Use the **isfield** (...) function.

14. EXCEPTIONS

Exceptions are a powerful tool for gracefully managing software errors caused by either programming errors or bad data. The general need for an exception mechanism might best be established by way of an example. Suppose you write a program that requests some data from a user, and then launches on a significant number of nested function calls to perform analysis on the data received. Somewhere in the depths of these function calls, the program calculates the square root of a value, but in this instance that value is negative. While MATLAB will gracefully take the square root of a number and produce a complex number, in this case, this is unacceptable. The cause of this problem is probably bad data entered by the user. However, the effect is discovered deep in the activation stack in the middle of some obscure numerical computation.

14.1. Historical Approaches

Early languages attempted to deal with this problem in one of two equally unpleasant ways:

- Some languages require any mathematical function that might produce an error to return the status of that calculation to the calling function. This did allow errors to be reported and processed, but had two unpleasant consequences. It was using up the ability of a function to return a value, and the writer of any function calling this function had to choose between testing for errors and solving the problem locally, or passing the error condition back to its calling function in the hope that somewhere the error would be dealt with.
- Perhaps worse than this are the languages that want to use a globally accessible variable (say, **ierror**) to report status. For example, if **ierror** were normally set to **0**, an error could be announced by setting its value to **-1**. While this frees the function from needing to return status, it does not relieve the calling function of the need to check and see if the **ierror** value is bad, and either solving the problem or elevating it. Furthermore, if an error does occur within a function, since it is now still returning a value, what value should it return if it is unable to complete its assigned calculation?

14.2. Concepts

Two concepts are necessary to implement the exception mechanism effectively:

- Throwing an exception: Whenever a problem occurs, the operating system is asked to suspend operations at that point in the activation stack and go back down the stack without completing any of the functions looking for a function equipped to handle this specific exception[1]. If no such function is found, the program is terminated and the exception is returned to the operating system.

- Catching an exception: A function able to deal with a specific exception uses a "**try** ... **catch**" construct to identify the suspect code, and resolve the problem. Between try and catch, it puts a code block containing the suspect code. After the catch statement that usually identifies the particular exception to be caught is a code block that should fix the problem.

In the example above, the general template for successfully interacting with the user might be as illustrated in Table 71. The Boolean successful flag will only be set if the data are processed without error.

```
successful = false
while <not successful>
    try
        <request data from then user>
        <process the data>
        successful = true
    catch
        <announce the error to the user>
    end
end
```

Table 71—Illustrating a try ... catch Block

14.3. MATLAB Implementation

MATLAB does not distinguish between the kinds of exceptions that can be thrown.

- To throw an exception, the program calls the **error(...)** function that takes one parameter, a string defining the error. If the exception is not caught, the string provided is displayed in red to the user. If the exception is caught, that string is ignored.
- To handle an exception, the suspect code is placed as the code block between the **try** and **catch** statements. If no error occurs in the code block, the **catch** statement is ignored. If

---

[1] In the Java language, while run-time exceptions are treated this way, the more general types of exception have an additional constraint. A method calling another method that might throw a general exception must either handle that exception by catching it, or must declare in its header that it, too, is capable of generating such an exception.

an error occurs, however, execution is suspended at that point. No further processing is performed, no data are returned from functions, and the code in the closest **catch** block is executed up to the associated **end** statement.

· In more complex situations where this function may not be able to actually handle the error, a further exception can be thrown from the **catch** block. This exception will escape from this **try** ... **catch** block, and must be caught (if at all) by another function or script deeper in the activation stack.

Table 72 illustrates a simple example. The objective is to have the user define a triangle by entering a vector of three sides, and to calculate the angle between the first two sides. The **acosd(...)** function computes the inverse cosine of a ratio. If that ratio is greater than one, there is something seriously wrong with the triangle, and **acosd** returns a complex number. This program detects that the answer is complex and throws an exception.

> ➤ Put the following code in a script and execute it, using the data indicated below.
> ➤ Then, edit the script to remove the try statement and the catch block and repeat the test.

```
clear
clc
OK = false
while ~OK
    try
        side = input('enter a triangle: ');
        a = side(1); b = side(2); c = side(3);
        cosC = (c^2 - a^2 - b^2)/(2 * a * b);
        angle = acosd(cosC);
        if imag(angle) ~= 0
            error('bad triangle')
        end
        OK = true;
        fprintf('the angle is %f\n', angle)
    catch
        disp('bad triangle - try again')
    end
end
```

Table 72—Exception Handling in MATLAB

```
enter a triangle: [3 4 8]
bad triangle - try again
enter a triangle: [3 4 6]
the angle is 62.720387
>>
```

Table 73—Executing the Example

Style Point:

1. Exception processing is for processing events that occur outside the normal thread of execution. While it may be tempting at times to use the exception mechanism as a clever means of changing the normal flow of program control, resist that temptation. It produces ugly, untraceable code and should be avoided.

PART II

PROCEDURAL PROGRAMMING

I know God will not give me anything I can't handle.
I just wish that He didn't trust me so much.

Mother Teresa 1910–1997

15. PLOTTING

There is a much quoted expression that "a picture is worth a thousand words," and this is never more appropriate than when talking about data. In Part I, we used some simple plot commands to display data to illustrate their behavior. The ability of MATLAB to present data reaches far beyond ordinary data plotting, and far beyond the limited confines of a text book. This chapter will present the fundamental concepts of the different forms in which data can be presented, but then leave to the reader the challenge of exploring the full range of capabilities available. I would make the case that you only really discover the power of MATLAB's plotting capabilities when you have some unusual data to visualize.

15.1. In General

Before considering the details of how each plotting mode works, we should set the context.

15.1.1. A Figure—The Plot Container

The fundamental container for plotting is a MATLAB *figure*. In a simple script, if you just start plotting data, a figure is automatically generated to present the data. You can manage the figures by calling the **figure** function. Each time **figure** is called, a new figure is made available, with the next higher figure number. The **figure** function actually returns a reference called a handle with which, in advanced plotting circumstances, you can change the attributes of the figure.

To clear the current figure, put the key word **clf** in the header of your script. To remove all the figures, put the keyword **close** at the beginning of your script.

15.1.2. Multiple Plots on One Figure—Subplots

Within the current figure, you can place multiple plots with the **subplot** command, as shown in Figure 26, which was generated by the code in Table 74.

15.1.3. Manually Editing Plots

When a figure has been created, you are free to manipulate many of its characteristics by using its menu items and tool bars. They provide the ability to re-size the plot, change the view characteristics, and annotate it with legends, axis labels, lines and text callouts.

Style Points:
1. Of course, most of these capabilities are also available to the script that creates the plots. Since you are very likely to want to generate a plot more than once, it is unwise to put a significant amount of manual effort into adjusting a plot. Better to experiment with the

manual adjustments and then find out how to make the same adjustments in the script that creates the plots. This also leaves you a permanent record of how the plot was generated.

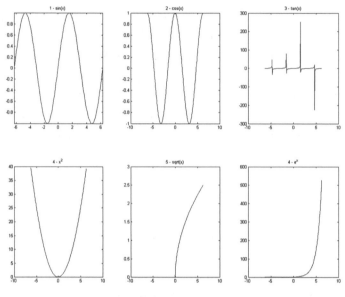

Figure 26—Subplots

```
clf                                        % Note 1

scrsz = get(0,'ScreenSize');               % Note 2
figure('Position',[1 scrsz(4)/1.2          % Note 3
        scrsz(3)/1.2 scrsz(4)/1.2]);
x = -2*pi:.05:2*pi;

subplot(2,3,1)                             % Note 4
plot(x, sin(x))
title('1 - sin(x)');
axis tight                                 % Note 5

subplot(2,3,2)
plot(x, cos(x))
title('2 - cos(x)');
```

(Continued)

Table 74—Subplots

```
subplot(2,3,3)
plot(x, tan(x))
title('3 - tan(x)');

subplot(2,3,4)
plot(x, x.^2)
title('4 - x^2');

subplot(2,3,5)
plot(x, sqrt(x))
title('5 - sqrt(x)');

subplot(2,3,6)
plot(x, exp(x))
title('4 - e^x');
```

Table 74—Subplots *(Continued)*

Notes:

1. **clf** clears the parameters of the current figure.
2. Request the size of the computer screen in pixels. Typically, screen attributes (**'ScreenSize'** and **'Position'** here) are 4-element vectors containing respectively the left edge location, the bottom edge, the width and the height.
3. Define a figure filling 80% of the screen (the default size is too small to show multiple plots).
4. **subplot(r, c, n)** divides the current figure into **r** rows and **c** columns of equally spaced plot areas, and then establishes the **nth** of these (counting across the columns first) as the current figure. You do not have to draw in all of the areas you specify.
5. **axis tight** removes as much white space as possible from the edges of the plots.

15.2. 2-D Plotting

Since we have already seen basic 2-D plotting at work, it should be sufficient to observe and comment on the simple example generated by the code in Table 75. The results are seen in Figure 27.

➢ **Build and run the following script:**

```
clear
clc
clf
x = linspace(-1.5, 1.5, 30);
y1 = x;
y2 = x.^2;
y3 = x.^3;
y4 = x.^4;
plot(x,y1,x,y2,x,y3,x,y4)            % Note 1
xlabel('x');                         % Note 2
ylabel('value');
title('powers of x')                 % Note 3
legend({'1','2','3','4'}, ...        % Note 4
          'Location','SouthEast')
```

Table 75—Simple 2-D Plot

Notes:

1. You might be wondering why use this ponderous form of the plot function where all the curves are generated with one call. It would indeed have been much simpler to iterate across the powers of x, and overlay the plots one at a time. The MATLAB operation **hold on** will allow multiple plots to be overlaid. However, there are two problems with that: a. the colors of each line must then be set manually, and b. legend displays cannot correlate to multiple plots. Plotting in this form automatically cycles the colors and generates the data for the legend.

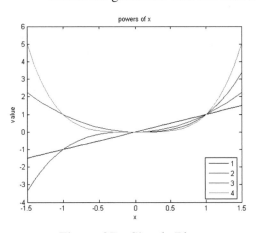

Figure 27—Simple Plot

2. **xlabel(...)** and **ylabel(...)** put labels on the axes.

3. **title(...)** titles the plot.

4. **legend(...)** puts the box identifying the individual lines on the screen. It requires a cell array (or parameter list) of the strings identifying each line. Since its default position is on the upper right corner of the plot, it is frequently necessary to relocate it to a position where it will not hide the data. See MATLAB's **help legend** command for more specifics.

You should also explore the following capabilities of 2-D plots that will be used extensively elsewhere in this text. Some of these ideas are illustrated in Figure 28.

- Line style: In the **plot(...)** command, after specifying the **x** and **y** data vectors, it accepts a string defining both the color of the plot and the marker type. For example, **plot(x, y, 'r+')** will mark the data with red '+' signs. Absent the symbol specifier, the color symbol specifies the color of the line. For example, **(plot x, y, 'g')** draws a green solid line. The symbols '–', '—', '.', and '..' specify different dotted and dashed lines as an alternative to the symbol markers. However, if you want both symbols and lines, you must call the plot function twice.
- Axis manipulation: There are a number of ways to customize the axes—refer to **help axes** and **help axis** for more information.

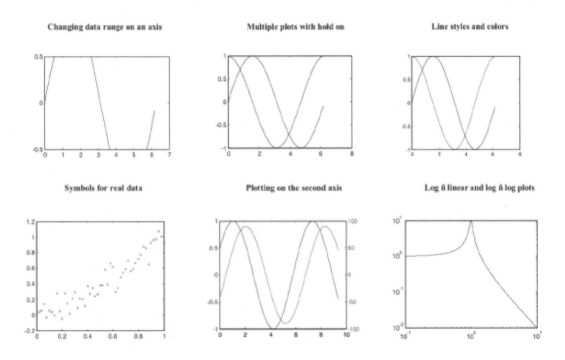

Figure 28—Styles of 2-D Plots

Style Point:

1. By convention, good engineers are expected to represent the data with appropriate line styles to avoid misleading the reader. For example, if you have some raw data that are only valid at the measurement points, they should be plotted with symbols only. Connecting

them with a line would imply that the data have some interpolated values between them, which may not be the case. On the other hand, if you calculate a theoretical curve that is good throughout the range of x, it should be plotted as a continuous curve, perhaps even at a better resolution (more x values) than the raw data samples.

15.3. 3-D Plotting

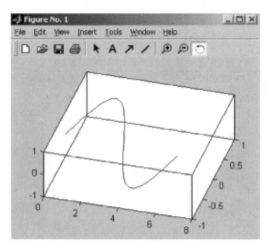

Figure 29—Rotated 2-D Plot

Before attacking the details of plotting in three dimensions, it should probably be noted that even two-dimensional plots in MATLAB are actually 3-D plots. Consider the picture in Figure 29 that was generated originally as a 2-D plot of sin(x) vs x. By selecting the 'Rotate 3D' icon on the tool bar and moving the mouse on your figure, it becomes apparent that what appeared to be a 2-D plot in the x-y plane is really a 3-D plot in the x-y-z plane "suspended in space" at z = 0.

We conclude that we can begin exploring the world of 3-D plotting by supplying vectors of x, y and z values to the `plot(...)`[1] function.

15.3.1. Linear 3-D Plots

Figure 30 illustrates this point by showing three curves plotted in three dimensions, using the script in Table 76. Each plot is in the z = x plane—the red curve at y = 0; the blue curve at y = 0.5; and the green curve at y = 1.

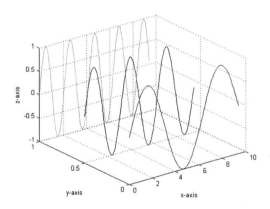

Figure 30—Simple 3-D Plots

We can generalize the concept further as shown in Figure 31 in which the x, y and z values plotted are computed as mappings of some linear parameter. On the left side, the parameter is a rotation angle theta varying from 0 to 10π (5 complete rotations) The x and y values are mapped from theta as sin(theta) and cos(theta)—the classic means of describing a circle as theta increases. The spiral effect is accomplished by plotting theta on the z axis.

The right half of Figure 31 illustrates a fully parameterized plot where the values of all three

---

[1] Actually, the function required is plot3(x, y, z) with attributes identical to plot(x, y).

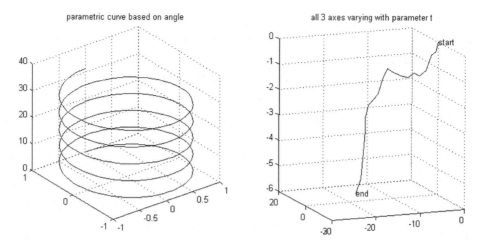

Figure 31—3-D Parametric Curves

coordinates are mappings of an independent parameter, t. This particular example is a plot of the random 3-D motion of a particle receiving random impulses in all three axes. Note the use of text anchored in x-y-z space to label points on the graph.

```
x=0:0.1:3.*pi;
y1=zeros(size(x));
z1=sin(x);
z2=sin(2.*x);
z3=sin(3.*x);
y3=ones(size(x));
y2=y3./2;
plot3(x,y1,z1,'r',x,y2,z2,'b',x,y3,z3,'g')
grid on
xlabel('x-axis'),ylabel('y-axis'),zlabel('z-axis')
```

Table 76—Simple 3-D Plots

```
subplot(1, 2, 1)
theta=0:0.1:10.*pi;
plot3(sin(theta),cos(theta),theta)
title('parametric curve based on angle');
grid on
subplot(1, 2, 2)
N = 20;
```
(Continued)

Table 77—Parametric 3-D Plots

```
dvx = rand(1, N) - 0.5    % random v changes
dvy = rand(1, N) - 0.5
dvz = rand(1, N) - 0.5
vx = cumsum(dvx);         % integrate to get v
vy = cumsum(dvy);
vz = cumsum(dvz);
x = cumsum(vx);           % integrate to get pos
y = cumsum(vy);
z = cumsum(vz);
plot3(x,y,z)
grid on
title('all 3 axes varying with parameter t')
text(0,0,0,'start');
text(x(N),y(N),z(N),'end');
```

Table 77—Parametric 3-D Plots *(Continued)*

15.3.2. Surface Plots

In Figure 31, we saw that data can be generated for all three axes based on one linear parameter. Perhaps the most dramatic graphics are produced by a different genre of 3-D graphics functions that produces images based on mapping a 2-D surface or "*plaid*."

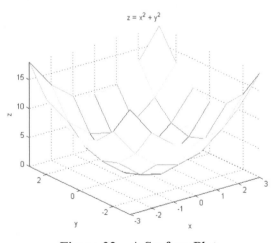

Figure 32—A Surface Plot

As we did above, we will begin with a simple example. Consider how we might plot the data in Figure 32. Before we look at the code, consider what the picture represents. Clearly, the independent variables are x and y, each covering the range from –3 to 3, each having 7 discrete values. As the caption indicates, the z values are calculated as the sum of x^2 and y^2. There are not, however, 7 z values as the range of x and y values might suggest, but 49! In order to plot the 3-D shape of our parabolic bowl, we must have a z value for every point on the x-y surface. Each of these points has a value of x corresponding to the reading on the x-axis, and a value of y from the y-axis.

The process of creating this plot therefore has three parts:

- Develop the underlying grid of points (the plaid) specifying the x-y location of every point on the x-y plane[2],
- Calculate the z values from the plaid, and then
- Call some kind of function that will accept the plaid and these z values to produce the plot.

The code to accomplish this is shown in Table 78.

```
x=-3:3;
y=-3:3;
[xx,yy]=meshgrid(x,y);          % Note 1
zz=xx.^2 + yy.^2;               % Note 2
mesh(xx,yy,zz)                  % Note 3
axis tight
title('z = x^2 + y^2')
xlabel('x'),ylabel('y'),zlabel('z')
```

Table 78—The Bowl Plot

Notes:

1. The **meshgrid(x, y)** function accepts the $x_{1 \times m}$ and $y_{1 \times n}$ vectors that bound the edges of the plaid, and then replicates the rows and columns appropriately to produce $xx_{m \times n}$ and $yy_{m \times n}$ containing the x and y values respectively of the complete plaid. This enables us in general to compute mappings for the 3-D coordinates of the figure we want to plot.

2. In this particular example, we map only the z coordinate, leaving the plaid (xx and yy) as the x and y coordinates of the figure.

3. **mesh(...)** is one of many functions that represent 3-D mappings of a plaid in different ways. Notice in the figure that the faces between line segments are solid white, and the line colors change with the z coordinate.

If you were to examine the values of **xx** and **yy** by removing the semicolon from the **meshgrid** call, you would see the results shown in Table 79. Notice that in general, if **x** is length **m** and **y** is length **n**, the **xx** values consist of the **x** vector in rows replicated **n** times, and the **yy** values consist of the **y** vector as a column replicated **m** times.

---

[2] Fortunately, there is a nice MATLAB function to accomplish this—meshgrid(.)

```
x=-3:3;
y=-3:3;
[xx,yy]=meshgrid(x,y)
xx =
      -3      -2      -1       0       1       2       3
      -3      -2      -1       0       1       2       3
      -3      -2      -1       0       1       2       3
      -3      -2      -1       0       1       2       3
      -3      -2      -1       0       1       2       3
      -3      -2      -1       0       1       2       3
      -3      -2      -1       0       1       2       3
yy =
      -3      -3      -3      -3      -3      -3      -3
      -2      -2      -2      -2      -2      -2      -2
      -1      -1      -1      -1      -1      -1      -1
       0       0       0       0       0       0       0
       1       1       1       1       1       1       1
       2       2       2       2       2       2       2
       3       3       3       3       3       3       3
```

Table 79—meshgrid Results

15.3.3. Simple Exercises

To begin to discover the range of rendering capabilities available, the student should perform the following simple exercises, all based on the code in Table 78:

1. Insert the line **hidden off** after **mesh(xx, yy, zz)**.
2. Change **mesh(xx, yy, zz)** to **surf(xx, yy, zz)**. Notice that the panels are now colored and the lines black. This form is also insensitive to the **hidden** parameter.
3. Replace **hidden off** with **shading flat**, and notice that the lines have disappeared.
4. Replace **shading flat** with **shading interp**, and notice that the surface is now smoothly contoured.
5. Insert the line **colormap 'summer'** after **mesh(xx, yy, zz)**. There are a number of built-in color maps to handle the shading. Look up **help colormap** for details.
6. Don't forget to rotate your images and examine them from different points of view using the "3D rotate" tool bar icon.

For the next few exercises, we will replace our do-it-yourself data with one of MATLAB's many built-in data sets. The function **peaks(n)** returns the complete **xx**, **yy**, **zz** data sets for drawing this odd shaped function with **n** facets along each axis. The code is shown in Table 80, and the resulting picture is shown in Figure 33. Note that **meshgrid** is done internally in the **peaks(...)** function, and the color map was restored by specifying **'default'**.

```
clear
clc
clf

[xx,yy,zz]=peaks(30);
surf(xx,yy,zz)
colormap 'default'
shading interp
axis tight
title('peaks')
xlabel('x'),ylabel('y'),zlabel('z')
```

Table 80—Using peaks(n)

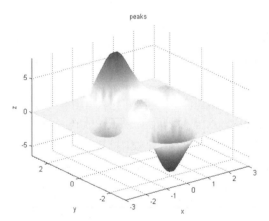

Figure 33—peaks(30)

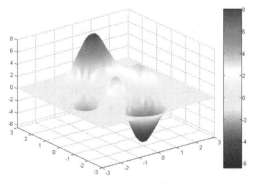

Figure 34—Added Color Bar

Now, continue with the next exercises using Table 80 as your code baseline.

7. Change the **surf(xx, yy, zz)** call to **surfc(xx, yy, zz)**. Notice the contour lines plotted on the x-y plane base.

8. Add the line **view(-45, 60)** which changes the viewing angle. This can program a different angle rather than needing to manually rotate the image after it is drawn. If you do rotate the image manually, the az, el numbers in the lower left corner are the values you need to enter in the **view(...)** function to replicate that view.

9. Change the **surfc(xx, yy, zz)** call to **surf(xx, yy, zz, yy)**. Here, we override the default color direction z with the y direction by supplying a 4th parameter to the **surfc(...)** function specifying the color values explicitly rather than implicitly.

10. Before the **surf(xx, yy, zz, yy)** call, add the line **c = del2(zz)**, and change

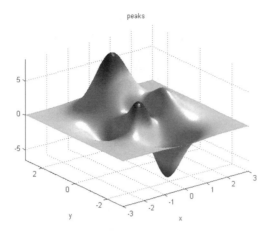

Figure 35—Illuminated Curvature Plot

`surf(xx, yy, zz, yy)` to `surf(xx, yy, zz, c)`. The `del2(...)` function computes the second derivative, or curvature, of the plot, so the coloring now highlights the areas of maximum curvature.

11. Add a color bar by inserting the command `colorbar` (Figure 34)—see the help menu for code that labels the color bar.

12. Finally, for a really eye-catching effect, change the parameter to `peaks` to `120`, and add the line `lightangle(60, 45)` at the bottom of the script. This illuminates the surface with a light at the specified azimuth and elevation

angle (degrees) (Figure 35). Try this effect without increasing the peaks parameter. You will see that the lighting effect highlights the facets on the figure due to the coarser resolution of the raw data.

15.4. Parametric Surfaces

Thus far, we have drawn beautiful pictures of typical 3-D plots in a Cartesian axis system where the x-y plaid was passed directly to the plotting function. The only coordinate actually mapped

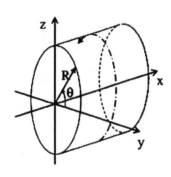

Figure 36—Parametric Cylinder

was the z axis. We now return to the concept briefly introduced in Section 15.3.1 when discussing Figure 31b. In that case, all three coordinate values were functions of (mappings of) one parameter, t. Consider first the construction of a cylinder as illustrated in Figure 36.

One could consider this as a sheet of paper rolled up in a circular shape. Now we could visualize that piece of paper as a plaid of values, not of x-y in this case, but perhaps x-θ. The range of x would be from 0 to the length of the cylinder, and the range of y would be 0 to 360°.

To plot this, one would then merely need to create a plaid in x and θ, and then decide on the mapping from θ to the y and z values of the cylinder. The code to accomplish this is shown in Table 81, and the resulting picture is shown in Figure 37.

```
facets = 120;  len = 2;  radius = 1;
thr = linspace(0, 2*pi, facets);
xr = linspace(0, len, facets);
[x, th] = meshgrid( xr, thr );
y = radius * cos(th);           % Note 1
z = radius * sin(th);
surf(x, y, z);
shading interp
colormap bone                   % Note 2
axis equal,axis tight,axis off  % Note 3
lightangle(60, 45)              % Note 4
alpha(0.8)                      % Note 5
view(-20, 35)
```

Table 81—Drawing a Simple Cylinder

Figure 37—Simple Cylinder

Figure 38—A Sphere

Notes:

1. The circular cross-section is achieved by using the parametric definition of a circle of a given radius.
2. Changing the color to a pleasant metallic scale.
3. Squaring up and removing the axes.
4. Illuminating the figure.
5. Setting the transparency of the surface so that a portion of the hidden details can show through.

Now, we construct a sphere as shown in Figure 38 starting with the cylindrical figure above. However, instead of using a constant radius in the x direction, calculate the radius in that direction by rotating a second angle, θ, from 0 to 180°. Think of this as mapping or "wrapping" a plaid with two angles as the independent variables around the sphere. The coordinate in the x direction would be r cosθ and the radii of the y-z circles would be r sinθ. The code for drawing this sphere is shown in Table 82.

We can assemble more complex solid bodies by constructing simple surfaces and concatenating the data before submitting it to the rendering machine.

```
factor = 120; radius = 1;
thr = linspace(0, 2*pi, facets); % range of theta
phir = linspace(0, pi, facets);  % range of phi
[th, phi] = meshgrid( thr, phir );
x = radius * cos(phi);
y = radius * sin(phi) .* cos(th);
z = radius * sin(phi) .* sin(th);
surf(x, y, z);
shading interp
colormap copper
axis equal, axis tight, axis off
lightangle(60, 45)
```

Table 82—Drawing a Sphere

Figure 39—A Solid Disk

The solid disk shown here in Figure 39 was constructed by drawing first the front face as a body of rotation, then the curved surface, and then the back face. If the angles of rotation are maintained in a consistent direction, the three sets of [x y z] arrays can be concatenated and submitted to the rendering software as before. The code for this drawing is in Table 83.

```
linear = 20;
rotational = 360;
len = 5; radius = 3;
ll = linspace(0, len, linear);
th1 = linspace(0, 2*pi, rotational);
r0 = linspace(0, radius, linear);
[r1, th] = meshgrid( r0, th1 );
x1 = zeros(size(r1));     % front disk
y1 = r1.*cos(th);
z1 = r1.*sin(th);
[l, th] = meshgrid(ll, th1);
x2 = l;                   % curved surface
y2 = radius*cos(th);
z2 = radius*sin(th);
x3 = len*ones(size(r1)); % back disk
[r3, th] = meshgrid(r0(end:-1:1), th1);
y3 = r3.*cos(th);                              (Continued)
```

Table 83—Drawing a Solid Disk

```
z3 = r3.*sin(th);
x = [x1 x2 x3];y = [y1 y2 y3];z = [z1 z2 z3];
surf(x, y, z);
shading interp
colormap copper
axis equal, axis tight, axis off
lightangle(60, 45)
```

Table 83—Drawing a Solid Disk *(Continued)*

Shapes of considerable complexity can be assembled in this manner. Consider, for example, the Klein bottle, a well-documented example of topological curiosity. The particular example shown in Figure 40 was constructed in the manner indicated above by assembling individually mapped articles.

The code, however, is a little too complex to be included here, and is left as an exercise for the reader.

Figure 40—Klein Bottle

15.5. Examples

15-1. Write the MATLAB commands to plot the equation $z = \cos(x^2 - y^2)$ with the following restrictions:

❑ Vary x and y between –2 and 2 with an increment of .1.
❑ The faces should be colored with no lines visible.

Make sure the plot is suitably labeled and titled.

15-2 We need to plot a hyperbolic paraboloid. This is special in mathematics due to the existence of a '*saddle point*' or '*minimax*' that exists at the origin. This function can be created from the equation $z = \dfrac{x^2}{4} - \dfrac{y^2}{4}$.

Write a MATLAB script to plot this function with the following restrictions:
a. Vary x and y between -3 and 3, increment in steps of .1.
b. Draw the picture as a wire frame with the lines colored to indicate the y value.
c. Put a color bar on the plot identifying the colors to values of y.

Make sure the plot is appropriately labeled and titled.

15-3 Write and test a function called *sineGraph* that graphs a sine function four times between the interval [start,stop] on the same graph. The values start and stop will be parameters of the function. The number of points per interval will vary across the plots. More specifically:

 a. The first time you graph the sine function, you should have two evenly spaced points, i.e. start and stop.
 b. The next plot should have 4 evenly spaced points—start, stop, and two between.
 c. The third has 8 evenly spaced points.
 d. The fourth has 256 points.

Make sure to include a legend, a title—'Multiple graphs on one plot'—and to label the axes. Make sure each line has a different color.

Test your function with the following intervals:

$$[0,\pi/2],[0,2\pi],[0,4\pi],[0,16\pi]$$

15-4 We want to plot the top half of a sphere that can be created from the equation $x^2 + y^2 + z^2 = r^2$, where r is the radius of the hemisphere. Write a MATLAB script to plot this function with the following restrictions:

 a. The hemisphere has a radius of 3 units.
 b. Vary x and y between -3 and 3, incremented in steps of .1.
 c. The surface should be smoothly colored in shades of gray with no likes apparent.

Make sure the plot is appropriately labeled and titled.

15-5 Plot the shape generated when you rotate the curve y = x^2 with x values from 0 to 2 in steps of 0.1 around the *y axis*.

15-6 Plot the shape generated when you rotate the curve y = x^2 with x values from 0 to 2 in steps of 0.1 around the x axis.

15-7 The equation $r = \sin\left(\dfrac{11\theta}{10}\right)$ creates a plot that looks similar to a "Slinky." Write a MATLAB script to plot the Slinky for $0 < \theta < 10\pi$. Make sure the plot is fully labeled and titled.

The x and y axes are defined as follows:

 x = $r*\cos(\theta)$
 y = $r*\sin(\theta)$

15-8 Write a script that will plot the function $f(x) = sin(x)$ for a user-specified range of values. Specifically, prompt the user for the start point and end point to use for the plot's x-axis, calculate the sine function over the values of x in the interval, and then plot those values. There should be 100 evenly spaced points along the plot's x-axis, including the start and end points.

You should also prompt the user for the title of this plot. Use this answer for the plot title and the y-axis label. Label the x-axis `x values`. *Hint:* Put `s` as the second parameter to `input(...)` in order to avoid entering the quote marks.

You may assume that the value of the end point will always be greater than the value of the start point.

15-9 Write a script to plot the parabolic mirror that is the body of rotation produced by rotating the curve $y = x^2$ about the y axis.

15-10 Write a script to plot the toroid shape that is the body of rotation produced by rotating the curve $(x-R)^2 + y^2 = r^2$ about the y axis. Use suitable values for r and R where r should be less than R.

Hint: It is probably a good idea to use the polar form of the circle:

$$x\text{-}R = r\cos(\theta)$$
$$y = r\sin(\theta)$$

15-11 You just realized that February 14th has passed and you haven't gotten anything for your Valentine. Since you are in the CS1371 class and your date is a CS major, sending the lucky person a MATLAB coded heart would seem like a cool and sincere thing to do. Make sure you follow each and every instruction carefully or your heart would turn out broken. Trust us.
   a. Create a new script called 'valentine.m'.
   b. Create 2 variables, 'x' and 'y' with range (0 to 2pi, interval 0.05) and (0 to 1, interval 0.05) respectively.
   c. Use the meshgrid function to generate the matrices xx and yy from x and y.
   d. Define: c = [0.1 + 0.9 * (pi – abs(xx – pi))/pi] .* yy.
   e. Define: aa = c .* cos(xx).
   f. Define: bb = c.* sin(xx).
   g. Define: zz = (-2)*aa.^3 + (3/2)*c.^2 + 0.5.
   h. Plot zz against aa and bb.

Voila! You are now all set to present your heart to your Valentine.

15-12 In this problem you will be creating two 3-D plots for comparison using subplot(. . .) in one row and two columns. Label all axes accordingly ("X-axis", "Y-axis", etc.). Give a title to your plot corresponding to the problem statement. Create the following plots in a script:
   a. In the first subplot, plot the function f(x,y)=x^2*cos(y) in the range x = -5:5 and y = -5:5 using 'mesh'. Title this plot "Using Mesh".
   b. In the second subplot, plot the same function as above, in the same range, but using 'surf'. Title this plot "Using Surf".

15-13 Georgia Tech wants to tear down the Campanile and build a new one that is ridiculously tall. However, before they build it, they need you to model it in MATLAB. Using the equation $z = 1/(x^2 + y^2)$ as the model, write a script that will plot the Campanile.

❑ Plot the function with both x and y between –0.75 and 0.75 in steps of 0.05.
❑ Set your axes such that all of the x,y domain is seen and z runs from 0 to 300.
❑ You must account for dividing by 0 (see eps).
❑ Make sure you use surf to plot your surface.
❑ Title the plot "Campanile" and label the axes.

16. MATRICES

In most mathematical discussions, the words "matrix" and "array" can be used interchangeably, and rightly so, because they store data in exactly the same form. Moreover, almost all the operations we can perform on an array can also be performed on a matrix—logical operations, concatenation, slicing and almost all of the arithmetic operations behave identically. The fact that some of the mathematical operations[1] are defined differently gives us a chance to pause and reflect on an important concept that will increase in importance when we begin to consider Object Oriented Programming.

16.1. Concept: Behavioral Abstraction

Recall the following concepts:

- Abstraction is the ability to ignore specific details and generalize the description of an entity.
- Data abstraction is the specific example of abstraction that we first considered whereby we could treat vectors of data (and later other collections like structures and arrays) as single entities rather than enumerating their elements individually.
- We also encountered procedural abstraction as functions that collect multiple operations into a form in which, once they are developed, we can overlook the specific details and treat them as a "black box," much as we treat MATLAB's built-in functions.

So we derive the concept of **behavioral abstraction**, which combines data and procedural abstraction, encapsulating not only collections of data, but also the operations that are legal to perform on that data.

One might attempt to argue that this is a new, irrelevant concept best ignored until "we just have to!" But consider the rules we have had to establish for what we can and cannot do with data collections we have seen so far. For example, can I add two arrays together? Yes, but only if they have the same number of rows and columns, or if one of them is a scalar (a 1×1 array). Can I add two character strings? Almost the same answer, except each string is first converted to a numerical quantity and the result is a vector of numbers and not a string. Can I add two cell arrays? No.

So at least some, and maybe all, MATLAB data collections also "understand" the set of operations that are permitted on the data. This encapsulation of data and operations is behavioral

---

[1] Multiplication, division and exponentiation.

abstraction. We can therefore differentiate arrays from matrices not by the data they collect, but by the operations that are legal to perform on them.

16.2. Matrix Operations

The arithmetic operations that differ between arrays and matrices are multiplication, division and exponentiation.

16.2.1. Matrix Multiplication

When we considered multiplying two arrays, we called this scalar multiplication, and it had the typical array operation characteristics:

- Either the two arrays must be the same size, or one of them must be scalar,
- The multiplication was indicated with the '.$\times$' operator,
- The result was an array with the same size as the larger original array, and
- Each element of the result was the product of the corresponding elements in the original two arrays.

This is best illustrated in the following diagram:

$$A_{(m \times n)} = \begin{bmatrix} a_{11} & a_{12} & \cdots & a_{1n} \\ a_{21} & a_{22} & \cdots & a_{2n} \\ \vdots & & \ddots & \\ a_{m1} & a_{m2} & \cdots & a_{mn} \end{bmatrix} \quad .* \quad B_{(m \times n)} = \begin{bmatrix} b_{11} & b_{12} & \cdots & b_{1n} \\ b_{21} & b_{22} & \cdots & b_{2n} \\ \vdots & & \ddots & \\ b_{m1} & b_{m2} & \cdots & b_{mn} \end{bmatrix}$$

$$\rightarrow \begin{bmatrix} a_{11} \times b_{11} & a_{12} \times b_{12} & \cdots & a_{1n} \times b_{1n} \\ a_{21} \times b_{21} & a_{22} \times b_{22} & \cdots & a_{2n} \times b_{2n} \\ \vdots & & \ddots & \\ a_{m1} \times b_{m1} & a_{m2} \times b_{m2} & \cdots & a_{mn} \times b_{mn} \end{bmatrix}$$

Figure 41—Scalar Multiplication

Scalar division and exponentiation have identical implementations.

Matrix multiplication is an entirely different logical operation, as illustrated in Figure 42. The logical characteristics of matrix multiplication are as follows:

- The two matrices do not have to be the same size. The only requirement is that the number of columns in the first matrix must equal the number of rows in the second.
- If, as illustrated, A is a m×n matrix, and B is a n×p, the result of A * B is a m×p matrix.
- The item at (i, j) in the result matrix is the scalar product of the ith row of A and the jth column of B.
- Whereas with scalar multiplication, A .* B gives the same result as B .* A, this is not the case with matrix multiplication. In fact, if A * B works, B * A will not work unless both matrices are square, and even then the results are different[2].
- Whereas with scalar multiplication, the original array A can be recovered by dividing the result by B, this is not the case with matrix multiplication unless both matrices are square[3].
- The identity matrix, sometimes given the symbol I_n, is a square matrix with n rows and n columns that is zero everywhere except on its major diagonal, which contains the value 1. I_n has the special property that when multiplied by any matrix A with n columns, the result is A. The MATLAB function **eye(rows, cols)** generates the identity matrix. We will need this property to derive matrix division below.

Figure 43 illustrates the mathematics for the case where a 3×2 matrix is multiplied by a 2×3 matrix resulting in a 3×3 matrix.

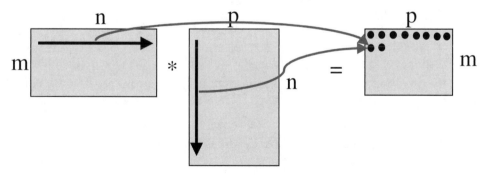

Figure 42—Matrix Multiplication in General

---

[2] Proof of this can be derived immediately from Figure 43 by eliminating the third row and column. All 4 terms of the result of A * B are different from B * A.

[3] The cumulative effect of the scalar products in each element of the result actually prevents the general matrix multiplication from being inverted by division.

$$A_{(3\times2)} = \begin{bmatrix} a_{11} & a_{12} \\ a_{21} & a_{22} \\ a_{31} & a_{32} \end{bmatrix} \quad * \quad B_{(2\times3)} = \begin{bmatrix} b_{11} & b_{12} & b_{13} \\ b_{21} & b_{22} & b_{23} \end{bmatrix}$$

$$\rightarrow \begin{bmatrix} (a_{11}\times b_{11}+a_{12}\times b_{21}) & (a_{11}\times b_{12}+a_{12}\times b_{22}) & (a_{11}\times b_{13}+a_{12}\times b_{23}) \\ (a_{21}\times b_{11}+a_{22}\times b_{21}) & (a_{21}\times b_{12}+a_{22}\times b_{22}) & (a_{21}\times b_{13}+a_{22}\times b_{23}) \\ (a_{31}\times b_{11}+a_{32}\times b_{21}) & (a_{31}\times b_{12}+a_{32}\times b_{22}) & (a_{31}\times b_{13}+a_{32}\times b_{23}) \end{bmatrix}$$

Figure 43—Simple Example of Matrix Multiplication

16.2.2. Matrix Division

Matrix division, as indicated above, is the logical process of reversing the effects of a matrix multiplication. The goal is this:

- Given $A_{n\times n}$, $B_{n\times p}$ and $C_{n\times p}$, where C = A * B, define the mathematical equivalent of C / A that will result in B.
- Since C = A * B, we are actually searching for some other matrix $K_{n\times n}$ by which we can multiply each side of the equation:

K * C = K * A * B

This multiplication would accomplish the division we desire if K * A were I_n, the identity matrix. If this were the case, multiplying C by K would result in I_n * B, or simply B by the definition of I(n) above. The matrix K is referred to as the inverse of A, or A^{-1}. The algebra for computing this inverse is messy but well defined—in fact, Gaussian elimination to solve linear simultaneous equations accomplishes the same thing. MATLAB has both functions (`inv(A)`) and operators ('back divide', \) (see below) that accomplish this. However, two things should be noted:

1. This inverse does not exist for all matrices—if any two rows or columns of a matrix are linearly related, the matrix is singular and does not have an inverse.
2. Only non-singular, square matrices have an inverse (just as a set of linear equations is only soluble if there are as many independent equations as there are unknown variables).

16.2.3. Matrix Exponentiation

For completeness, we mention here that matrix operations include exponentiation. However, this does not suggest that one would encounter $A_{n \times n} \wedge B_{n \times n}$ in the scope of our applications[4]. Rather, our usage of matrix exponentiation will be confined to A^k where k is any non-zero integer value. The result for positive k is accomplished by multiplying A by itself k times (using matrix multiplication). The result for negative k is accomplished by inverting A^{-k}.

16.3. MATLAB Implementation

16.3.1. Matrix Multiplication

Matrix multiplication is accomplished by using the "normal" multiplication symbol as illustrated below:

```
    ➢  In the Command Window, enter the following:

A = [2 5 7; 1 3 42]
A =
     2      5      7
     1      3     42
>> B = [1 2 3]'
B =
     1
     2
     3
>> A * B
ans =
    33
   133
>> I2 = eye(2)
I2 =
     1      0
     0      1
>> I2 * A
ans =
     2      5      7
     1      3     42
>>
```

Table 84—Matrix Multiplication

---

[4] There is in fact meaning in matrix exponentials with non-scalar exponents, but this involves advanced concepts with eigenvalues and eigenvectors. See the MATLAB help files for more detail.

16.3.2. Matrix Division

Matrix division is accomplished in a number of ways, all of which are equivalent. Returning to the problem statement above, we are given that **A**, **B** and **C** are square matrices and **C = A * B**. If we are actually given the matrices **C** and **B**, we can compute **A** in one of the following ways:

- **A = C * inv(B)**—using the MATLAB **inv(...)** function to compute the inverse of B;
- **A = B \ C**—"back dividing" **B** into **C** to produce the same result; or
- **A = C / B**—implicitly performing a similar operation; according to the MATLAB help system, this really computes **(C'\B')'**.

Since the order in which the matrix multiply was done affects the value of the result, care must be taken to ensure that the appropriate inversion or division is used. Both multiplying by the inverse and the normal divide nullify the effect of the array that did the post-multiplication. Back dividing nullifies the effect of the matrix that did the pre-multiplication. See the examples below for illustrations.

➢ **Make a script containing the following:**

```
A = magic(3)                    % Note 1
M = magic(6);
B = M(1:2:end, 2:2:end)
disp('C = A * B')
AB = A * B                      % Note 2
disp('D = B * A')
BA = B * A
disp('C * inv(B)')
AB * inv(B)                     % Note 3
disp('C / B = A * B / B')
AB / B
disp('B \ D = B \ B * A')
B \ BA                          % Note 4
disp(' B / B ')
B / B                           % Note 5
disp(' B \ B ')
B \ B
```

Table 85—Matrix Division

Notes:

1. Construct two 3×3 matrices, **A** and **B**.
2. Pre-multiply and post-multiply **B** by **A**; recall that we expect this to produce different answers.
3. Since we defined `inv(A)` as that function that produces the result **A** * `inv(A)` = **I**, this should produce a matrix with the same values as **A**. Also, dividing **AB** by **B** should produce the same.
4. Here, back dividing **B** into **BA** should also produce a matrix equal to **A**.
5. Verify that normally dividing **B** by **B** and back dividing **B** into **B** both produce **I**.

```
  ➢   The results should be as follows:

A =
      8        1        6
      3        5        7
      4        9        2
B =
      1       26       24
      9       22       20
      5       12       16
C = A * B
C =
     47      302      308
     83      272      284
     95      326      308
D = B * A
D =
    182      347      236
    218      299      248
    140      209      146
C * inv(B)
ans =
     8.0000    1.0000    6.0000
     3.0000    5.0000    7.0000
     4.0000    9.0000    2.0000
C / B = A * B / B
ans =
     8.0000    1.0000    6.0000
     3.0000    5.0000    7.0000
     4.0000    9.0000    2.0000              (Continued)
```

Table 86—Matrix Division Output

```
B \ D = B \ B * A
ans =
      8.0000      1.0000      6.0000
      3.0000      5.0000      7.0000
      4.0000      9.0000      2.0000
  B / B
  ans =
        1        0        0
        0        1        0
        0        0        1
  B \ B
  ans =
        1        0        0
        0        1        0
        0        0        1
```

Table 86—Matrix Division Output *(Continued)*

16.4. Applications

We consider two typical examples of the application of matrix operations.

16.4.1. Rotating Coordinates

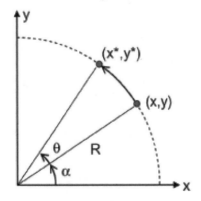

Figure 44—Coordinate Rotation

We can move points around on a plot by adding coordinate offsets or multiplying them by scalar quantities. However, the need frequently arises to rotate the coordinates of a graphical object by some angle. The mathematics involved are relatively straightforward in two dimensions, as illustrated in Figure 44. If the original point location is (x, y) at angle α to the X axis and you wish to rotate that point by the angle θ about the origin of coordinates, the mathematics are as follows:

$$x^* = x \cos \theta - y \sin \theta$$
$$y^* = x \sin \theta + y \cos \theta$$

This can be expressed as a matrix multiplication as follows:

$$\begin{bmatrix} x^* \\ y^* \end{bmatrix} = \begin{bmatrix} \cos \theta & -\sin \theta \\ \sin \theta & \cos \theta \end{bmatrix} * \begin{bmatrix} x \\ y \end{bmatrix}$$

Since points can always be translated by adding a vector before or after rotation, there is no loss of generality in rotating points about the origin of coordinates.

➤ Write the following function:

```
function transformation = rotation(angle)
% rotate a coordinate system by the angle (radians)
transformation = [ cos(angle), -sin(angle)
                   sin(angle), cos(angle) ];
```

➤ Write the following script to test it:

```
x =    [3, 10
        1, 3];
plot(x(1,:), x(2,:))
axis ([0 15 0 15])
hold on
angle = 0;
for angle = 0.05:0.05:1
    A = rotation(angle);
    xr = A * x;
    plot(xr(1,:), xr(2,:))
end
```

Table 87—Coordinate Rotation

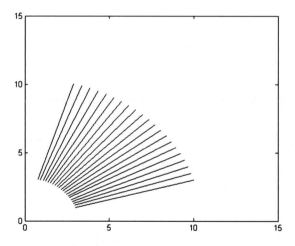

Figure 45 shows the plot resulting from this script.

Figure 45—Rotation Output

16.4.2. Solving Simultaneous Linear Equations

A typical example of a simultaneous equation problem might take this form: Consider two straight lines on a plot with the general form:

$$A_{11}\, x + A_{12}\, y = c_1$$
$$A_{21}\, x + A_{22}\, y = c_2$$

These lines intersect at some point [x, y] that is the solution to both of these equations. The equations can be rewritten in matrix form:

```
A * V = c
```

where c is the column vector `[c1 c2]`′ and V is the required result, the column vector `[x y]`′. The solution is obtained by eliminating A from the left side of the equation using the back divide operator:

```
V = A \ c
```

Recall that back divide, like the `inv(...)` function will fail to produce a result if the matrix is singular, i.e., has two rows or columns that have a linear relationship. In the specific example of two intersecting lines, this singularity occurs when the two lines are parallel, in which case there is no point of intersection.

16.4.3. Curve Fitting

A specific example of simultaneous equation solution occurs when seeking the best polynomial fit to a set of data points. The problem is this: You are given two vectors of points x and y, and want to find the coefficients of the best polynomial of order n that fits the data. The polynomial is of the form:

$$y = C_n x^n + C_{n-1} x^{n-1} \ldots + C_1 x + C_0$$

The best fit is usually defined as the polynomial that minimizes the sum of the squared difference between the actual Y value and the value of the polynomial.

The solution, found in any good calculus book, produces the following set of simultaneous equations:

$$
\begin{bmatrix}
\sum x^{2n} & \sum x^{2n-1} & \ldots & \sum x^{n+2} & \sum x^{n+1} & \sum x^{n} \\
\sum x^{2n-1} & \sum x^{2n-2} & \ldots & \sum x^{n+1} & \sum x^{n} & \sum x^{n-1} \\
\vdots & & \ddots & & & \vdots \\
\sum x^{n+1} & \sum x^{n} & \ldots & \sum x^{3} & \sum x^{2} & \sum x \\
\sum x^{n} & \sum x^{n-1} & \ldots & \sum x^{2} & \sum x & n
\end{bmatrix}
*
\begin{bmatrix}
C_n \\
C_{n-1} \\
\vdots \\
C_1 \\
C_0
\end{bmatrix}
\begin{bmatrix}
\sum x^{n} y \\
\sum x^{n-1} y \\
\vdots \\
\sum x\, y
\end{bmatrix}
$$

which is an equation of the general form $A_{(n+1)\times(n+1)} * C_{(n+1)\times 1} = B_{(n+1)\times 1}$. To solve this, we merely perform the back divide in the usual way:

$$C = A \setminus B$$

The example in Table 88 illustrates the computation of a linear fit. It reads a file of fuel consumption records and computes the curve fit of order 1, a linear curve fit. The resulting plot is shown in Figure 46; the red crosses show the raw data, and the blue line is the least squares linear fit.

➤ **Write the following script:**

```
% the file gasoline.dat contains two data columns:
% the miles driven
% the gas used, e.g:
% 444.41, 13.8
% 754.08, 21.0
% 1178.6, 33.8
% 1617.7, 46.7
% 2008.6, 57.4
% 2356.5, 66.1
r = dlmread('gasoline.dat');
x = r(:,2)';
y = r(:,1)';
plot(x, y, 'rx');
hold on
title('gas vs miles');
ylabel('miles');
xlabel('gallons');

c = [ sum(x.^2) sum(x); sum(x) 1];
rhs = [sum(x.*y); sum(y)]
a = c \ rhs;
plot(x, a(1)*x + a(2))
fprintf('average mpg = %f\n', a(1) );
```

Table 88—Linear Curve Fit

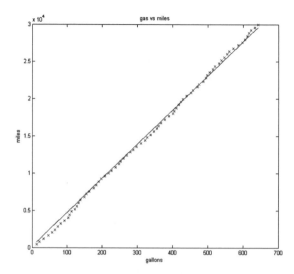

Figure 46—Gas Mileage Results

Notes:

1. MATLAB has some built-in functions that perform this function automatically up to n=6— look up **polyfit(...)** and **polyval(...)** in the help files.

2. You must be careful that higher-order polynomial fits do not impose their own shape on your ideas of the data rather than following the data. This is especially true when there is not an abundance of data. Consider the following slightly extreme example where, with limited samples, the polynomial fits can mislead you. The data are actually for the expression **y = erf(x)**, shown in green on the figure. The blue lines are the attempts by **polyfit(...)** to

➤ **Write the following script:**

```
N = 8
x = linspace(0, 2, N);
y = (1 - exp(-x));
plot(x, y, 'g')
hold on
y = y + (rand(1,N)-0.5);
plot(x, y, 'rx')
for n = 1:6
    p = polyfit(x, y, n);
    yp = polyval(p, x);
    plot(x, yp);
end
```

Table 89—Polynomial Fit Test

fit the data with the polynomial order increasing from 1 to 6. Clearly, as the order of the fit increases, the noise on the data has more and more influence over the results.

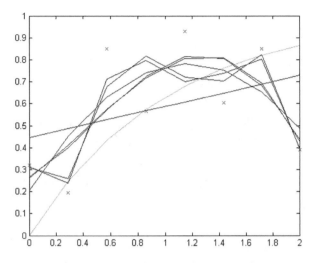

Figure 47—Polynomial Fit Results

16.5. Examples

16-1 Do the following matrix exercises:
  a. Create a five-by-six matrix, A, that contains random numbers between 0 and 10.
  b. Create a six-by-five matrix, B, that contains random numbers between 0 and 10.
  c. Find the inverse of matrix A*B and store it in the variable, C.
  d. Create a new matrix D that is the same as A except that all values less than 5 are replaced by zero. (Do not use iteration to create D.)
  e. Create a new matrix F that is the same as A except that all values less than 5 are replaced by zero; use iteration to create F.
  f. Create a new matrix G that is the "horizontal" reverse of A. For example:

```
[1 2 3          [3 2 1
 3 2 5    =>     5 2 3
 1 7 4]          4 7 1]
```

  g. Find the minimum value among all the elements in A and store your answer in the variable H.

16-2 Which of the following statements are true?
  a. `eye(5)` is equivalent to `eye(5,5)`.
  b. `size(eye(size(A)))` is equal to `size(A)`.
  c. Typing "`eye`" at the command prompt will produce an error.

16-3 Write a short script to solve the system of linear equations:

$$2x + 5y + 7z = 9$$
$$3x + 2y + 3z = 2$$
$$x + 3y + 2z = 5$$

16-4 As the enthusiastic and motivated student that you are, you decided to go out and buy plenty of pens for all your classes this semester. This spending spree occurred at the unfortunate time before you realized your engineering classes rendered little use for "ink." So now, you're left with 4 different types of pens and no receipt—you only remember the total amount you spent, and not the price of each type of pen.

You decide to get together with three of your friends who coincidentally did the same thing as you, buying the same 4 types of pens and knowing only the total amount. In order to find the price of each individual pen, you create a matrix called data, where each column represents a different type of pen and each row represents a different person.

```
           pen1   pen2   pen3   pen4
data =      3      6      2      5    <-you
            4      7      5      2    <-friend 1
            1      3      12     6    <-friend 2
            2      8      2      4    <-friend 3
```

You then generate a column vector "totals" which contains the totals each of you and your friends spent on the pens.

```
totals =    19.60
            18.78
            25.59
            19.26
```

Using the matrix **data** and the vector **totals**, find the column vector **prices** that contains the price of each type of pen.

16-5 World leaders have decided to come up with a single currency for the world. This new currency called the Eullar is defined by the following:

❑ Seven dollars and three Euros make seventy-one Eullars.
❑ One dollar and two Euros make twenty Eullars.

You are a reputable economist and your job is to find out the value of a dollar in terms of Eullars. Write a script to compute and print the value of the dollar in Eullars. For example, your script might print "1 Dollar = 4.64 Eullars".

17. FILE I/O

We have already seen and used examples of the use of your computer's file system to store and retrieve both data and programs. Your script and function files were stored in your current directory, and could be invoked from there by name from the command window. It is also possible to save your complete workspace with the **save** command and reload it with the **load** command. See help on these two topics for more details[1]. We turn to the general case of file I/O where we expect to load data from external sources, process that data and perhaps save data back to the file system with enhancements created by MATLAB.

17.1. Concept

Serial I/O: In general, any computer file system saves and retrieves data as a sequential (serial) stream of characters, as illustrated in Figure 48. Mixed in with the characters that represent the

Figure 48—Reading a Data File

values of the data are control characters ("delimiters") that specify the organization of the data. When a program opens a file by name for reading, it continually requests values from the file until the end of the file is reached. As the data are received, the program must identify the delimiting characters and reformat the data to reconstruct the organization of the data as represented in the file.

Figure 49—Writing to a File

Similarly, when writing data to a file, the program must serialize the data as illustrated in Figure 49. In order to preserve the organization of the data, the appropriate delimiting characters must be inserted into the serial character stream.

---

[1] There are very few occasions where this is a really good idea—the save command retains only the results of a computation and not the details of how the results were achieved. When the amount of computation you do is more than a few lines long, it should be done and saved as a script, not in the command window. In that case, saving the script retains how you computed the data. The only time I use save and load is when a large amount of computation is required to create the data—see the sort data analysis program in Section 22.5.

17.2. Approach

When you think about it, when you are trying to process data from some unknown source, it is going to be difficult to write MATLAB code without some initial exploration of the nature and organization of the data. So a good habit would be to explore the data in a file by whatever means you have available and then commit to processing the data according to your observations.

17.3. Implementation

Most programming languages require the programmer to write detailed programs to read and write files, especially those produced by other application programs or data acquisition packages. Fortunately for MATLAB programmers, much of this messy work has been built into special file readers and writers. The following table identifies the type of data, the name of the appropriate reader and writer, and the internal form in which MATLAB returns the data. You should consult the help documentation for details of the usage of each reader and writer of interest.

File Content	Ext	Reader	Writer	Data Format
Plain text	Any	`textread`	`fprintf`	Specified in the function calls
Comma-separated numbers	CSV	`csvread`	`csvwrite`	Double array
Tab-separated text	TAB	`dlmread`	`dlmwrite`	Double array
General delimited text	DLM	`dlmread`	`dlmwrite`	Double array
Excel worksheet	XLS	`xlsread`	`xlswrite`	Double or cell array
Lotus 123 worksheet	WK1	`wk1read`	`wk1write`	Double or cell array
Scientific data in Common Data Format	CDF	`cdfread`	`cdfwrite`	Cell array of CDF records
Flexible Image Transport System data	FITS	`fitsread`		Primary or extension table data
Data in Hierarchical Data Format	HDF	`hdfread`		HDF or HDF-EOS data set
Extended Markup Language (XML)	XML	`xmlread`	`xmlwrite`	Document Object Model node
Image data[2]	Various	`imread`	`imwrite`	True color, grayscale or indexed image
Audio file[3]	AU or WAV	`auread or` `wavread`	`auwrite`	Sound data and sample rate
Movie	AVI	`aviread`		MATLAB movie

Table 90—File I/O Operations

---

[2] See Chapter 19.
[3] See Chapter 18.

17.3.1. Exploration

The types of data of immediate interest are the text files and spreadsheets. Later, we will see chapters that cover sound files and images in depth. We will not be processing MATLAB movies or the other special-purpose data types. Notice in the table above that the delimited text files are presumed to contain numerical values, whereas the spreadsheet data may be either numerical data stored as doubles, or string data stored in cell arrays. Typically, text files are delimited by a special character (comma, tab or anything else) to designate the column divider and a new line character to designate the rows. Once the data are imported, all of MATLAB's normal array and matrix processing tools can be applied. The exception to this rule is the plain text reader that must be provided with a format specifier to define the data, and the names of the variables in which the data are to be stored.

So when you are approached with a file of data, the file extension (that part of the file name after the '.') gives you a significant clue to the nature of the data. If it is the output from, for example, a spreadsheet, you should open the data in that spreadsheet tool to explore their contents and organization. Typically, spreadsheet data will not open well in a plain text editor. If you do not recognize the file extension as coming from a spreadsheet, try opening the file in a plain text editor like Notepad, and see if the data are legible. You should be able to discern the field delimiters or the format of each line if the file contains plain text.

17.3.2. Reading and Using the Data

The types of data of immediate interest are the text files and spreadsheets. Later, we will see chapters that cover sound files and images in depth.

Consider the typical set of data in an Excel spreadsheet named "grades.xls" illustrated in Table 91. The MATLAB `xlsread(...)` function does a really nice job of separating out the text and numerical portions of the spreadsheet, as illustrated in Table 92.

name	age	grade
fred	19	78
joe	22	83
sally	98	99
charlie	21	56
mary	23	89
ann	19	51

Table 91—Typical Spreadsheet Data

```
>> [n, t] = xlsread('grades.xls')    % Note 1
n =
      19     78                        % Note 2
      22     83
      98     99
      21     56
      23     89
      19     51
t =
     'name'          'age'      'grade'  % Note 3
     'fred'           ' '          ' '
     'joe'            ' '          ' '
     'sally'          ' '          ' '
     'charlie'        ' '          ' '
     'mary'           ' '          ' '
     'ann'            ' '          ' '
```

Table 92—xlsread Importing Data

Notes:

1. The parameter to **xlsread(...)** is the name of the file; you can ask for up to 3 return variables: the first will hold all the numerical values in an array of doubles, the second will hold all the text data in cell arrays, and the third, if you request it, holds both string and numerical data in cell arrays.

2. The numerical rows and columns in an array of doubles.

3. The string data in a cell array.

   On the other hand, if, thinking you were improving your chances of recovering the data, you saved this data from Excel as a comma separated file 'grades.csv', the data would appear as seen in Table 93. If you tried to read this with MATLAB, the result would be the ugly yelling at you seen in Table 94.

```
name,age,grade
fred,19,78
joe,22,83
sally,98,99
charlie,21,56
mary,23,89
ann,19,51
```

Table 93—csv Data File

```
>> d = csvread('grades.csv')
??? Error using ==> textscan
Mismatch between file and format string.
Trouble reading number from file (row 1, field 1) ==> name,
Error in ==> dlmread at 130
    cresult  = textscan(fid,'',nrows,...
Error in ==> csvread at 45
    m=dlmread(filename, ',', r, c);
>>
```

Table 94—Trying to Use csvread(...)

17.3.3. Processing the Data

Clearly, as a result of our preliminary exploration, we can extract the information we need by processing the Excel data. So armed with some understanding of the data produced when we read the file with **xlsread(...)**, we could write the script shown in Table 95, and achieve the results shown in Table 96.

```
[n, t] = xlsread('grades.xls');
for i = 1:length(n)
    fprintf('%s, aged %d, scored %d\n', ...
        t{i+1}, n(i,1), n(i,2) );
end
```

Table 95—Processing the Grade Data

```
fred, aged 19, scored 78
joe, aged 22, scored 83
sally, aged 98, scored 99
charlie, aged 21, scored 56
mary, aged 23, scored 89
ann, aged 19, scored 51
```

Table 96—Processing Results

17.3.4. Saving Results to a File

When we have performed significant amounts of work on a set of data, we need appropriate means for saving the results in a form that can be restored to MATLAB for future operations. The write functions corresponding to specific file functions are listed on Table 90. If you need to write a file of a specific type, look up the name on that table and check its usage with the MATLAB help files.

17.4. Examples

17-1 You have a client who wants you to work on her old data files. She's an engineer, and wants you to use MATLAB for the project. Luckily, all of the old data is stored in simple tab-delimited text files. Unluckily, the first row of every data file is full of meaningless numbers. As a quick check to verify that you're capable of solving her problems, she has asked you to write a few MATLAB functions.

  a. First, write a MATLAB function called **readData** that takes the name of a tab-delimited text file and returns a 2-dimensional array of the data in the file, skipping the first row of data.

  b. Now, using your **readData** function from part a, write another function **maxMerge** that takes the name of two of these tab-delimited files and returns a single 2-dimensional array where each element of the array is the larger of the corresponding elements from the two data files.

Example:

File 1			File 2			maxMerge		
0	0	0	0	0	0			
10	20	30	2	4	8	10	20	30
45	55	63	16	32	64	45	55	64
80	90	99	128	56	512	128	90	512

Notice that the first row is ignored, as specified by the requirements of the **readData** function.

17-2 You are provided the file 'data.xls' which contains two columns of numbers—each column contains 1371 elements, starting from Row 1. Create a script that does the following:

  a. The first column, A, represents your x values. Read these numbers from the file and save to a vector called **xData**.

  b. Column B is your y values. Read the numbers from the file and save them in the vector **yData**.

  c. Make a plot of the x vs. y values, and title your plot 'Excel Plot'.

Hint: See "**help xlsread()**" to learn how the **xlsread()** function reads in data from **.xls** files.

17-3 You are provided with two files: atlanta.txt and ttimes.txt. Each are delimited files that should read correctly using dlmread(). We need to explore and plot the data in these files.

Hints: The file atlanta.txt contains the end points of a large number of roads throughout the city. The x coordinate and y coordinate of each end of the road are in adjacent columns. There is also a column for the class of road (1-6) that could be used to color the roads differently. The file ttimes.txt contains values of the travel times from certain x-y coordinate locations (on the same scale as the map) to the center of the city. If you look carefully, you will see that it contains all the data that would have come from a meshgrid(.) call. The first few columns define the indices in the meshgrid where that line of data belongs.

Follow these steps.
   a. Read the file atlanta.txt, determine the columns defining the roads and plot the roads using the function `line(...)`.
   b. Read the file ttimes.txt, figure out the three appropriate columns and plot this data using `surf(...)`.
   c. Title the plot and label the axes.

17-4 You are provided with an Excel spreadsheet World_Data.xls. Do the following:
   a. Find the names of the 10 most populous countries.
   b. Plot the population growth for each for as many years as data are available. Don't forget a title, suitable axis labels and a legend.

18. SOUNDS

18.1. Concept

Physics of Sound: Any sound source produces sound in the form of pressure fluctuations in the air. While the air molecules move infinitesimal distances in order to propagate the sound, the important part of sound propagation is that pressure waves move rapidly through the air by causing air molecules to "jostle" each other. These pressure fluctuations can be viewed as analog signals—data that has essentially an enormous, continuous range of values. These signals have two attributes—their amplitude, and their frequency characteristics.

In absolute terms, sound is measured as the ***amplitude*** of pressure fluctuations on a surface like an ear drum or a microphone. However, this is usually reported in decibels where the intensity of a sound in decibels is calculated as:

$$I_{DB} = 10 \log_{10}(I / I_0)$$

- where I is the measured pressure fluctuation,
- and I_0 is a reference pressure usually established as the lowest pressure fluctuation a really good ear can detect, 2×10^{-4} dynes / cm.^{2}

To give you an idea of the dynamic range of these pressure measurements, a not-too-painful sound level of, say, 100db has an amplitude 10^{10} (10 billion) times as loud as the lowest perceivable sound.

Also, sounds are pressure fluctuations at certain ***frequencies***. The human ear can hear sounds as low as 50 Hz, and as high as 15 kHz. Voices on the telephone sound slightly odd because the upper frequency is limited by the telephone equipment to 4 kHz. Typically, hearing damage due to exposure to excessive sound levels causes an ear to lose sensitivity to high and/or low frequencies.

18.2. Recording and Playback

Early attempts at sound recording concentrated first on mechanical, and later magnetic, methods for storing and reproducing sound. The phonograph/record player depended on the motion of a needle in a groove as a cylinder or disk rotated at constant speed under the playback head. Not surprisingly when you see the incredible dynamic range required, even the best stereos could not reproduce high-quality sound. Later, analog magnetic tape in various forms replaced the phonograph, offering less wear on the recording, and better, but still limited, dynamic range. Digital recording has almost completely supplanted analog recording, and will be the subject of the rest of this chapter.

Of course, sound amplitude in analog form is unintelligible to a computer—it must be turned into an electrical signal by a microphone, amplified to suitable voltage levels, digitized and stored as illustrated in Figure 50. The key to successful digital recording and playback—whether by digital tape machines, compact disks or computer files—is the design of the analog-to-digital (A/D) and digital-to-analog (D/A) devices. The reader should remember that this is still low-level data. Each word coming out of the A/D or going into the D/A merely represents the pressure on the microphone at a point in time.

Two parameters govern the sound quality:

· How quickly they record samples of the sound (the sampling rate), and
· The size of the digital word holding the sound value (the resolution).

The background theory of sampling is too deep for this text. Interested readers should look up Nyquist on a good search engine. For our purposes, we want the sampling rate to be twice the highest frequency you are likely to encounter, usually around 20,000 samples per second. The resolution of the recorded data is usually either 8 bits (-128 to 127) or 16 bits (-32,768 to 32767). 8 bit resolution offers very limited dynamic range, and is used only for recording speech. Even 16 bit resolution does not have sufficient resolution to capture the complete 100dB range discussed above.

However, none of this discussion has much value when we are reading files of sound data previously recorded. To read a file, we must receive not only the data stream, but also information indicating the sample frequency, Fs, and the word size.

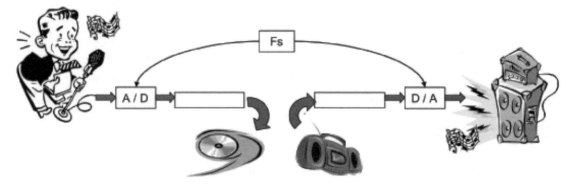

Figure 50—Sound Recording and Playback

18.3. MATLAB Implementation

As noted on Table 90, MATLAB offers the tools for reading sound files in two formats: `.wav` files (`wavread(...)`), and `.au` files (`auread(...)`). Both return three variables: the vector of sound values in the range (0 ... 1), the sampling frequency in Hz (samples per second) and the number of bits used to record the data (8 or 16).

A number of .**wav** files are included with code sources for this book to demonstrate certain aspects of sound files. Examine the following example comparing two recordings of the identical sound bite recorded at 16 bit and 8 bit resolution respectively.

```
>> [b16, F16, n] = wavread('brooklyn16.wav');
>> fprintf('bit size of b16 is %d\n', n);
bit size of b16 is 16
>> sound(b16, F16)            % Note 1
>> [b8, F8, n] = wavread('brooklyn8.wav');
>> fprintf('bit size of b8 is %d\n', n);
bit size of b8 is 8
>> sound(b8, F8)             % Note 2
```

Table 97—Sound Resolution Experiment

Notes:

1. This command plays the sound file read into b16 at the frequency specified in the file.
2. This plays the 8 bit version. Unless you have very good audio equipment and a really good musical ear, in spite of the discussion of the ideal physics, it is very hard to distinguish between 8 bit and 16 bit recording quality.

18.4. Time Domain Operations

We first consider three kinds of operation on sound files in the time domain: slicing, playback frequency changes, and sound file frequency changes.

18.4.1. Slicing and Concatenating Sound

Consider the problem of constructing an "audio ransom note" by choosing and assembling words from published speeches. This exercise is strictly experimental in nature, but can produce some interesting results. There are a number of web sites that offer free .wav files containing memorable speech fragments from movies, TV shows and cartoons[1].

The resource center for this text contains a sampling of such files. In particular, it has the "Apollo 13" speech "Houston, we have a problem," "Frankly, my dear . . ." from "Gone with the

---

[1] Beware, however, when looking for materials. Some web sites store .wav files in a compressed form that MATLAB cannot decode. When you find a file, save it to disk and make sure that MATLAB's wavread(. . .) functiuon can open it correctly.

Wind," and "You can't handle the truth..." from "A Few Good Men." The following exercise describes the process of assembling parts of these speeches into a semi-coherent conversation. Consider the following scripts:

```
➤ Step 1—find the location of problem speech

[houston, Fsh] = wavread('a13prob.wav');
plot(houston)²;
sound(houston, Fsh);
```

Table 98—Finding the Problem

The result of this script is similar to the left half of Figure 51. The sound file in **A13prob.wav** includes more than we need. By listening to the speech using the function **sound(...)**, and judiciously zooming and panning the plot, it is possible to narrow down the location in the file where the problem speech starts at about 111000.

```
➤ Step 2—extracting the problem speech

subplot(1, 2, 1)
plot(houston);
clip = 110000;
prob = houston(clip:end)*2;
subplot(1, 2, 2)
plot(prob)
```

Table 99—Extracting the Problem

Notice that on listening to the sound, it appeared to be too soft, so we doubled its amplitude. The right half of Figure 51 is the speech we need to start our speech collage.

---

² plot(...) with only one parameter treats the data as the y values, and uses the index of the data as the x axis values.

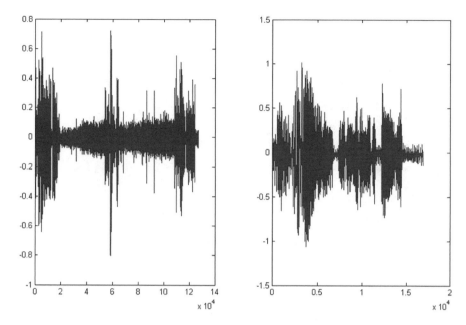

Figure 51—Cropping the Problem Speech

By a very similar process, we remove "my dear" from the "Frankly, my dear. . ." speech, reducing its amplitude by a half, resulting in Figure 52.

> ➢ Step 3—removing 'my dear'

```
[damn, Fsd] = wavread('givdamn2.wav');
subplot(1, 2, 1)
plot(damn);
lo = 4500;
hi = 8700;
sdamn = [damn(1:lo); damn(hi:end) ] * .5;
subplot(1, 2, 2)
plot(sdamn);
```

Table 100—Removing 'My Dear'

Finally, we assemble the complete speech. We might have observed that the sound data are stored as column vectors rather than row vectors. The concatenation therefore requires semicolons to assemble column vectors, resulting in the picture in Figure 53.

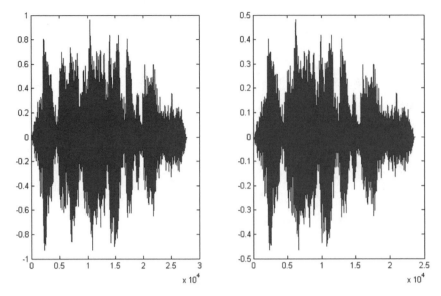

Figure 52—Removing 'My Dear'

➤ Step 4—assembling the speech

```
[truth, Fst] = wavread('truth1.wav');
speech = [prob; sdamn; truth * .7];
plot(speech);
sound(speech, Fst);
```

Table 101—Assembling the Speech

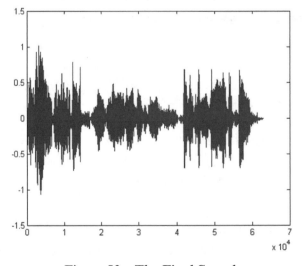

Figure 53—The Final Speech

18.4.2. Changing Sound Frequency—Poorly

The second time domain exercise is to manipulate the file 'piano.wav' to produce a snippet of music. This file is a recording[3] of a single note played on a piano. Other files provided in the resource center are the same note played on a variety of instruments.

Musically speaking, if a sound is played at twice its natural frequency, it is heard as one musical octave higher. The steps from one note to the next higher octave are divided into 7 steps, 5 whole note steps and 2 half note steps, for a total of 12 half note steps. These 12 half steps are arranged in geometric order where the ratio between half steps is $2^{1/12}$.

There are a few practical issues to deal with in this simple example:

- Since they are played at different frequencies, we cannot concatenate different notes in the same sound file.
- Changing the playback frequency also changes the duration of the note since it consumes more or less data items in a given period of time. We therefore have to manage the number of data items sent to the **sound(...)** function.
- The **sound(...)** function starts playing the sound, but immediately continues to the next line of code. It is therefore necessary to pause until the sound is finished playing before continuing to process the next sound.

Consider the following code that plays a major scale with the piano note, and saves the values of the frequencies and durations.

```
[note, Fs] = wavread('piano.wav');
duration = floor(length(note)/8);
wait = duration / Fs;
whole = 2^(1/6);
half = 2^(1/12);
for i = 1:8
    dur(i) = duration;
    freq(i) = Fs;
    sound(note(1:duration), Fs);
    pause(wait)
    if (i == 3) || (i == 7)
        Fs = Fs * half;
        duration = round(duration * half);
    else
        Fs = Fs * whole;
        duration = round(duration * whole);
    end
end
```

Table 102—Playing a Scale

---

[3] Credit: http://chronos.ece.miami.edu/~dasp/samples/samples.html.

Now we extend the above script by using an array of note frequencies and durations to play a simple tune. The form of the tune specification is illustrated in Figure 54.

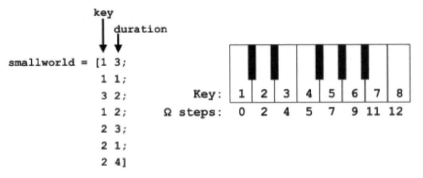

Figure 54—Structure of a Tune File

```
%           pitch length
smallworld = [ 1 3; 1 1; 3 2; 1 2; 2 3; 2 1; 2 4]
l = length(smallworld);
for i = 1:l
    f = freq(smallworld(i,1));
    d = dur(smallworld(i,1)) * smallworld(i,2);
    sound(note(1:d), f);
    pause(wait*smallworld(i,2));
end
```

Table 103—Playing a Simple Tune

18.4.3. Changing Sound Frequency—Well

The third time domain exercise is to manipulate the piano note file to produce a snippet of music at the same playback frequency throughout. In order to change the note frequency without changing the playback frequency, we have to remove the appropriate number of data samples from the original data file. It turns out, as illustrated in the script in Table 104, that MATLAB's array indexing is more general than we have so far discussed.

```
[note Fs] = wavread('piano.wav');
base = length(note);
sound(note, Fs);
pause(base/Fs);  % playing time of note
sound(note(ceil(1:1.3:end)), Fs);   % Note 1
pause(base/(1.3*Fs));
sound(note(ceil(1:0.5:end)), Fs);   % Note 2
```

Table 104—Changing a Note Frequency

Notes:
1. Here, we request a vector at a spacing of 1.3. As you will observe if you run this script, MATLAB does exactly what we might have hoped—removing data samples at regular intervals to reduce the length of the vector by a factor of 1/1.3, thereby raising the note frequency.
2. Perhaps even more remarkable, if the step size is less than 1, MATLAB replicates sufficient data points (in this case, every data point) to increase the size of the file, thereby lowering the frequency of the note.

Table 105 shows a script that uses this function to play the C Major scale on the piano. It repeatedly shortens the vector **newNote** to increase the frequency of the note played.

```
[note, Fs] = wavread('piano.wav');
half = 2^(1/12);
whole = half^2;
C = 266;
oldF = C;
newNote = note;
for index = 1:8
    sound(newNote, Fs);
    pause(.5);
    if (index == 3) || (index == 7)
        mult = half;
    else
        mult = whole;
    end
    newF = oldF * mult;
    newNote = newNote(ceil(1:mult:end));
    oldF = newF;
end;
```

Table 105—Playing a Scale

Table 106 illustrates a script to build a playable **.wav** file using the technique above. It uses the array **steps** to decide how many half-tone steps are necessary to reach the nth note on the scale, and the array **doremi** to define the tune. The array **doremi** has the format illustrated in Figure 54—the first column specifies the pitch (the note on the scale), and the second the duration in "beats". The script sets the beat time to be 0.2 seconds.

The goal of the script is to put the notes into a single sound array called **tune** rather than playing the notes "on the fly," as illustrated in Figure 55.

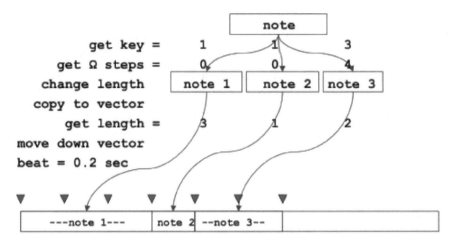

Figure 55—Constructing a Tune Vector

This is accomplished by:

- Creating an empty array, **tune**, of the appropriate length (the length of the original note plus the total number of beats in the song)
- Initializing **storeAt** to store the first note at the start of the tune
- Iterating across the **tune** definition array **doremi** with the following steps:
  - Starting with the original **note**
  - Deciding how many times to raise the **note** array by half a step
  - Raising the **note** to the right pitch and saving it as **theNote**
  - Adding that **theNote** vector to the **tune** vector starting at **storeAt**
  - Moving the **storeAt** variable down the **tune** vector a distance equivalent to the duration of that note.

When all the notes have been added to the tune file, play the tune and save it as a **.wav** file.

```
[note, Fs] = wavread('piano.wav');
half = 2^(1/12);
doremi = [1 3; 2 1; 3 3; 1 1; 3 2; 1 2; 3 4; 2 3;
          3 1; 4 1; 4 1; 3 1; 2 1; 4 8; 3 3; 4 1;
          5 3; 3 1; 5 2; 3 2; 5 4; 4 3; 5 1; 6 1;
          6 1; 5 1; 4 1; 6 4 ];
dt = .2;
nCt = floor(dt*Fs);
s = sum(doremi);
```
(Continued)

Table 106—Building a Tune File

```
overall = s(2)*nCt + length(note);
tune = zeros(overall,1);
ln = length(doremi);
storeAt = 1;
for index = 1:ln
    sndi = doremi(index,1);
    pow = steps(sndi)
    theNote = note(ceil(1:half^pow:end));
    noteLength = length(theNote);
    noteEnd = storeAt + noteLength - 1;
    tune(storeAt:noteEnd,1) =  theNote;
    storeAt = storeAt + doremi(index,2) * nCt;
end
sound(tune, Fs)
wavwrite(tune, Fs, 'dohAdeer.wav')
```

Table 106—Building a Tune File *(Continued)*

18.5. The Fast Fourier Transform

As we saw above, typically, a time history display shows you the amplitude of the sound as a function of time, but makes no attempt at showing the frequency content. In general, a spectrum display shows the amount of sound energy in a given frequency band throughout the duration of the sound analyzed, but ignores the time at which the sound at that frequency was generated.[4]

Figure 56—A Typical Amplifier[5]

We frequently encounter the results of applying the Fourier Transform to a sound file. Many acoustic amplifiers include two features that allow you to customize the sound output:

· A spectral display indicating the amount of sound energy (vertically) in different frequency bands (horizontally), and
· Filter controls to change the relative amplification in different frequency bands.

These features are illustrated in Figure 56—the spectral display in the top right, and the filter controls in the bottom center. To achieve the motion of these bands, the transformation between

---

[4] Way beyond the scope of this course, MATLAB provides a Wavelets toolbox that allows you to experiment with Wavelet transforms that can present a 3-D plot of both the time and frequency dependency of sound energy.

[5] Credit to WinAmp.

a segment of the sound file and the spectral display runs periodically. Typically, perhaps 20 times a second, 1/20th second of sound file is analyzed and transformed.

The mathematics of the Fourier transform are beyond the scope of this book. However, we can make use of the tools it offers without concerning ourselves with the mathematics. There are a number of implementations of the Fourier transform, perhaps the most commonly used is the Fast Fourier Transform (fft). The fft uses clever matrix manipulations to optimize the mathematics needed to generate the forward (time to frequency) and reverse (frequency to time) transforms.

Figure 57 illustrates the overall process of transforming between the time domain and frequency domain. It starts with a simple sound file, a vector of **N** sound values in the range (−1.0 to 1.0), which, if played back at a sample frequency **Fs** entries per second, reproduces the sound. Examining the parameters involved, we see the following:

- **N**—the number of samples;
- **Fs**—the sampling frequency;
- **Δt**—the time between samples, is computed as **1/Fs**; and
- **tmax**—the maximum time is **N × Δt**.

The fft consumes a file with these parameters and produces a frequency spectrum with a corresponding set of parameters. It consists of the same number, **N**, of data points, each of which are complex values with real and imaginary parts[6]. The frequency values are "folded" on the plot so that zero frequency occurs at either end of the spectrum, and the maximum frequency occurs in the middle, at spectrum data point **N/2**.

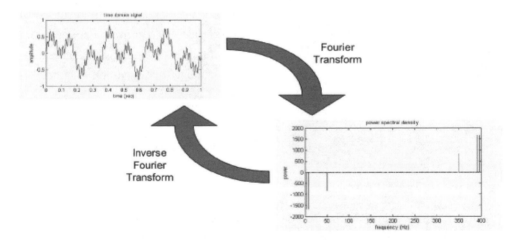

Figure 57—Overview of the Fast Fourier Transform

---

[6] Many displays plot the magnitude of the spectrum values, but to accomplish the inverse transform, the complex values must be retained.

The equivalent parameters for the spectrum data are:

- **N**—the number of samples;
- Δ**f**—the frequency difference between samples, is computed as **1/tmax**;
- **fmax**—the maximum frequency **is** ½ **x N x** Δ**f**.

The inverse fft, **ifft(...)** takes a spectrum array with these parameters and reconstructs the time history. This pair of functions provides a powerful set of tools for manipulating sound files.

Table 107 illustrates a script that creates 10 seconds of an 8 Hz sine wave, plots the first second of it, performs the **fft**, and plots the real and imaginary parts of the spectrum. Notice the following:

- a sine wave in the time domain transforms to a line in the frequency domain because all its energy is concentrated at that frequency—8Hz in this example.
- Since the **fft** is a linear process, multiple sine or cosine waves added together at different frequencies have additive effects in the spectrum.
- As stated above, the resulting spectrum is complex (with real and imaginary parts) and symmetrical about its center, the point of maximum frequency.[7]
- The real part is mirrored about the center; the imaginary part is mirrored and inverted.
- The phase part of the complex spectrum retains the position of the sine wave in the time domain—it would be totally real for a cosine wave symmetrically placed in time, and totally imaginary for a sine wave in the same relationship.
- The detailed explanation for the large value of the amplitude of the peaks in the spectrum is beyond the scope of this text. It should suffice to observe that the spectral energy that was spread across the time domain has been integrated into this one value in the frequency domain[8].

```
subplot(2, 2, 1)
dt = 1/400              % sampling period (sec)
pts = 10000             % number of points
f = 8                   % frequency
t = (1:pts) * dt;       % time array for plotting
x = sin(2*pi*f*t);                                  (Continued)
```

Table 107—Transforming a Simple Sine Wave

---

[7] On the MATLAB plot, of course, one cannot make the frequency axis labels reduce from the center to the end.

[8] The math involved requires integrating $\sin^2 wt$ across the time signal that results in $t/2 + $ <a fluctuating term>. Since t is in fact 10,000 samples, the steady state value of the spectral amplitude is $N/2 = 5,000$.

```
df = 1 / t(end)         % the frequency interval
fmax = df * pts / 2
plot(t(1:end/25), x(1:end/25));
title('time domain sine wave')
ylabel('amplitude')
xlabel('time (sec)')
subplot(2,2,3)
Y = fft(x);             % perform the transform
f = (1:pts) * 2 * fmax / pts;
                        % frequencies for plotting
plot(f, real(Y))
title('real part')
xlabel('frequency (Hz)')
ylabel('energy')
subplot(2,2,4)
plot(f, imag(Y))
title('imaginary part')
xlabel('frequency (Hz)')
ylabel('energy')
```

Table 107—Transforming a Simple Sine Wave *(Continued)*

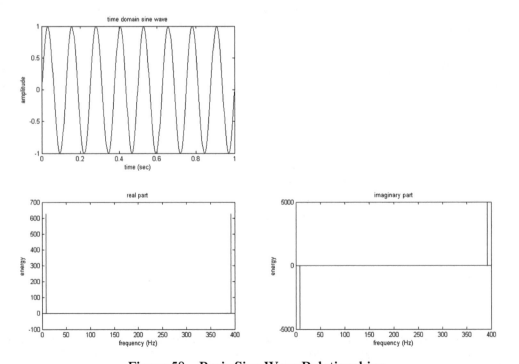

Figure 58—Basic Sine Wave Relationships

18.6. Frequency Domain Operations

We will consider three applications in the frequency domain—analyzing the spectral quality of different musical instruments, inserting a sine wave into the frequency domain, and digital filtering.

18.6.1. Analyzing Instrument Sounds

Table 108 is a function that reads the **.wav** file of an instrument from the music samples in the University of Miami's Audio and Signal Processing Laboratory.[9] All the instruments are carefully playing a note at about 260 Hz. Table 109 is the script that uses this function to plot the data in Figure 59.

It is interesting to notice that:

- all the instruments have significant amounts of energy at even multiples of the source frequency.
- The flute and piano are perhaps the purest tones with the least harmonics.
- The brass, on the other hand, have most of their energy in the 2nd, 3rd and 4th harmonics rather than the base frequency.
- The strings have very strong 3rd harmonic components, and
- Those instruments with noticeable vibrato when played (flute, violin and cello) show a marked fuzziness in their spectral peaks.

```
function inst(name, ttl)

[x, Fs] = wavread([name '.wav']);
N = length(x);
dt = 1/Fs ;         % sampling period (sec)
t = (1:N) * dt;     % time array for plotting
Y = abs(fft(x));    % perform the transform
mx = max(Y);
Y = Y * 100 / mx;
df = 1 / t(end) ;   % the frequency interval
fmax = df * N / 2 ;
f = (1:N) * 2 * fmax / N;
up = floor(N/10);
plot(f(1:up), Y(1:up) );
title(ttl)
xlabel('frequency (Hz)')
ylabel('energy')
```

Table 108—Instrument Analysis Function

---

[9] http://chronos.ece.miami.edu/~dasp/samples/samples.html.

In principle, these characteristic spectral "signatures" can be used to synthesize the sound of instruments, and even to identify individual instruments when played in groups.

```
rows = 4
cols = 2
subplot(rows, cols, 1)
inst('sax','Saxophone');
subplot(rows, cols, 2)
inst('flute', 'Flute');
subplot(rows, cols, 3)
inst('tbone','Trombone');
subplot(rows, cols, 4)
inst('piano', 'Piano');
subplot(rows, cols, 5)
inst('tpt', 'Trumpet');
subplot(rows, cols, 6)
inst('mutetpt', 'Muted Trumpet');
subplot(rows, cols, 7)
inst('violin', 'Violin');
subplot(rows, cols, 8)
inst('cello', 'Cello');
```

Table 109—Instrument Script

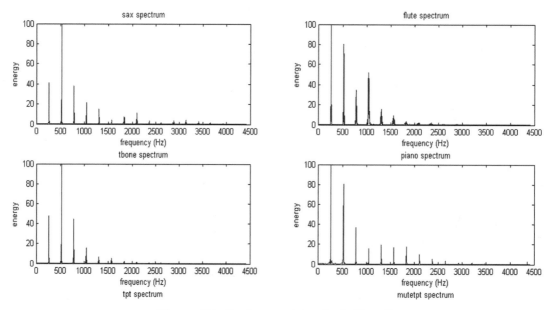

Figure 59—Instrument Analysis Results

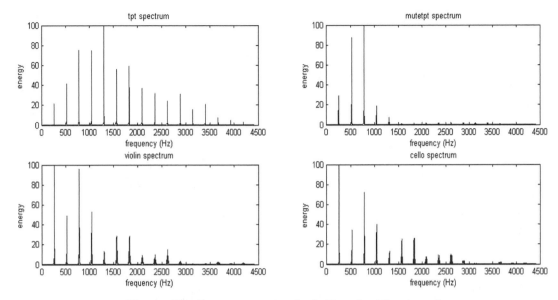

Figure 59—Instrument Analysis Results *(Continued)*

18.6.2. Adding Sounds to the Spectrum

Table 110 shows a script for building a signal with two sine waves (3 Hz and 8 Hz) in the time domain, performing the fft, adding a 50Hz wave in the spectrum and using ifft(. . .) to reconstruct the new time history. Figure 60 shows the results.

```
rows = 2;
cols = 2;
% set up two sine waves
dt = 1/400      % sampling period (sec)
N = 10000       % number of points
f1 = 3          % first frequency
f2 = 8          % second frequency
t = (1:N) * dt; % time array for plotting
x = sin(2*pi*f1*t) + sin(2*pi*f2*t);
subplot(rows, cols, 1)
plot(t(1:(1/dt)), x(1:(1/dt)))
title('original signal')
xlabel('time (sec)')
df = 1 / t(end) % the frequency interval
fmax = df * N / 2
```
(Continued)

Table 110—Adding a Sine Wave

```
Y = fft(x);      % perform the transform
f = (1:N) * 2 * fmax / N; % frequencies for plotting
subplot(rows, cols, 2)    % plot the imaginary part
plot(f(1:N/3), imag(Y(1:N/3)))
title('imag spectrum')
xlabel('frequency (Hz)')
% find the maximum value and location
[level1, index1] = max(imag(Y(1:(N/2))).^2)
[level2, index2] = max(imag(Y((N/2+1):end)).^2)
newF = 50
newBasic = 50 / df
newI1 = newBasic + 1
newI2 = N - newBasic + 1
newV = complex(0, -sqrt(level1)/2)
Y(newI1) = newV;
Y(newI2) = -newV;
subplot(rows, cols, 4)    % plot the imaginary part
plot(f(1:N/3), imag(Y(1:N/3)))
title('imag spectrum with added signal')
xlabel('frequency (Hz)')
y = ifft(Y);
subplot(rows, cols, 3)
plot(t(1:(1/dt)), y(1:(1/dt)))
title('reconstructed the new signal')
xlabel('time (sec)')
```

Table 110—Adding a Sine Wave *(Continued)*

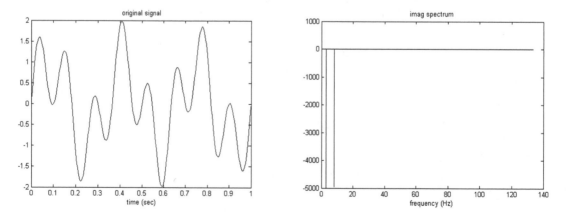

Figure 60—Adding Sine Wave in the Spectrum

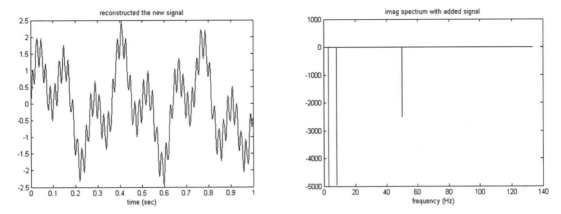

Figure 60—Adding Sine Wave in the Spectrum *(Continued)*

18.6.3. Manipulating the Spectrum

Adding pure sine waves to the spectrum is reasonable straightforward as long as the symmetry of the spectrum components is preserved, and other simple operations are possible. Consider, for example, an apparently simple project. Compare the spectra of the trumpet and the muted trumpet shown on the third row of Figure 59. One might consider operating on the spectrum to apply "digital muting" to the trumpet spectrum. The code in Table 111 implements a crude approximation to such an effort, manually defining the location of the 3rd harmonic, and reducing that to 20% of its original size, and then zero filling the spectrum above that to remove all other harmonics. Figure 61 suggests that the resulting spectrum is superficially similar to a muted trumpet, but if you run the script and listen, even an untrained ear would observe that the sound is not really the same as a real muted trumpet.

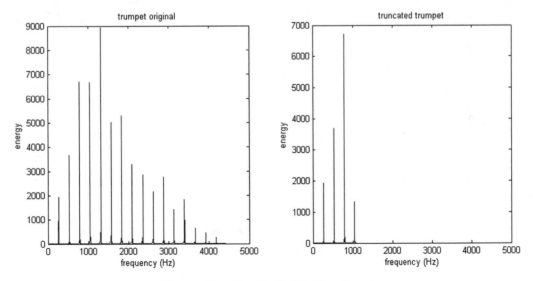

Figure 61—Synthetic Muting Spectra

```
[x, Fs] = wavread('tpt.wav');
N = length(x);
sound(x, Fs)
dt = 1/Fs ;          % sampling period (sec)
t = (1:N) * dt;      % time array for plotting
pause(t(N));
Y = fft(x);          % perform the transform
df = 1 / t(end) ;    % the frequency interval
fmax = df * N / 2 ;
f = (1:N) * 2 * fmax / N;
subplot(1, 2, 1);
frac = floor(N/10);
plot(f(1:frac), abs(Y(1:frac)));
title('trumpet original')
xlabel('frequency (Hz)')
ylabel('energy')
subplot(1, 2, 2);
fhalf = 925; %Hz
ihalf = floor(fhalf / df);
foff = 1100; %Hz
ioff = floor(foff / df);
Y(ihalf:end-ihalf) = Y(ihalf:end-ihalf) * 0.2;
Y(ioff:end-ioff) = 0;
plot(f(1:frac), abs(Y(1:frac)));
title('truncated trumpet')
xlabel('frequency (Hz)')
ylabel('energy')
y = abs(ifft(Y));
mx = max(y);
y = y / mx;
disp('synthetic muted');
sound(y, Fs);
pause(t(N));
disp('real muted');
[x, Fs] = wavread('mutetpt.wav');
mx = max(x);
x = x / mx;
sound(x, Fs)
```

Table 111—Synthetic Muting

18.6.4. Truncating the Spectrum

It is also possible (and left as an exercise for the reader) to truncate the spectrum by deleting, for example, the half of the spectrum located symmetrically in the middle and then performing the inverse transform. The impact of this activity in the time domain is surprising.

18.6.5. Digital Filtering

It is beyond the scope of this text to discuss digital filtering in general, except to observe some practical considerations.

1. Firstly, real data are not nice and tidy like the sine waves we used in some examples. Even the instrument spectra in the examples above which appeared so nice and clean at the resolution at which they were plotted are actually quite fuzzy "up close." Figure 62 shows a close-up of the base of one of the harmonics of the trumpet spectrum.

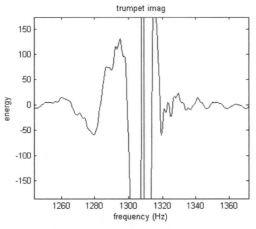

Figure 62—Details of Trumpet Spectrum

2. These instrument examples were carefully recorded in a quiet environment for test purposes. Real data very rarely have nice, quite spectral patches.

3. blanking in the frequency domain such as was done in the muting example above only works tolerably well when the spectrum is essentially zero in that region. Notice that the cutoff frequencies for that example were regions of zero spectral content. If data manipulation in the spectrum introduces sharp data discontinuities, these discontinuities become very loud clicks or "ringing" in the time domain.

4. Practical digital filtering actually involves multiplying the spectrum by smoothed shapes designed to produce certain spectral effects.

5. Most digital filtering actually has to be accomplished in real-time using totally different techniques.

18.7. Examples

18-1 Read in the file bubble.wav and perform the following operations on its data.

    a. Store the sampling period in the variable **dt**.

    b. Store the duration of the sound in the variable **t**.

    c. Store the number of samples in the variable **n**.

    d. Store the difference in frequency between the samples (after the fft) in the variable **df**.

e. Store the maximum frequency in the variable **f_max**.

f. Create an array containing the frequency at each sample in the variable **f**.

g. Create a new sound that has double the frequency of the original sound in the variable **sound_Double**.

h. Create a new sound that is the same as the original except that the pitch is raised by 5 half tones. Store your answer in the variable **raised_pitch**.

i. Plot the original sound, **sound_Double**, and **raised_pitch** all in the same row of a figure using **subplot**. Label each plot accordingly.

j. Play each of the sounds at a sampling frequency of 22050 Hz in the following order:

original sound, **sound_Double**, and **raised_pitch**

k. Plot the sound waveform in both the time and frequency domains. Label your plots appropriately. Use **figure** to start a new figure, and **subplot** (one row, two columns).

18-2 Write and test a script to assemble your own speech from speeches in the resource center or on the Web.

18-3 Write a script to play your favorite tune on one of the instruments in the resource center.

18-4 Write a script to construct a 10 second signal with sine waves of unit amplitude and frequencies 5 Hz and 12 Hz at a sampling rate of 1000 samples per second. Perform the fft on this signal, and remove the 5000 elements in the center of the spectrum. Then, perform the inverse transform, plot and explain your observations.

18-5 When plotting the results from applying a Fast Fourier transform to a sampled sound file, what would be appropriate labels for the x and y axis?

a. x: 'time'   y: 'frequency'

b. x: 'frequency'   y: 'time'

c. x: 'time'   y: 'power'

d. x: 'frequency'   y: 'amplitude'

e. x: 'time'   y: 'amplitude'

18-6 You want to read in a sound 'myfile.wav' and perform a Fast Fourier transform on it. Which of the following lines of code would accomplish this with no errors?

```
a. [a, b] = wavread('myfile.wav'); r = fft(a, b);
b. [c, d] = wavread('myfile.wav'); s = fft(d, c);
c. [e, f] = wavread('myfile.wav'); u = fft(e);
d. [g, h] = wavread('myfile.wav'); t = fft(h);
```

18-7   Congratulations, because of your success while working with acmeClothes over the past few weeks, the company has requested your help again. An agent for acmeClothes has recorded the average clothes rating for the company in a file, **confused.wav**. However, the file has been all scrambled up. Your job is to read the file in, unscramble it, and play it back.

Store your modified waveform (the one that has been unscrambled) in the variable **mySound**. Here is how the file was scrambled:

    a. The file was amplified to 10 percent of its original amplitude.

    b. The order of the words in the file was reversed. Each word in the sound file took one second to say. This means what was the first second in the original sound file is now the last second, and the last second in the original sound file is now the first second.

    c. The file was reversed.

19. IMAGES

19.1. Concepts

Before we confine ourselves the practical, computational reality, we should consider the general nature of what an image is. The easiest answer would be that an image is a two-dimensional sheet on which the color at any point can have essentially infinite variability. However, we must immediately confine ourselves to the conventional representation of images required for most digital display processors. This is illustrated in Figure 63. We can represent any given image as a 2-D array of points usually referred to as *pixels*, each of which is "painted" by blending variable amounts of the three primary colors, red green and blue[1].

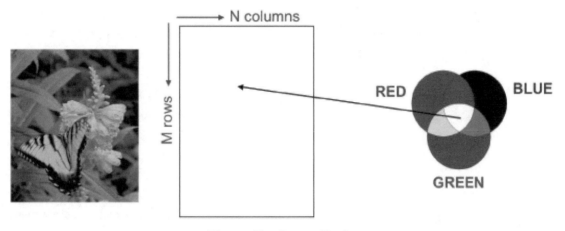

Figure 63—Image Basics

The resolution of the picture is measured by the number of pixels per unit of picture width and height. This governs the fuzziness of its appearance in print, and controls the maximum size of good quality photo printing. The color resolution is measured by the number of bits in the words containing the R-G-B components. Since one value generally exists for each of the MN pixels in the array, increasing the size of the pixel color will have a significant effect on the stored size of the image. Typically, 8 bits (values 0–255) are assigned to each color. By combining the three color values, there are actually 2^{24} different combinations of color available to a true-color image—many more possible combinations than the average eye can detect.

---

[1] Notice that this is not the same blending process used in painting with oils or water colors where the third primary color is yellow, and the combination process is reversed—increasing saturation of the primary colors tends towards black, not white.

19.2. Image Types

Our source for images to process are data files captured by cameras, scanners and graphic arts systems, and occur in a wide variety of file formats. According to the MATLAB documentation, it recognizes files in TIFF, PNG, HDF, BMP, JPEG (JPG), GIF, PCX, XWD, CUR and ICO formats. The various file formats are usually identified by the file extension, but can be defined explicitly for MATLAB.

The result of reading image files is one of three basic internal representations of the image: true color, gray scale or color mapped. Computationally, it is possible to convert a color mapped image to true color[2], but true color or black and white images cannot normally be converted to color mapped format without loss of fidelity in the color representation.

19.2.1. True Color and Gray Scale Images

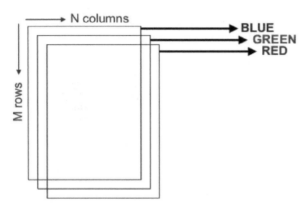

Figure 64—True Color Image Storage

True color images are stored according to the scheme shown in Figure 64 as an MxNx3 array where every pixel is directly stored in three layers of the 3-D array. The first layer contains the red value, the second layer the green value and the third layer the blue value. The advantage of this approach, as the name suggests, is that every pixel can be represented as its true color value without compromise. The only disadvantage is the size of the image in memory since there are three color values for every pixel.

Gray scale images are also directly stored, but save the black-to-white intensity value as a single number rather than three values.

19.2.2. Color Mapped Images

Color mapped or indexed images keep a separate color map either 256 items long (for maximum economy of memory) or up to 32,768 items long. Each item in the color map contains the red, blue and green values of a color respectively.

As illustrated in Figure 65, the image itself is stored as an MxN array of indices into the color map. So for example, a certain pixel index might contain the value 143. The color to be shown at that pixel location would be the 143rd color set (R-G-B) on the color map.

---

[2] Of course, this conversion will do nothing for the color fidelity of the resulting image.

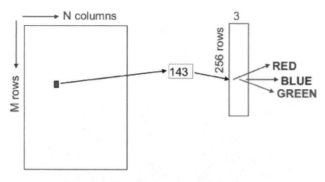

Figure 65—Color Mapped Image

If the color map is restricted to 256 colors, the picture itself can consist of 8 bit values, but the choice of colors is very restricted, and normal pictures of scenery—sky, for instance—take on a "layered color" appearance. They can be used, however, for cartoon pictures where limited color choices are not a problem. Using a larger color map provides a larger, but still sometimes restrictive, range of color choices, but of course, the indices in the picture array must be 16 bit values.

19.2.3. Reading and Writing Images

Unlike the sound readers that have a separate function for each supported sound file type, MATLAB uses only one image reader, **imread(...)** for all image file types. We will not attempt to describe its behavior for all the image file types—the MATLAB help file for **imread(...)** is extremely detailed if you need to read files other than the most common.

We will confine our discussion to the most common file types: Windows bitmap files (BMP), GIF files, and files compressed according to a standard algorithm originally proposed by the Joint Photographic Experts Group (JPEG). These file types happen to return the two data structures described above; JPEG images are decoded as true color images; GIF files and BMP are returned as color mapped images.

Similarly, there is only one function for writing files: **imwrite(...)** that can be used to write most common file formats.

19.3. Operating on Images

Since images are stored as arrays, it is not surprising that we can employ the normal operations of creation, slicing and concatenation.

19.3.1. Creating a Collage

As a motivating example, consider the two images shown in Figure 66. Each are 1600x1200 JPEG images such as can be taken with any good digital camera. However, the cute factor is a little low. What we really want for our family album is a collage consisting of the cute dog without most of the background and the lake picture. Furthermore, it would be nice to have a brown-colored frame and a light yellow mat setting off the two pictures.

Figure 66—Original Images

Before we begin coding, we should draw a diagram in detail to understand what we are trying to achieve. The diagram is shown in Figure 67, the resulting collage is shown in Figure 68, and the code is shown in Table 112.

Notice that two different manipulations are required: cropping will eliminate the extraneous background in the dog picture. However, now, the lake picture is twice the size of the dog picture. It therefore has to be shrunk by a factor of 2 in each dimension. The easiest way to accomplish that is to eliminate every other row and every other column of the lake picture. This will reduce its resolution, but still retain enough to be pleasant to the eye.

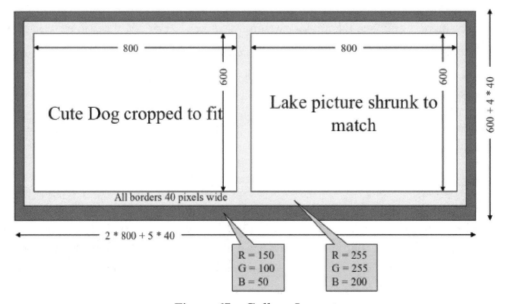

Figure 67—Collage Layout

Figure 68—Resulting Collage

Study the notes in the code for a full understanding of the implementation of this picture.

```
clear
clc
clf

dog = imread('Pep.jpg');
lake = imread('Lake.jpg');
[rows, cols, clrs] = size(dog);          % Note 1
pheight = rows/2; pwidth = cols/2
border = 40;
overallw = 2*pwidth + 5 * border;
overallh = pheight + 4 * border;
frameR = 150; frameG = 100; frameB = 50;
mattR = 255; mattG = 255; mattB = 200;
% make the outside frame
frame = uint8(ones( overallh, overallw ));% Note 2
collage = uint8(zeros( overallh, overallw, 3 ));
collage(:, :, 1) = frame * frameR;       % Note 3
collage(:, :, 2) = frame * frameG;
collage(:, :, 3) = frame * frameB;
% insert the matt
matt = uint8(ones( overallh - 2*border, ... % Note 4
                overallw - 2*border ));
```
                                                  (Continued)

Table 112—Collage Script

```
collage(border+1:overallh-border,...
        border+1:overallw-border,1) = matt * mattR;
collage(border+1:overallh-border,...
        border+1:overallw-border,2) = matt * mattG;
collage(border+1:overallh-border,...
        border+1:overallw-border,3) = matt * mattB;
% crop the dog picture
left = 180;  % a judgment call              Note 5
dogCr = dog( end - pheight + 1: end,...
             left + 1: left + pwidth, :);
collage(2*border+1:2*border + pheight,...   % Note 6
        2*border+1:2*border + pwidth, :) = dogCr;
% shrink the lake picture
lakeSh = lake( 1:2:end, 1:2:end, :);
collage(2*border+1:2*border + pheight,...   % Note 7
        3*border+pwidth+1:3*border+2*pwidth,:)...
                                        = lakeSh;
image(collage)
axis equal                                  % Note 8
axis off
imwrite(collage,'collage.jpg','jpg')
```

Table 112—Collage Script *(Continued)*

Notes:

1. Be careful requesting the size of 3-D (and more) arrays. If you leave off variables—as here, you might be tempted not to ask for colors because you know it's 3—the **size(...)** function multiplies together the remaining dimension sizes! So **[r,c] = size(dog)** would return **r = 1200** and **c = 4800**!

2. JPEG files store the colors as 8 bit unsigned integers, of type **uint8**. Since **ones(...)** naturally produces an array of type **double**, we have to cast it to type **uint8** by calling the function **uint8(...).**

3. This loads the three color layers with the values specified in **FRAMER** etc.

4. The rectangle for the matt is two borders smaller (one each side / end) than the frame, and must be positioned one border in from the frame edge in the collage.

5. Looking at the dog picture, we must decide where to cut off the background. Considering the rows, it is pretty clear that the bottom rows should be kept. However, we need to cut off a little to the left and a lot to the right, so setting a variable for the left cutoff allows one to look at the results and adjust the position of the dog in the clipped picture.

6. The clipped dog picture is inserted into the collage two borders from the top and 2 borders from the left.

7. The shrunken lake picture is inserted into the collage two borders from the top and 3 borders plus the width of the dog picture from the left.

8. In cleaning up, the two axis commands make sure that the x and y scales are equal to avoid distortion in the image, and turn off the unwanted numerical boundaries. The image is then written out as a JPEG file.

19.3.2. Changing Color Maps

Figure 69[3] is an example of a GIF format file that is read into MATLAB as a 270x180 array of indices in **uint8** form, and a 256x3 array of **doubles** representing the color values in the range 0 .. 1. All of the cropping and shrinking operations used above are available with this image format together with the ability to replace the color map with a different map. There are a number of color maps built into MATLAB that can be substituted. For instance, the picture in Figure 70 was created by reading the L-1011 image, rendering it and then replacing the color map. The code to do this is:

Figure 69—A GIF Image

```
[pln map] = imread('L1011.bmp');
image(pln); colormap(map);
pause;
colormap bone;
```

19.4. Advanced Image Manipulation

We include here a couple of examples of more advanced image manipulation to offer some ideas of the scope and power that MATLAB provides. The first, an artistic artifice uses some simple built-in array operators to create the effect of a Kaleidoscope. The second more practical section discusses the issues associated with edge detection.

Figure 70—Bone Color Map

---

[3] Copyright Lockheed Martin Corporation

19.4.1. Creating a Kaleidoscope

Figure 71 illustrates the geometric manipulation necessary to create a kaleidoscope picture, Figure 72 shows the results, while Table 113 and Table 114 show the code used to generate the images. The overall logic flow matches the figure below:

- Disassemble the picture into 4 quadrants
- Rotate each quadrant the appropriate number of 90° turns
- Mirror the quadrant
- Rotate the mirrored quadrant back to its original orientation

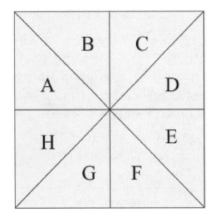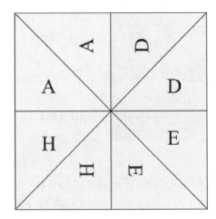

Figure 71—Creating a Kaleidoscope

Figure 72—Kaleidoscope Pictures

```
sb  = imread('sqbutter.jpg');
subplot( 1, 2, 1);
cols = length(sb);
image(sb);
mid = cols/2
subplot( 1, 2, 2);
img = [diagMirror( sb(1:mid,     1:mid, :), 0 ) ...
       diagMirror( sb(1:mid,     mid+1:end, :), 3 );
       diagMirror( sb(mid+1:end, 1:mid, :), 1 ) ...
       diagMirror( sb(mid+1:end, mid+1:end, :), 2 )];
image(img);
```

Table 113—Script for Kaleidoscope

```
function sq = diagMirror(A, code)
% mirror this square diagonally
% code = represents the number of
%               90 deg left rotations

for c = 1:3  % tacky to do a layer at a time, but
             % tril must see a 2-D array
    layer = A(:,:,c);
    trin = tril(rotated(layer, code));
           % rotate the image back after mirroring
    sq(:,:,c) = rotated(trin + trin', 4 - code);
end

function B = rotated(A, code)
n = code;
if n == 4
    n = 0
end
B = A;
for i = 1:n
    B = rot90(B);
end
```

Table 114—Diagonal Mirror Function

19.4.2. Detecting Edges

While images are powerful methods of delivering information to the human eye, they have limitations when being used by computer programs. Our eyes have an astonishing ability to see an

Figure 73—C-130 Image

image such as that shown in Figure 73 and interpret its content. Even a novice observer would have no difficulty seeing that it is a picture of an aircraft in flight. An experienced observer would be able to identify the type of aircraft as a Lockheed C-130, and perhaps some other characteristics of the aircraft.

While our eyes are excellent at interpreting images, computer programs need a lot of help. One operation commonly performed to reduce the complexity of an image is edge detection. Here the complete image is replaced by a very small number of points that mark the edges of "interesting artifacts." However, a simple program attempting to perform

Figure 74—C-130 Outline

such an apparently "simple" task also uncovers some of the obvious limitations of image understanding.

Figure 74 shows the results from a simple program attempting to paint the outline of the aircraft in white by putting a white pixel at an identified edge. The key feature used to identify an edge is a selected intensity threshold. An edge is defined as a pixel where some of the surrounding pixels are brighter than the threshold, and some dimmer.

While this has greatly reduced the complexity of the picture content, it has actually introduced more uncertainty. For example, can you now determine whether the aircraft is flying towards you or away from you? On the original picture, a study of the subtleties of shading at the nearest wing roots suggests it is flying away, but all that information has been lost. Can you even determine whether the engines are turning? Obviously so in the picture, but not on the outline.

The particular program used to generate this picture is shown in Table 115.

```
pic = imread('C-130.jpg');
[rows, cols, cl] = size(pic);

amps = uint16(pic(:,:,1))...
     + uint16(pic(:,:,2))...
     + uint16(pic(:,:,3));
up = max(max(amps))
dn = min(min(amps))
fact = .5
thresh = uint16(dn + fact * (up - dn))

pix = amps(2:end, 2:end);
ptl = amps(1:end-1, 1:end-1);
 pt = amps(1:end-1, 2:end);
 pl = amps(2:end, 1:end-1);

allup = and(and((pix > thresh),(pt > thresh)),...
            and((pl  > thresh), (ptl  > thresh)));
alldn = and(and((pix <= thresh), (pt <= thresh)),...
            and((pl <= thresh), (ptl <= thresh)));
edges = and(not(allup), not(alldn));
layer = zeros(rows-1, cols-1);
layer(edges) = 1;
outline(:,:,1) = layer;
outline(:,:,2) = layer;
outline(:,:,3) = layer;
image(outline)
imwrite(outline, 'c-130 edges.jpg','jpg')
```

Table 115—Edge Detection Script

Note:

Notice that the program determines the minimum and maximum intensity of the picture, and then sets the threshold to some fraction of those values.

19.5. Examples

19-1 Consider the following "image" (assume it is a perfect square), saved under the file 'mysquare.jpg':

1	2
3	4

And the following code:

```
b = imread('mysquare.jpg');
[n,m,l] = size(b);
a = b(1:end, 1:n/2, :);
c = b(1:end, (n/2 + 1):end, :);
b = [c a];
imshow(b);
```

Which of these will the picture shown on the last line most resemble?

a.

1	2
3	4

b.

2	1
4	3

c.

1
2
3
4

d.

3
4
1
2

19-2   Given an image file called 'american_flag.jpg' in which the colors are only red, white, and blue, and the following code:

```
af = imread('american_flag.jpg');
[r1,c1] = find(af(:,:,1) == 255 ...
          && af(:,:,2) == 0 ...
          && af(:,:,3) == 0);
[r2,c2] = find(af(:,:,1) == 0 ...
          && af(:,:,2) == 0 ...
          && af(:,:,3) == 255);
[r3,c3] = find(af(:,:,1) == 255 ...
          && af(:,:,2) == 255 ...
          && af(:,:,3) == 255);
af(r1,c1,:) = 0;
af(r2,c2,:) = 255;
af(r3,c3,2:3) = 0;
image(af)
```

What happens in the resulting image?

19-3   Given the following code:

```
buzz = imread('GTBuzz.jpg');
```

Which of the following lines of code would cause buzz to be displayed in the most green color?

a. `buzz(:, :, 1) = 0;`

b. `buzz(:, :, 1) = 255;`

c. `buzz(:, :, 2) = 0;`

d. `buzz(:, :, 2) = 255;`

e. `buzz(:, :, 3) = 0;`

f. `buzz(:, :, 3) = 255;`

19-4 The edge detection algorithm in Section 19.4.2 applies only to true color images. Rewrite it to apply it to bit mapped images.

19-5 Write a script that reads the image 'uselessTA.jpg' and converts it into a RGB matrix. The script then displays a sub-image of uselessTA.jpg. The sub-image starts at pixel number 50 on both the x and y axis. The height and width of the sub-image are each 50 pixels.

19-6 Consider this code that reads in an image saved as 'myimage.jpg':

```
b = imread('myimage.jpg');
[m,n,l] = size(b);
count = 0;
for i = 1:m
  for j = 1:n
    if ( <A> (double(b(i, j, <B> )))) == <C>
        count = count + 1;
    end
  end
end
```

What would you put in the place of **<A>**, **<B>** and **<C>** to give you the number of completely white pixels in the image?

19-7 You are provided an image and your job is to convert the full-sized image to one that is 1/4 of the original size. Normally when image processing software is required to resize an image, a complex resizing algorithm is used to accomplish the conversion. We will attempt to duplicate this conversion.

Write a function called *resizeMe* that takes in a string as an input corresponding to an image file name. The function should then resize the image to 1/4 its original size and display it.

Additionally your function should use the built-in function `imwrite` to create an image file containing the new image, named with the original file name preceded by 'SM'. For example, if the original filename is called 'yellow_bird.jpg', the new file should be called 'SMyellow_bird.jpg'.

Note: Your function should work with ALL .jpg files! So be sure to test it with multiple files of different sizes. Remember image matrices have to be of type `uint8`, so make sure to cast the result at the end.

You must use iteration to accomplish this task.

Hint: To generate a pixel in the smaller image, take the average of 4 pixels that make up a square at that position in the original image.

19-8   Write a function called ***IMrotate*** that takes in an image matrix and a number. The number represents the number of times the function will rotate the image by 90 degrees. A negative number signifies counter-clockwise rotation and a positive one signifies clockwise rotation.

Hint: Rotating counter-clockwise once is the same as rotating clockwise three times.

20. NUMERICAL METHODS

Real-world data is rarely in such a form that you can use it immediately. This section[1] discusses four fundamental techniques for operating on real data to recover the required information:

- Interpolation to "fill in holes" in sparse data;
- Curve fitting to remove random noise from data samples;
- Numerical integration to compute a cumulative sum; and
- Numerical differentiation to compute its rate of change.

20.1. Interpolation

Interpolation is a technique by which we estimate a variable's value between two known values. There are a number of different techniques for this, but in this section we present the two most common types of interpolation: linear interpolation and cubic-spline interpolation. In both techniques, we assume that we have a set of data points which represents a set of x-y coordinates for which y is a function of x; that is, $y = f(x)$. We then have a value of x that is not part of the data set for which we want to find the y value. (See Figure 75.)

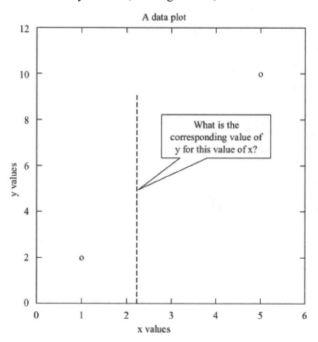

Figure 75—Interpolation Between Data Points

---

[1] Chapter 8 of Etter, Kuncicki & Moore "Introduction to MATLAB® 7" ISBN 0-13-147492-8.

20.1.1. Linear Interpolation

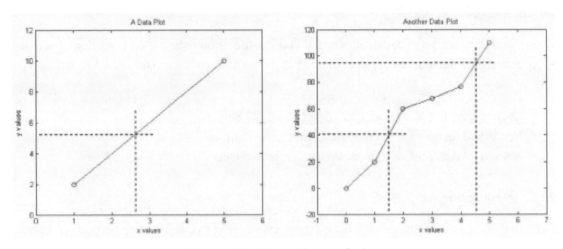

Figure 76—Linear Interpolation

Linear interpolation is one of the most common techniques for estimating data values between two given data points. With this technique, we assume that the function between the points can he estimated by a straight line drawn between the points. (See Figure 76.) If we find the equation of a straight line defined by the two known points, we can find y for any value of x. The closer together the points are, the more accurate our approximation is likely to be. Of course, we could use this equation to extrapolate points past our collected data. This is rarely wise, however, and often leads to large errors.

20.1.2. The `interp1` Function

Hint: The last character in the function name **interp1** is a one. Depending on the font, it may look like the letter L.

The MATLAB function that performs interpolation, **interp1**, has two forms. Each form assumes that vectors **x** and **y** contain the original data values and that another vector **x_new** contains the new point or points for which we want to compute interpolated **y_new** values. (The **x** values should be in ascending order, and the **x_new** values should be within the range of the x values.) These forms are demonstrated in the following examples.

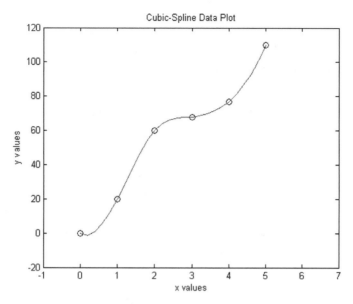

Figure 77—Cubic-Spline Interpolation

The points in Figure 76 and Figure 77 were generated with the following commands:

```
x = 0:5;
y = [0, 20, 60, 68, 77, 110];
```

Suppose we would like to find a value for **y**, if **x** = **1.5**. Unfortunately, **1.5** is not one of the elements in the **x** vector, so we'll need to perform an interpolation:

```
interp1(x, y ,1.5)
```

which returns:

```
ans =
        40
```

We can see from Figure 76 that this answer corresponds to a linear interpolation between the **x**, **y** points at **(1,20)** and **(2,60)**. The function **interp1** defaults to linear interpolation unless otherwise specified.

If, instead of a scalar value of new **x** values, we define an array of new **x** values, the function returns an array of new **y** values:

```
new_x = 0:0.2:5;
new_y = interp1(x,y,new_x);
```

The new calculated points are plotted in Figure 78. They all fall on a straight line connecting the original data points. The commands to generate the graph are:

```
plot(x, y, new_x, new_y, 'o')
axis([-1,7,-20,120])
title('linear Interpolation Plot')
xlabel('x values')
ylabel('y values')
```

If we wish to use a cubic spline interpolation approach, we must add a fourth argument to the **interp1** function. The argument must be a string. The choices are:

'nearest'	nearest neighbor interpolation
'linear'	linear interpolation—which is the default
'spline'	piecewise cubic spline interpolation (SPLINE)
'pchip'	shape-preserving piecewise cubic interpolation
'cubic'	same as **'pchip'**
'v5cubic'	the cubic interpolation from MATLAB 5, which does not extrapolate, and uses **'spline'** if X is not equally spaced.

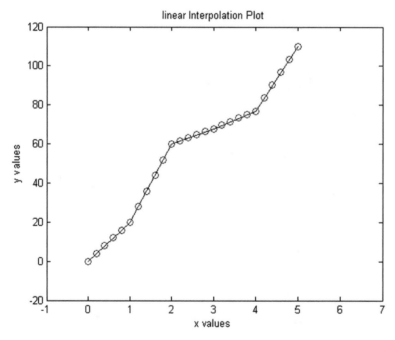

Figure 78—Interpolated Data Points

To find the value of **y** at **x = 1.5** using a cubic spline, type

```
interp1(x, y, 1.5, 'spline')
```

which returns

```
ans =
     42.2083
```

Referring to Figure 77, we see that this corresponds to our graph of a cubic spline. To generate a vector of new y values, we use the same procedure as before:

```
new_y = interp1(x, y, new_x, 'spline');
```

The results are plotted in Figure 79. The original points are connected with a straight line. The curved plot is constructed from the calculated points. (Remember, all MATLAB plots are constructed of straight line segments, but these are close enough together to approximate a curve.) The commands needed to generate Figure 79 are

```
plot(x, y, '-x', new_x, new_y, '-o')
axis([-1,7,-20,120])
title('Spline Interpolation Plot')
xlabel('x values')
ylabel('y values')
```

MATLAB provides two-dimensional (**interp2**) and three-dimensional (**interp3**) interpolation functions, which are not discussed here. Refer to the help feature for more information.

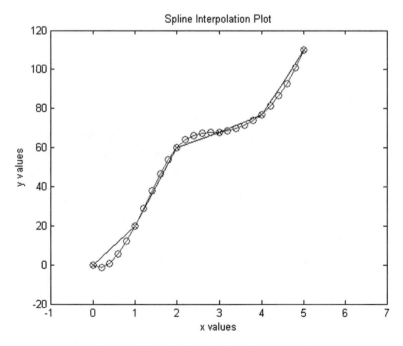

Figure 79—Cubic-Spline Interpolation

20.1.3. Cubic-Spline Interpolation

A cubic spline is a smooth curve constructed to go through a set of points. The curve between each pair of points is a third-degree polynomial that has the general form:

$$a_0 x^3 + a_1 x^2 + a_2 x + a_3$$

which is computed so that it provides a smooth curve between the two points and a smooth transition from the third-degree polynomial between the previous pair of points. See Figure 77. A total of five different cubic equations were used to generate this smooth function that joins all six points.

20.1.4. The `spline` Function

MATLAB implements the cubic spline with the `spline(...)` function with the same form as `interp1(...)`:

```
new_y = spline(x, y, new_x);
```

20.2. Curve Fitting

Assume that we have a set of data points collected from an experiment. After plotting the data points, we find that they generally fall in a straight line. However, if we were to try to draw a straight line through the points, only a couple of the points would probably fall exactly on the line. A least-squares curve fitting method could be used to find the straight line that is the closest to the points, by minimizing the distance from each point to the straight line. Although this line can be considered a "best fit" to the data points, it is possible that none of the points would actually fall on the line of best fit. (Note that this method is very different from interpolation, because the curves used in linear interpolation and cubic-spline interpolation actually contained all of the original data points.) In this section, we first discuss fitting a straight line to a set of data points, and then we discuss fitting a polynomial to a set of data points.

20.2.1. Linear Regression

Linear regression is the name given to the process that determines the linear equation that is the best fit to a set of data points in terms of minimizing the sum of the squared distances between the line and the data points. To understand this process, we first consider the following set of data values:

```
x = 0:5;
y = [0 20 60 68 77 110];
```

If we plot these points, it appears that a good estimate of a line through the points is $y = 20 x$, as shown in Figure 80. This process is sometimes called "eyeballing it" meaning that no calculations were done, but it looks like a good fit.

The following commands were issued to generate the plot:

```
y2 = 20 * x;
plot(x, y, 'o', x, y2);
axis([-1 7 -20 120])
title('Linear Estimate')
xlabel('Time (sec)')
ylabel('Temperature (degrees F)')
grid
```

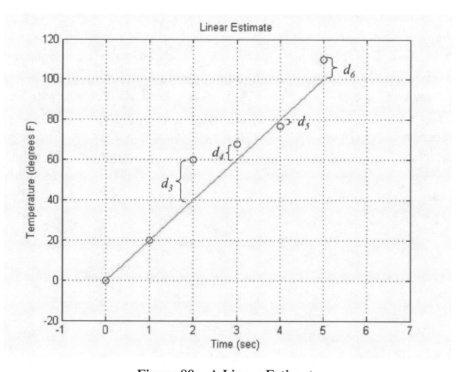

Figure 80—A Linear Estimate

Looking at the plot, we can see that the first two points appear to fall exactly on the line, but the other points are off by varying amounts. We need the ability to compare the quality of the fit of this line to other possible estimates, so we first find the difference between the actual y value and the value calculated from the estimate (in this case, $y = 20x$).

x	y(actual)	y2(calculated)	difference = y−y2
0	0	0	0
1	20	20	0
2	60	40	20
3	68	60	8
4	77	80	−3
5	110	100	10

Now, the question is how to combine these differences to evaluate this estimate. If we were to sum the differences, some of the positive and negative values would cancel each other out and give a result that could over-state the accuracy of the estimate. To avoid this problem, we could add the absolute value of the differences, or we could square them. The *least squares technique* uses the latter approach where the measure of the quality of the fit is the sum of the squared distances between the points and the linear estimates. This sum can be computed with the following command:

```
>> sum_sq = sum((y-y2)^2)
```

For this set of data, the value of **sum_sq** is **573**.

If we drew another line through the points, we could compute the sum of squares that corresponds to the new line. Of the two lines, the better fit is provided by the line with the smaller sum of squared distances. MATLAB uses techniques from calculus to minimize the sum of squared distances and arrive at the best-fit line. The MATLAB commands for doing this are described in Section 20.2.3 below. Figure 81 shows the best fit results of a linear regression analysis for our data. The corresponding sum of squares is **356.8190**, a significant improvement over our original guess.

We call it linear regression when we derive the equation of a straight line, but more generally it is called polynomial regression. The linear equation used to model the data is a first-order polynomial.

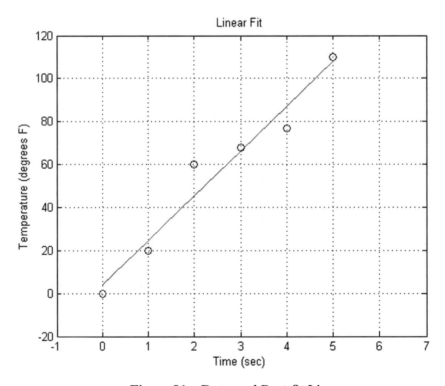

Figure 81—Data and Best-fit Line

20.2.2. Polynomial Regression

Linear regression is a special case of the polynomial regression technique. Recall that a polynomial with one variable can be written by using the following formula:

$$f(x) = a_0 x^n + a_1 x^{n-1} + a_2 x^{n-2} + a_3 x^{n-3} + \dots a_{n-1} x + a_n$$

the degree of a polynomial is equal to the largest value used as an exponent. Therefore, the general form of a cubic (or third order) polynomial is :

$$g(x) = a_0 x^3 + a_1 x^2 + a_2 x + a_3$$

Note that a linear equation is also a polynomial of degree one.

In Figure 82, we plot the original set of data points that we used in the linear regression example, along with plots of the best-fit polynomials with degrees two through five. Note that, as the degree of the polynomial increases, the number of points that fall on the curve also increases. If a set of $n + 1$ points is used to determine an nth degree polynomial, all n points will fall on the polynomial.

20.2.3. The `polyfit` and `polyval` functions

The MATLAB function for computing the best fit to a set of data with a polynomial is **polyfit**. This function has three arguments: the **x** coordinate of the data points, the **y** coordinate of the data points, and the degree **n** of the polynomial. The function returns the coefficients, in descending powers of **x**, of the **nth** degree polynomial used to model the data. For example, using the data

```
x=0:5; y=[0,20,60,68,77,110]
```

the function

```
polyfit(x, y, 1)
```

returns

```
ans =
     20.8286   3.7619
```

So the first-order polynomial that best fits our data is:

$$f(x) = 20.8286x + 3.7169$$

Similarly, we can find other polynomials to fit the data by specifying a higher order in the polyfit equation. Thus,

```
polyfit(x, y, 4)
```

returns

```
ans =
     1.5625  -14.5231 38.6736 -3.4511 -0.3770
```

which corresponds to the 4th order polynomial:

$$f(x) = 1.5625 \ x^4 - 14.5231 \ x^3 + 38.6736 \ x^2 - 3.4511 \ x - 0.3770$$

We could use these coefficients to create equations to calculate new values of y. For example,

```
Y_first_order_fit = 20.8286 * x + 3.7619;
```

and

```
y_fourth_order_fit = 1.5625 * x^4 ...
    - 14.5231 * x^3 + 38.6736 * x^2 ...
    - 3.4511 * x-0.3770
```

or we could use the function **polyval** provided by MATLAB to accomplish the same thing.

The **polyval** function is used to evaluate a polynomial at a set of data points. The first argument of the **polyval** function is a vector containing the coefficients of the polynomial (in an order corresponding to decreasing powers of x), and the second argument is the vector of x values for which we want to calculate corresponding y values.

Fortunately, the polyfit function can provide us the first input:

```
coef = polyfit(x,y,1);
y_first_order_fit = polyfit(coef,x);
```

These two lines of code could be shortened to one line by nesting functions:

```
y_first_order_fit = polyval(polyfit(x,y,1),x);
```

We can use our new understanding of the **polyfit** and **polyval** functions to write a program to create the plots in Figure 82:

```
x = 0:5;
fine_x = 0:.1:5;
y = [0 20 60 68 77 110];
for order = 2:5
    y2=polyval(polyfit(x,y,order), fine_x);
    subplot(2,2,order-1)
    plot(x, y, 'o', fine_x, y2)
    axis([-1 7 -20 120])
    ttl = sprintf('Degree %d Polynomial Fit', order );
    title(ttl)
    xlabel('Time (sec)')
    ylabel('Temperature (degrees F)')
end
```

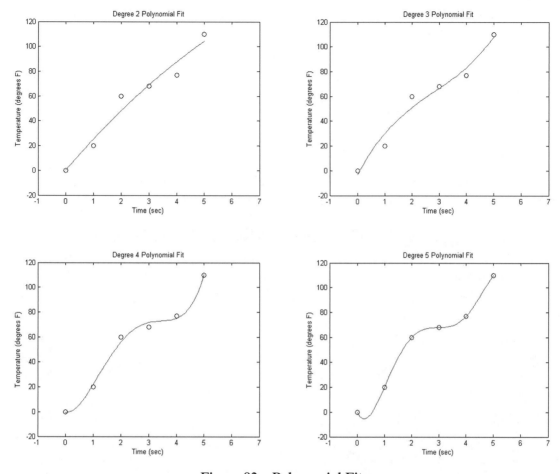

Figure 82—Polynomial Fits

The two new functions discussed in this section are summarized as follows:

polyfit(x,y,n)   Returns a vector of **n + 1** coefficients that represents the best-fit polynomial of degree **n** for the **x** and **y** coordinates provided. The coefficient order corresponds to decreasing powers of **x**.

polyval(coef,x)   Returns a vector of polynomial values **f(x)** that correspond to the **x** vector values. The order of the coefficients corresponds to decreasing powers of **x**.

20.3. Using the Interactive Fitting Tools

MATLAB 7 includes new interactive plotting tools that allow you to annotate your plots without using the command window. The software also includes basic curve fitting, more complicated curve fitting, and statistics tools.

20.3.1. Basic Fitting Tools

To access the basic fitting tools, first create a figure:

```
x = 0:5;
y = [0 20 60 68 77 110];
plot(x, y, 'o')
axis([-1 7 -20 120])
```

These commands create a graph with the same data used in previous sections.

To activate the curve fitting tools, select Tools → Basic Fitting from the menu bar on the figure. The Basic Fitting window opens on top of the plot (see Figure 83). By checking linear and cubic and show equations, the plot shown in Figure 84 is generated.

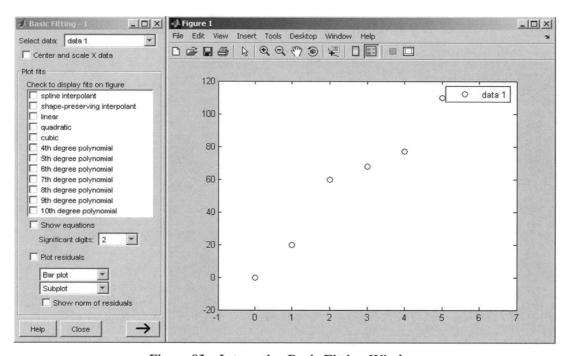

Figure 83—Interactive Basic Fitting Window

Checking the plot residuals box generates a second plot, showing how far each data point is from the calculated line, as shown in Figure 85. Residuals are the difference between the actual and the calculated data points.

In the lower right-hand corner of the Basic Fitting window is an arrow button. Selecting that button twice opens the rest of the Basic Fitting window Figure 86. The center panel of the window shows the results of the curve fit and offers the option of saving those results into the workspace. The right-hand panel allows you to select x values and calculate y values based on the equation displayed in the center panel.

In addition to the Basic Fitting window, you can also access the Data Statistics window (Figure 87) from the figure menu bar. Select Tools-> Data Statistics from the figure window. This window allows you to calculate statistical functions interactively, such as mean and standard deviation, based on the data in the figure, and allows you to save the results to the workspace.

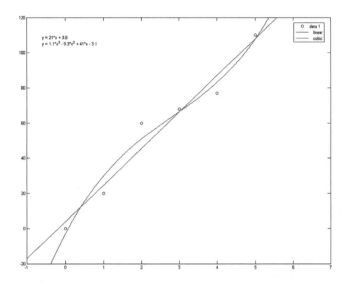

Figure 84—Plot Generated Using the Basic Fitting Window

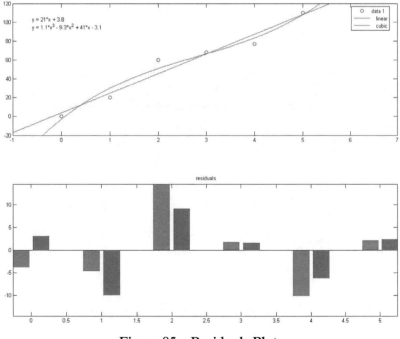

Figure 85—Residuals Plot

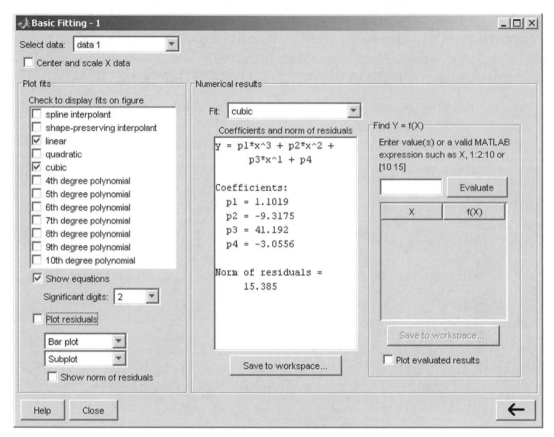

Figure 86—Basic Fitting Window

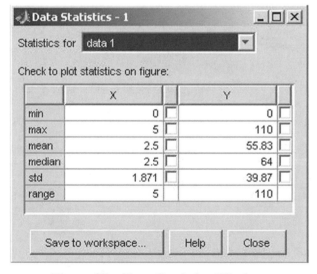

Figure 87—Data Statistics Window

20.3.2. Curve Fitting Toolbox

In addition to the basic fitting utility, MATLAB contains toolboxes to help you perform more specialized statistical and data fitting operations. In particular, the Curve Fitting toolbox contains a GUI (graphical user interface) that allows you to fit curves with more tools than just polynomials.

Before you access the curve fitting toolbox, you'll need a set of data to analyze. We can use the following data:

```
x = 0:5;
y = [0 20 60 68 77 110];
```

To open the curve fitting toolbox, type:

```
cftool
```

This launches the curve fitting tool window. Now you'll need to tell the curve fitting tool what data to use. Select the data button, which will open a data window. The data window has access to the workspace and will let you select an independent *(x)* and dependent *(y)* variable from a drop-down list. (See Figure 88.)

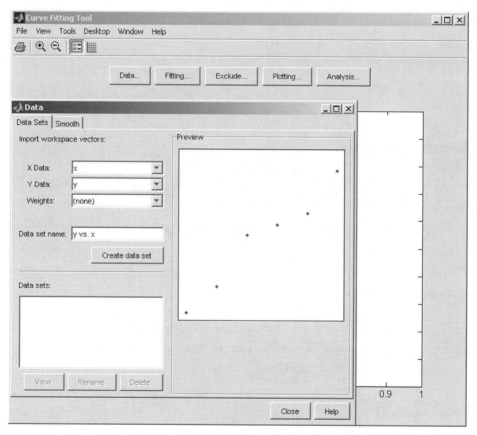

Figure 88—The Curve Fitting and Data Windows

In our example, from the drop-down lists, you should choose x and y, respectively. You can assign a data set name, or MATLAB will assign a name for you. Once you've chosen variables, MATLAB plots the data. At this point you can close the data window.

Going back to the Curve Fitting Tool window, you now select the Fitting button, which offers you choices of fitting algorithms. Select New Fit, and select a fit type from the type of fit list. You can experiment with fitting choices to find the best one for your graph. We chose an interpolated scheme, which forces the plot through all the points, and a third order polynomial. The results are shown in Figure 89.

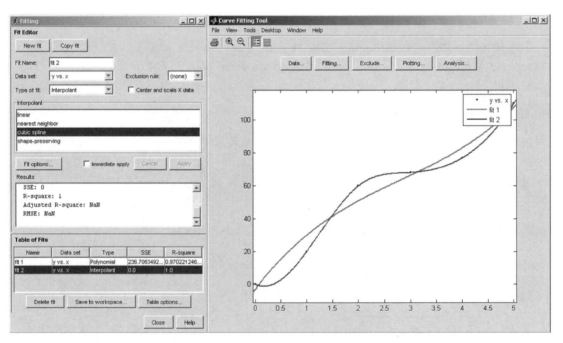

Figure 89—Curve Fitting Windows

20.4. Numerical Integration

The integral of a function *f(x)* over the interval *[a,b]* is defined to be the area under the curve of *f(x)* between *a* and *b,* as shown in Figure 90. If the value of this integral is *K,* the notation to represent the integral of *f(x)* between *a* and *b* is:

$$K = \int_a^b f(x)\, dx$$

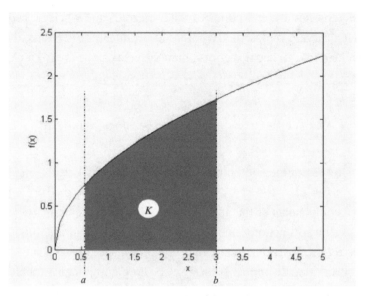

Figure 90—Integrating a Function

For many functions, this integral can be computed analytically. However, for a number of functions, the integral cannot easily be computed analytically and thus requires a numerical technique to estimate its value. The numerical evaluation of an integral is also called quadrature, a term that comes from an ancient geometrical problem.

The numerical integration techniques estimate the function $f(x)$ by another function $g(x)$, where $g(x)$ is chosen so that we can easily compute the area under $g(x)$. Then, the better the estimate of $g(x)$ to $f(x)$, the better will be the estimate of the integral of $f(x)$. Two of the most common numerical integration techniques estimate $f(x)$ with a set of piecewise linear functions or with a set of piecewise parabolic functions. If we estimate the function with piecewise linear functions, we can compute the area of the trapezoids that compose the area under the piecewise linear function; this technique is called the **trapezoidal rule**. If we estimate the function with piecewise quadratic functions, we can compute and add the areas of these components; this technique is called **Simpson's rule**.

20.4.1. Trapezoidal Rule and Simpson's Rule

If the area under a curve is represented by trapezoids and if the interval *[a,b]* is divided into n equal sections, then the area can be approximated by the formula (trapezoidal rule):

$$K_T = \frac{b-a}{2n}(f(x_0) + 2f(x_1) + 2f(x_2) + \ldots + 2f(x_{n-1}) + f(x_n))$$

where the x_i values represent the end points of the trapezoids and where $x_0 = a$ and $x_n = b$.

If the area under a curve is represented by areas under quadratic sections of a curve, and if the interval *[a,b]* is divided into *2n* equal sections, then the area can be approximated by the formula (Simpson's rule):

$$K_s = \frac{h}{3} \left(f(x_0) + 4f(x_1) + 2f(x_2) + 4f(x_3) + \ldots + 2f(x_{2n-1}) + 4f(x_{2n-1}) + f(x_{2n}) \right)$$

where the x_i values represent the end points of the sections and where $x_0 = a$ and $x_{2n} = b$, and $h = (b-a)/(2n)$.

If the piecewise components of the approximating function are higher degree functions (the trapezoidal rule uses linear functions, and Simpson's rule uses quadratic functions), the integration techniques are referred to as Newton-Cotes integration techniques.

The estimate of an integral improves as we use more components (such as trapezoids) to approximate the area under a curve. If we attempt to integrate a function with a singularity (a point at which the function or its derivatives are infinity or are not defined), we may not be able to get a satisfactory answer with a numerical integration technique.

20.4.2. Solving Practical Problems

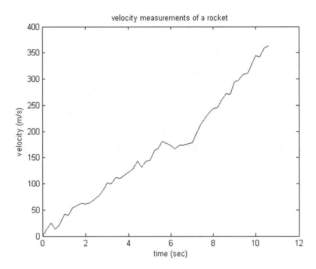

Figure 91—Velocity of a Sounding Rocket

In practice, we are frequently supplied with some practical data representing the behavior of an object over time. For example, we might be given data that represents the velocity of a sounding rocket, such as is plotted in Figure 91. We need to approximate the altitude of the rocket over time by integrating this data using the usual formula:

$$h(t) = \int v(t)\, dt$$

We will accomplish this by developing a function to perform this integration using a variant of the Trapezoidal Rule that permits the time values to be irregularly spaced. The algorithm will compute the sum of the 6 areas shown in Figure 92.

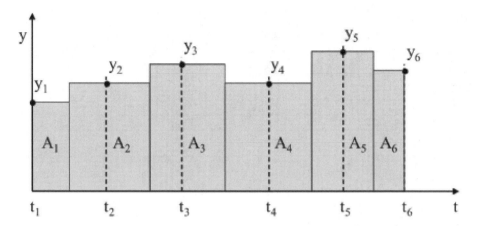

Figure 92—Trapezoidal Rule Implementation

There are two special cases in this algorithm: A1 and An. If we assume that the spaces between the areas fall at the mid-point between the time samples, the expressions for the areas are:

$$A_1 = y_1 * (t_2 - t_1) / 2$$
$$A_i = y_i * (t_{i+1} - t_{i-1}) / 2 \quad \text{for } i = 2 .. n\text{-}1$$
$$A_n = y_n * (t_n - t_{n-1}) / 2$$

Table 116 shows the function that computes this integral, making use of MATLAB's cumulative sum function, **cumsum(...)**. Table 117 shows code to test this function integrating the rocket velocity in Figure 91 to compute its altitude. Figure 93 shows the resulting plot.

```
function h = trapezoid( t, v )
% given v(t), find h(t), the integral of v(t) dt
%   h = trapezoid( t, v )
h = 0.5 * cumsum( [v(1)*(t(2) - t(1)) ...
    v(2:end-1).*(t(3:end) - t(1:end-2)) ...
    v(end)*(t(end) - t(end-1)) ] );
```

Table 116—Trapezoidal Integration

```
v =[ 0.0 15.1 25.1 13.7 22.2 41.7 ...
    39.8 54.8 57.6 62.6 61.6 63.9 69.6 ...
    76.2 86.7 101.2 99.8 112.2 111.0 ...
    116.8 122.6 127.7 143.4 131.3 143.0 ...
    144.0 162.7 167.8 180.3 177.6 172.6 ...
```
(Continued)

Table 117—Testing Numerical Integration

```
    166.6 173.1 173.3 176.0 178.5 ...
    196.5 213.0 223.6 235.9 244.2 244.5 ...
    259.4 271.4 270.5 294.5 297.6 ...
    308.7 310.5 326.6 344.1 342.0 358.2 362.7 ];

lv = length(v);
t = (0:lv-1) * 0.2;
h = trapezoid(t, v);
plot(t, v, t, h/5)
legend({'velocity' 'altitude/5' })
title('velocity and altitude of a rocket')
xlabel('time (sec)')
ylabel('v (m/s), h(m/5)').
```

Table 117—Testing Numerical Integration *(Continued)*

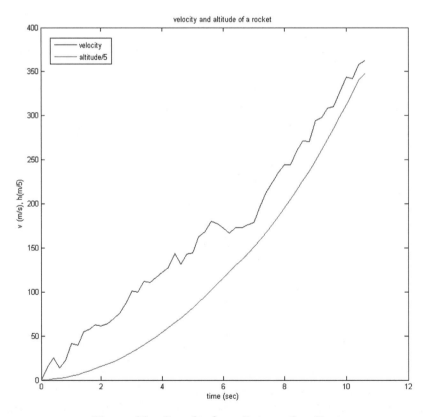

Figure 93—Results from Integration Test

20.5. Numerical Differentiation

The derivative of a function $f(x)$ is defined to be a function $f'(x)$ that is equal to the rate of change of $f(x)$ with respect to x. The derivative can be expressed as a ratio, with the change in $f(x)$ indicated by $df(x)$ and the change in x indicated by dx, giving

$$f'(x) = \frac{df(x)}{dx}$$

There are many physical processes for which we want to measure the rate of change of a variable. For example, velocity is the rate of change of position (as in meters per second), and acceleration is the rate of change of velocity (as in meters per second squared). It can also be shown that the integral of acceleration is velocity and that the integral of velocity is position. Hence, integration and differentiation have a special relationship, in that they can be considered to be inverses of each other: The derivative of an integral returns the original function, and the integral of a derivative returns the original function, to within a constant value.

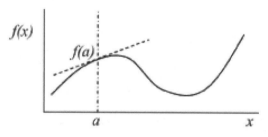

Figure 94—Derivative of f(x) at x = a

The derivative $f'(x)$ can be described graphically as the slope of the function $f(x)$, where the slope of $f(x)$ is defined to be the slope of the tangent line to the function at the specified point. Thus, the value of $f'(x)$ at the point a is $f'(a)$, and it is equal to the slope of the tangent line at the point a, as shown in Figure 94.

Because the derivative of a function at a point is the slope of the tangent line at the point, a value of zero for the derivative of the function at the point x_k indicates that the line is horizontal at that point. Points with derivatives of zero are called **critical points** and can represent a local maximum, a local minimum, or an inflexion point. (The point may also be the **global** maximum or minimum as shown in Figure 95, but more analysis of the entire function would be needed to determine this.)

If we evaluate the derivative of a function at several points in an interval and we observe that the sign of the derivative changes, then a local maximum or a local minimum occurs in the interval. The behavior of the curvature at

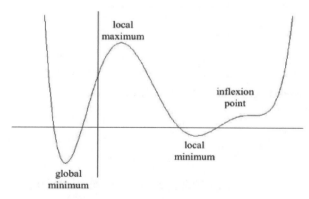

Figure 95—Example of a Function with Critical Points

these points [the derivative of $f'(x)$] can be used to determine whether a critical point represents an inflexion point, a local maximum or local minimum. More specifically, if the curvature at an critical point is positive, then the value of the function at the critical point is a local minimum; if negative, then the value of the function at the critical point is a local maximum; if zero, it is an inflexion point.

20.5.1. Difference Expressions

Numerical differentiation techniques estimate the derivative of a function at a point x_k by approximating the slope of the tangent line at x_k using values of the function at points near x_k. The approximation of the slope of the tangent line can be done in several ways, as shown in Figure 96.

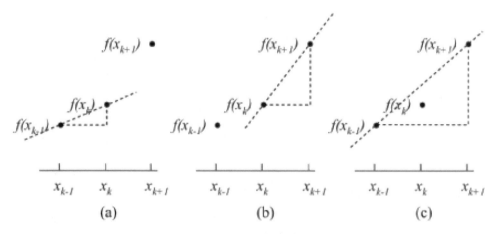

Figure 96—Techniques for Computing f′ (x$_k$)

Figure 96(a) assumes that the derivative at x_k is estimated by computing the slope of the line between $f(x_{k-1})$ and $f(x_k)$, as in

$$f'(x_k) = \frac{f(x_k) - f(x_{k-1})}{x_k - x_{k-1}}$$

This type of derivative approximation is called a **backward difference approximation**. Figure 96(b) assumes that the derivative at x_k is estimated by computing the slope of the line between $f(x_k)$ and $f(x_{k+1})$, as in

$$f'(x_k) = \frac{f(x_{k+1}) - f(x_k)}{x_{k+1} - x_k}$$

This type of derivative approximation is called a **forward difference approximation**. Figure 96(c) assumes that the derivative at x_k is estimated by computing the slope of the line between $f(x_{k-1})$ and $f(x_{k+1})$, as in

$$f'(x_k) = \frac{f(x_{k+1}) - f(x_{k-1})}{x_{k+1} - x_{k-1}}$$

This type of derivative approximation is called a **central difference approximation,** and we usually assume that x_k is half way between x_{k-1} and x_{k+1}. The quality of all of these types of derivative computations depends on the distance between the points used to estimate the derivative; the estimate of the derivative improves as the distance between the two points decreases.

The second derivative of a function $f(x)$ is the derivative of the first derivative of the function:

$$f''(x) = \frac{df'(x)}{dx}$$

This function can be evaluated using slopes of the first derivative. Thus, if we use backward differences, we have

$$f''(x_k) = \frac{f(x_k) - f'(x_{k-1})}{x_k - x_{k-1}}$$

Similar expressions can be derived for computing estimates of higher derivatives.

20.5.2. The `diff` Function

The **diff** function computes differences between adjacent values in a vector, generating a new vector with one less value than the original. If the **diff** function is applied to a matrix, it operates on the columns of the matrix as if each column were a vector. A second, optional argument specifies the number of times to recursively apply **diff**. Each time **diff** is applied, the length of the vector is reduced in size. A third, optional argument specifies the dimensions in which to apply the function. The forms of **diff** are summarized as follows:

`diff(V)`

For a vector **V**, **diff** returns:

      `[V(2)-V(1)  V(3)-V(2)  ...  V(n)-V(n-1)]`

`diff(M)`

For a matrix **M**, **diff** returns the matrix of column differences:

      `[M(2:end,:)  -  M(1:end-1,:)]`

`diff(M,n,dim)`

Look up the general form of **diff** in the help files if you need it.

To illustrate, we define vectors x, y, and z as follows:

```
>> x = [0 1 2 3 4 5];
>> y = [2 3 1 5 8 10];
>> z = [1 3 5; 1 5 10];
```

Then the vector generated by **diff(x)** is:

```
ans =
     1  1  1  1  1
```

Then the vector generated by **diff(y)** is:

```
ans =
     1  -2  4  3  2
```

If you execute **diff** twice, the length of the returned vector is 4:

```
>> diff(y,2)
ans =
    -3  6  -1  -1
```

The **diff** function can be applied to either dimension of matrix z:

```
>> diff(z,1,1)
ans =
      0      2      5
```

```
>> diff(z,1,2)
ans =
      2      2
      4      5
```

An approximate derivative *dy/dx* can be computed by using **diff(y) ./ diff(x)** as shown in Table 118.

```
% Evaluate f(x) and f'(x)
%
x = -7:0.1:9;
f = 0.0333*x.^6—0.3*x.^5 ...
      —1.3333*x.^4 + 16*x.^3 —187.2*x;
df = diff(f)./diff(x);
xd = x(2:end);
plot(xd, df)
```

Table 118—Plotting the Derivative df/dx

Note that these values of *df/dx* are correct for both the forward difference equation and the backward difference equation. The distinction between the two methods for computing the derivative is determined by the values of the vector **xd**, which correspond to the derivative **dy**. If the corresponding values of **xd** are [1,2,3,4,5], **dy** computes a backward difference. If the corresponding values of **xd** are [2,3,4,5,6], **dy** computes a forward difference.

20.5.3. Estimating Critical Points of a Function

As an example, consider the function given by the following polynomial. We want to compute an approximation to the locations of its critical points (the points of zero slope). These approximations will be found by marking the x values at which adjacent values of the slope change sign.

$$f(x) = 0.0333 \, x^6 - 0.3 \, x^5 - 1.3333 \, x^4 + 16 \, x^3 - 187.2 \, x$$

A plot of this function is shown in Figure 95. Recall that the zeros of the derivative correspond to the points of zero slope. The local minima and maxima (or critical points) of this function occur at –5.2, -1.9, 2.6, 5.8, and 6.2. You can use the **find** function to identify the critical points of a function. Assume that we want to compute the derivative of this function over the interval **[-4, 5]**. We can perform this operation using the **diff** function, as shown in the following script, where **xd** represents the **x** values corresponding to the derivative:

The plot of f'(x) is shown in Figure 97. Using values of **df** and **xd** from the previous script, we take the product of the slopes of adjacent points, and then use the **find** function to determine the indices *k* of the x values for which that product is negative. These indices are then used with the vector **xd** to print the approximation to the locations of the critical points:

```
% Estimate the critical points of f'(x)
%
product = df(1:end-1) .* df(2:end);
critical = xd( find(product < 0) );
```

Table 119—Finding the Critical Points

This produces the result:

```
critical =
          -5.2000   -1.9000    2.6000    5.8000    6.2000
```
[2]

---

[2] Notice that the point at about x = 6 that was described earlier as an inflexion point in fact has a very small excursion of f'(x) below 0, hence producing two closely spaced estimates of the critical point where we expected one. Since the original function was designed with an exact point of inflexion here, this may be a minor artifact resulting from the numerical differentiation.

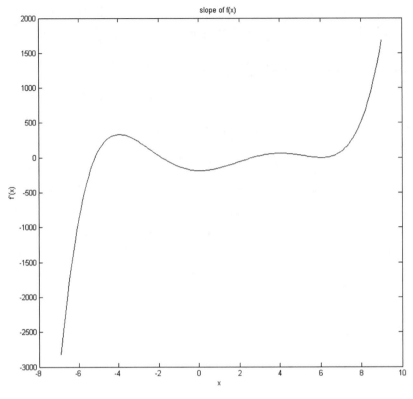

Figure 97—Slope of f(x)

20.6. Putting It All Together

Returning to the sounding rocket example from Section 20.4.2 above, suppose we are asked to find the acceleration of the rocket as well as its velocity and position. The complete script (using the velocity values from above) is shown in Table 120, and the resulting plot is shown in Figure 98.

```
lv = length(v);
t = (0:lv-1) * 0.2;
h = trapezoid(t, v);

acc = diff(v) ./ diff(t);
plot(t, v, t, h/5, t(2:end), acc)
legend({'velocity' 'altitude/5' 'acceleration'})
title('vel, alt and acc measurements of a rocket')
xlabel('time (sec)')
ylabel('v (m/s), h(m/5) and acc(m/sec^2)')
```

Table 120—Combined Differentiation and Integration

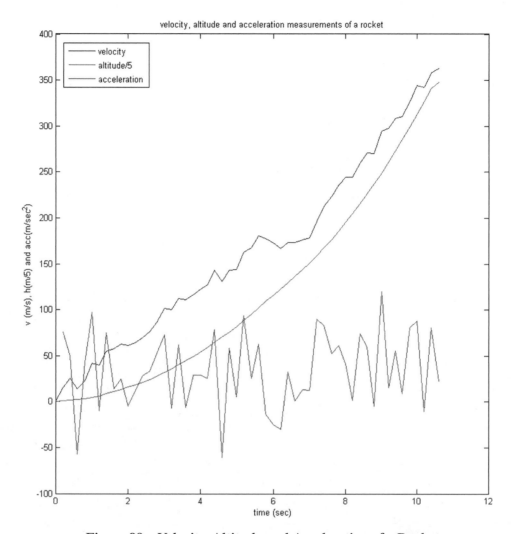

Figure 98—Velocity, Altitude and Acceleration of a Rocket

The results illustrate the problems associated with differentiating inherently noisy signals—where the integration smoothed the velocity data, differentiating that data amplified the undesirable effects of the noise on the velocity measurements. To improve the quality of our results, we might consider fitting curves of various orders to the velocity data before differentiation. Such a study is shown in Table 121, with the results plotted in Figure 99.

```
for plt = 1:6
    order = plt*3;
    subplot(2, 3, plt)
    c = polyfit(t, v, order);
    y = polyval(c, t);
    plot(t, v, t, y);
    str = sprintf('order %d', order);
    title(str);
    legend({'velocity' 'fitted vel'})
    xlabel('time (sec)')
    ylabel('vel (m/s)')
end
```

Table 121—Study of the Polynomial Order

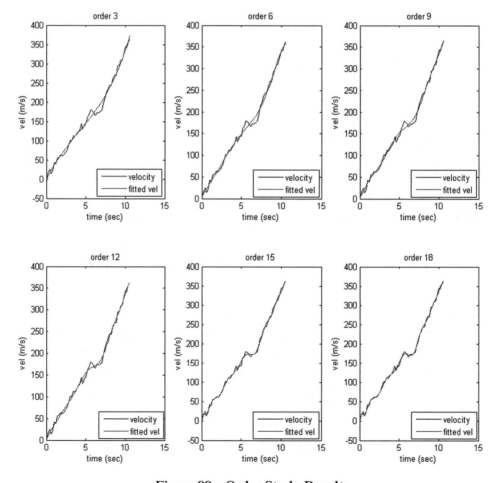

Figure 99—Order Study Results

With a considerable amount of data, we can push the order of the fit to match the data quite well, including the odd looking "kink" in the middle. Table 122 shows the code to differentiate the smoothed velocity, and Figure 100 shows the resulting plot.

```
c = polyfit(t, v, 12)
vs = polyval(c, t);
acc = diff(v) ./ diff(t);
accs = diff(vs) ./ diff(t);
treal = [0 6 6.2 7 7.2 t(end)];
g = 9.81;
areal = g * [3 3 -1 -1 5 5];
plot(t, v, t(2:end), acc, t(2:end), ...
                     accs, treal, areal)
title('attempt to smooth the acceleration')
xlabel('time (sec)')
ylabel('v (m/s) and acc(m/sec^2)')
```

Table 122—Effect of Smoothing the Velocity Before Differentiating

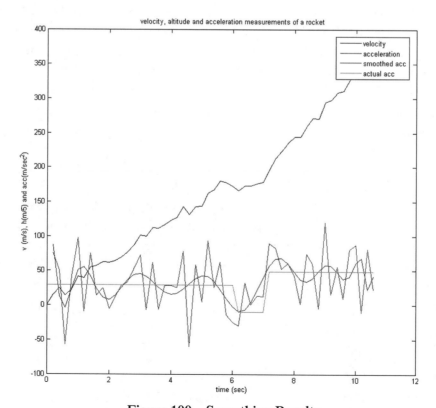

Figure 100—Smoothing Results

While this appears to have somewhat improved the situation, we also show the truth about the actual acceleration used to compute the rocket velocity profile. Being a two-stage rocket, this consisted of 6 seconds of acceleration at 3g, a second of falling at –g while the first stage motor detached, and the remaining time at 5g. As we can now see, while the curve fitting managed to smooth out the worst of the computed spikiness in the data and it was trying to track the discontinuity in the acceleration profile, it is also beginning to model the character of the noise on the velocity rather than the underlying truth. While we could re-examine the choice if order of the polynomial, and try a less aggressive fit, we would find that the data would track the noise less carefully, but also not follow the central velocity oddity as well. We seem to be trapped between fitting to the artifact we do want, and smoothing out artifacts we don't want . . .

Moral: Curve fitting can sometimes help to clean up nasty looking data. However, there may be some clues in the source of the data (in our case, a sounding rocket that could be multi-stage) and the character of the data (in our case, the odd discontinuity between burns) that might lead you to different and better interpretation of the data. Looking again at the velocity profile in the light of the actual data, it can be seen that the velocity profile is not as noisy as first appeared. Rather, it is two linear segments with a discontinuity in the middle. We leave it to the reader to construct piecewise fits to the data to improve the acceleration estimates . . .

Finally, in the examples discussed in this section, we assumed that we had the equation of the function to be differentiated, and thus we could generate points of the function. In many engineering problems, the data to be differentiated are collected from experiments. Thus, we cannot choose the points to be close together to get a more accurate measure of the derivative. In these cases, it might be a good solution to use alternative techniques that allow us to determine an equation for a polynomial that fits a set of data and then compute points from the equation to use in computing values of the derivative.

20.7. Examples

20-1. The subject of thermodynamics makes extensive use of tables. Although many properties can be described by fairly simple equations, others either are poorly understood, or the equations describing their behavior are very complicated. It is much easier just to tabulate the data. For example, consider the data for steam at 0.1 MPa (approximately 1 atm), given in the following table. These data could be used to analyze the geysers shown in Figure 8.7.

Temperature, C	u, Internal Energy, kJ/kg[3]
100	2506.7
150	2582.8
200	2658.1

---

[3] Data from "Steam Tables. SI units" by Joseph H. Keenan, Fredrick G. Keyes, Philip G Hill, and Joan G. Moore, New York, John Wiley and Sons, 1918.

Temperature, C	u, Internal Energy, kJ/kg
250	2733.7
300	2810.4
400	2967.9
500	3131.6

a. Use linear interpolation to determine the internal energy at 21.5° C.

b. Use linear interpolation to determine the temperature if the internal energy is 2600 kJ/kg.

20-2. Electric power plants use steam as a "working fluid" (see Figure 8.8). The science of thermodynamics makes extensive use of tables when systems such as a power plant are analyzed. Depending on the system of interest you may only need a portion of the table, such as this:

Temperature C	Specific Volume m^3/kg	Internal Energy kJ/kG	Enthalpy kJ/kg
100	1.6958	2506.7	2676.2
150	1.9364	2582.8	2776.4
200	2.172	2658.1	2875.3
250	2.406	2733.7	2974.3
300	2.639	2810.4	3074.3
400	3.103	2967.9	3278.2
500	3.565	3131.6	3488.1

Notice that this table is spaced at 50-degree intervals at first, and then at 100-degree intervals. Assume that you have a project that requires you to use this table, and you would prefer not to have to perform a linear interpolation every time you use it. Use MATLAB to create a table, applying linear interpolation, with a temperature spacing of 25 degrees.

20-3. Determining how much water will flow through a culvert is not as easy as it might first seem. The channel could have a non-uniform shape, obstructions might influence the flow, friction is important, etc. A numerical approach allows us to fold all of those concerns into a model of how the water actually behaves.

Consider these data collected from an actual culvert:

height, ft	flow, ft^3/sec
0	0
1.7	2.6
1.95	3.6
2.60	4.03
2.92	6.45
4.04	11.22
5.24	30.61

Compute a best-fit linear, quadratic, and cubic fit for the data, and plot them on the same graph. Which model best represents the data? (Linear is first order, quadratic is second order, and cubic is third order.)

20-4. The population of the earth is expanding rapidly, as is the population of the United States. MATLAB includes a built-in data file called **census** that contains U.S. census data since 1790. The data file contains two variables, **cdate** which contains the census dates, and **pop** which lists the population in millions. To load the file into your workspace, type

>> **load census**

Use the curve fitting toolbox to find an equation that represents the data.

20-5. Generate $f(x) = x^2$ for **x = [-3 -1 0 2 5 6]**

   a. Compute and plot the linear and cubic-spline interpolation of the data points over the range [-3:0.05:6]

   b. Compute the value of $f(4)$ using linear interpolation and cubic-spline interpolation. What are the respective errors when the answer is compared with the actual value of $f(4)$?

20-6. Assume that the following set of temperature measurements is taken from the cylinder head in a new engine that is being tested for possible use in a race car:

time, sec	temperature, °F
0	0
1.0	20
2.0	60
3.0	68
4.0	77
5.0	110

   a. Compare plots of these data, assuming linear interpolation and assuming cubic-spline interpolation for values between the data points, using time values from 0 to 5 in increments of 0.1 s.

   b. Using the data from part (a), find the time value for which there is the largest difference between its linear-interpolated temperature and its cubic-interpolated temperature.

20-7. Assume that we measure temperatures at three points around the cylinder head in the engine from Problem 6, instead of at just one point. The set of data is then the following:

time, sec	temp1	temp2	temp3
0	0	0	0
1.0	20	25	52
2.0	60	62	90
3.0	68	67	91
4.0	77	82	93
5.0	110	103	96

a. Assume that these data have been stored in a matrix with six rows and four columns. Determine interpolated values of temperature at the three points in the engine at 2.6 seconds using linear interpolation.

b. Using the information from part (a) determine the time when the temperature reached 75° at each of the three points in the cylinder head.

20-8. The guidance system for a spacecraft often uses a sensor called an accelerometer, which is an electromechanical device that produces an output voltage proportional to the applied acceleration. Assume that an experiment has yielded the following set of data:

Acceleration	voltage
4	0.593
2	0.436
0	0.061
2	0.425
4	0.980
6	1.213
8	1.646
10	2.158

a. Determine the linear equation that best fits this set of data. Plot the data points and the linear equation.

b. Determine the sum of the squares of the distances of these points from the line of best fit determined in part (a).

c. Compare the error sum from part (b) with the same error sum computed from the best quadratic fit. What do these sums tell you about the two models for the data?

20-9. Compute *tan(x)* for `x = [-1:0.05:1]`.

a. Compute the best-fit polynomial of order four that approximates *tan(x)*. Plot *tan(x)* and the generated polynomial on the same graph. What is the sum of square error of the polynomial approximation for the data points in *x?*

b. Compute *tan(x)* for `x = [-2:0.05:2]`. Using the polynomial generated in part (a), compute values of *y* from -2 to 2, corresponding to the x vector just defined. Plot *tan(x)* , and the values generated from the polynomial on the same graph. Why aren't they the same shape?

20-10. The following data set represents the time and altitude values for a sounding rocket that is performing high-altitude atmospheric research on the ionosphere.

a. Determine the equation that best represents the data, using the interactive curve fitting tools available in MATLAB 7.

b. Plot the altitude data. The velocity function is the derivative of the altitude function. Using numerical differentiation, compute the velocity values from these data, using a backward difference. Plot the velocity data. (Note that the rocket is a two-stage rocket.)

c. The acceleration function is the derivative of the velocity function. Using the velocity data determined from part (b), compute the acceleration data using backward difference. Plot the acceleration data.

Time, sec	Altitude, m
0	60
10	2,926
20	10,170
30	21,486
40	33,835
50	45,251
60	55,634
70	65,038
80	73,461
90	80,905
100	87,368
110	92,852
120	97,355
130	100,878
140	103,422
150	104,986
160	106,193
170	110,246
180	119,626
190	136,106
200	162,095
210	199,506
220	238,775
230	277,065
240	314,375
250	350,704

20-11. **Simple root finding**. Although MATLAB makes it easy to find the roots of a function, sometimes all that is needed is a quick estimate. This can be done by plotting a function and zooming in very close to see where the function equals zero. Since MATLAB draws straight lines between data points on a plot, it is good to draw circles or stars at each data point, in addition to straight lines connecting the points. Plot the following function, and zoom in to find the roots:

```
>> n = 5;
>> x = linspace(0, 2*pi, n);
>> y = x .* sin(x) + cos(1/2*x).^2-1./(x-7);
>> plot(x, y, '-o')
```

20-12. Consider the data points in the following two vectors:

```
>> x = [0.1 0.3 5 6 23 24];;
>> y = [2.8 2.6 18.1 26.8 486.1 530]
```

a. Determine the best-fit polynomial of order 2 to the data. Calculate the sum of squares for your results. Plot the best-fit polynomial for the six data points.

b. Generate a new x vector containing 250 points evenly spaced between 0.1 and 25. Using the coefficients from part (a), generate and plot the corresponding y values.

c. Compute and an estimate of dy/dx using the new values in part (b).

d. Compute 2nd and 3rd order polynomial fit to the derivative data in part (c). Plot each polynomial. Why is the use of polynomial fits to derivative data important?

20-13 The function $f(x)$ is defined by $f(x) = 4\ e^x$. Plot this function over the interval [0, 1] with a suitable number of points. Use numerical integration techniques to estimate the integral of $f(x)$ over [0, 0.5] and [0, 1]. Compare these results to the theoretical answer.

20-14 Re-examine the travel time plot in Example 17-3. As is common with real data, here are some ugly discrepancies that cause the plot to seem unrealistic. Apply the techniques presented in this chapter to removing these anomalies, and re-plot the corrected data.

21. BIG O

The subject of this chapter may seem to be a digression from the main thread of problem solving using MATLAB. How many times this semester have you asked yourself, "Just how good is my algorithm?" Probably not very often, if ever. After all, we've been creating relatively simple programs that work on a small finite set of data. Our functions execute and return an answer with a second or two. You may have noticed that the edge detection program in Table 115 takes a number of seconds to run.

However, as the problems become more complex and the volume of data increases, we need to consider whether we are solving the problem in the most efficient manner. In extreme cases, processes manipulating huge amounts of data like the inventory of Walmart, or a national telephone directory might only be possible with highly efficient algorithms.

Big O is an algebra that permits us to express how the amount of work done in solving a problem relates to the amount of data being processed. It is a gross simplification for software engineering analysis purposes based on some sound, but increasingly complex theory[1].

21.1. Definitions and Symbology

Big O is a means of estimating the worst-case performance of a given algorithm when presented with a certain number of data items, usually referred to as N. In fact, the actual process attempts to determine the limit of the relationship between the work done by an algorithm and N as N approaches infinity. Mathematically, given an input of size N, we seek the asymptotic upper bounds of the algorithm in terms of time/space (how long will it take to execute/how much memory will it require)?

We record the Big O of an algorithm as O(<expression in terms of N>). For example:

- $O(1)$ describes the situation where the computing cost is independent of the size of the data.
- $O(N)$ describes the situation where the computing cost is proportional to the size of the data.
- $O(2^N)$ describes the situation where the computing cost doubles each time one more piece of data is added.

At this point, we should also observe some simplifying assumptions:

1. We are not concerned with constant multipliers on the Big O of an algorithm. As rapidly as processor performance and languages are improving, multiplicative improvements can

---

[1] interested readers should look up little-O, Big-Ω, little-ω, and Big-Θ.

be achieved merely by acquiring the latest hardware or software. Big O is a concept that supports qualitative algorithm improvement. We therefore choose to ignore constant multipliers on Big O analyses.

2. We are concerned with the performance of algorithms as N approaches infinity. Consequently, When the Big O is expressed as the sum of multiple terms, we keep only the term with the highest power of N.

21.2. Specific Big O Examples

On the basis of algorithms we have already discussed, we will look at examples of the most common Big O classes.

21.2.1. O(1)—Independent of N

O(1) describes the ideal case of an algorithm or logical step whose amount of work is independent of the amount of data. The most obvious example is accessing or modifying an entry in a vector. Since all good languages permit direct access to elements of a vector, the work of these simple operations is independent of the size of the vector.

21.2.2. O(N)—Linear with N

O(N) describes an algorithm whose performance is linearly related to N. Copying a vector of size N is an obvious example, as is searching for a specific piece of data in such a vector. One might argue that occasionally, one would find the data as the first element. There is an equal chance that we would be unlucky and find the item as the last element. On average, we would claim that the performance of this search would be the mean of these numbers: (N + 1) / 2. However, applying the simplification rules of section 21.1 above, we first reject the 1 as being N to a lower power leaving N/2, and then reject the constant multiplier, leaving O(N) for a linear search.

21.2.3. O(logN)—Binary Search

Consider searching for a number—say, 89—in a sorted vector such as that illustrated in Figure 101. One could use a linear search as above without taking advantage of the ordering of the data. However, a better algorithm might be as follows:

· Go to the middle of the vector (approximately) and compare that element (the 59) to the number being sought.
· If this is the desired value, exit with the answer.
· If the number sought is less than that element, since the data are ordered, we can reject the half of the array to the right of, and including, the 59.

- Similarly, if the number sought is greater than that element, we can reject the half of the array to the left of, and including the 59.
- Repeat these steps with the remaining half vector until the number is found, or the size of the remaining half is zero.

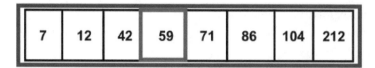

Figure 101—Binary Search Example

Now, consider how much data can be covered by each test—a measure of the work done as shown in Table 123.

Comparisons	Coverage, N
1	1
2	2
3	4
4	8
5	16
.	.
.	.
W	2^{W-1}

Table 123—Work for a Binary Search

In general, we can state that the relationship in general is expressed as:

$$N = 2^{W-1}$$

However, we need the expression for the work, W, as a function of N. We therefore take the log base 2 of each side so that

$$W = \log_2 N + 1$$

Now, we simplify, first removing the 1, and then realizing that one can convert $\log_2 N$ to $\log_x N$ merely by multiplying by $\log_2 x$. Consequently, since we reject constant multipliers as irrelevant, we lose interest in representing the specific base of the logarithm, leaving the work for a binary search as O(logN).

21.2.4. O(N²)—Proportional to N²

$O(N^2)$ describes an algorithm whose performance is proportional to the square of N. It is a special case of $O(N \times M)$ which describes any operation on an NM array or image.

21.2.5. O(2^N)—Exponential growth or worse

Occasionally, we run across really nasty implementations of simple algorithms. For example, consider the recursive implementation of the Fibonacci algorithm in Section 13.8.1. In this implementation, fib(N) = fib(N-1) + fib(N-2). So each time we add another term, the previous two terms have to be calculated again, doubling the amount of work. If we double the work when 1 is added to N, in general, the Big O is $O(2^N)$.

In the case of this particular algorithm, there is a simple iterative solution with O(N).

21.3. Analyzing Complex Algorithms

We can easily calculate the Big O of simple algorithms. For more complex algorithms, we determine the Big O by breaking the complex algorithm into simpler abstractions, in the same manner as Section 10.3 above. We would continue that process until the abstractions can be characterized as simple operations on defined collections for which we can determine their Big O's. The Big O of the overall algorithm is then determined from the individual components by combining them according to the following rules:

- If two components are sequential (do A and then do B), you add their Big O values.
- If components are nested (for each A, do B) you multiply their Big O values.

For example, we will see the Merge sort algorithm in Section 22.3. It can be abstracted in the following way:

- Perform a binary division of the data and then
  - *For each* binary step, merge all the data items.

Analysis proceeds as follows:

- The binary division is O(logN); there are O(logN) steps, and each merge touches all the data (O(N)).
- The overall algorithm then costs O(logN) + O(N) * O(logN).

We remove the first term because its growth is slower, leaving O(NlogN) as the overall algorithm cost.

22. SORTING

In general terms, sorting a collection of data will organize the data items in such a way that it is possible to search for a specific item using a binary search rather than a linear search. While this concept is nice in principle when dealing with simple collections like an array of numbers, it is more difficult in practice with real data. For example, telephone books are always sorted by the person's last name. While this facilitates searching by last name, it does not help if you are looking for the number of a neighbor whose name you do not know. That search would require sorting the data by street name.

There exist a large number of methods for sorting data. We present here four representative samples of techniques for which there are circumstances making them the best technique to use. We first describe the techniques, and then compare the performance and offer circumstances in which you would apply each technique.

22.1. Insertion Sort

Insertion sort is conceptually the easiest sorting technique to visualize. Given the original collection of objects to sort, it begins by initializing an empty collection. For example, if the collection were a vector, you might allocate a new vector of the same size, and initialize an "output index" to the start of that vector. The algorithm then traverses the original vector inserting each object from that vector in order into the output vector. This usually requires "shuffling" the objects in the new vector to make room for the new object. Figure 102 illustrates the situation where the first 4 numbers of the original vector have been inserted into the new vector, the algorithm finds the place to insert the next value (10) and then moves the 12 across to make space for it.

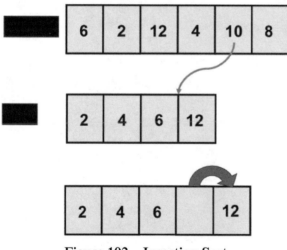

Figure 102—Insertion Sort

Table 124 shows the MATLAB code for insertion sort on a vector of numbers. The algorithm works for any collection of objects that can be compared to each other.

We will refer later to the Selection Sort algorithm that is similar in concept to Insertion Sort. Rather than sorting as the new data is put into the new vector, however, the selection sort algorithm repeatedly finds and deletes the smallest item in the original vector and puts it directly into the new vector.

Both Insertion sort and Selection Sort are $O(N^2)$ if used to sort a whole vector.

```
function b = insertionsort(a)
% This function sorts a vector,
% using the insertion sort
% algorithm
%
b = [];
i = 1;
sz = length(a);
while i <= sz
    b = insert(b, a(i) );
    i = i + 1;
end


function b = insert(a, v)
% this function inserts the value
% v in order into the array a
i = 1;       % initialization
sz = length(a);
done = 0;
while i <= sz    % find insertion point
    if v < a(i)
        done = 1;
        j = sz + 1;
        while j > I  % make space
            a(j) = a(j-1);
            j = j - 1;
        end
        a(i) = v;  % insert the value
        i = sz + 1;
    else
        i = i + 1;
    end
end
if done == 0 % might be the last entry
    a(sz+1) = v;
end
b = a;  % return the new array
```

Table 124—Insertion Sort

22.2. Quick Sort

As its name suggests, the quick sort algorithm is one of the fastest sorting algorithms[1]. It is designed to sort an array "in place." The quick sort algorithm is recursive, and uses an elegant approach to subdividing the original vector. Figure 103 illustrates this process. The algorithm proceeds as follows:

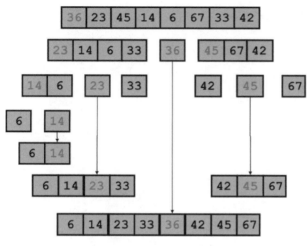

Figure 103—Quick Sort

- The terminating condition occurs when the vector is of length 1, which is obviously sorted.
- A "pivot point" is then chosen. Some sophisticated versions go to some trouble to calculate the most effective pivot point. We will be content to choose the first item in the vector.
- The vector is then subdivided by moving all of the items less than the pivot to its left, and all those greater than the pivot to its right, thereby placing the pivot in its final location in the result.
- The items to the left and right of the pivot are then recursively sorted by the same algorithm.
- The algorithm always converges because these two halves are always shorter than the original vector.

Table 125 is the MATLAB code for the quick sort algorithm. The partitioning algorithm looks a little messy, but is just performing the array adjustments noted above. It starts with i and j outside the vector to the left and right. It then keeps moving each towards the middle as long as the values at i and j are on the proper side of the pivot. When this process stops, i and j are looking at data items that are out of order. They are swapped, and the process repeated until i passes j. Quick Sort is O(NlogN).

---

[1] Unfortunately, while this algorithm can be coded and demonstrated in MATLAB, the efficiency of the implementation is not as fast as the algorithm could be. The reason is that MATLAB does not allow a function to have direct access to the items in an array passed to it. Consequently, each function call must take the time to copy the result back to the calling program.

```
 function b = quicksort(a,  from,  to)
 %   This function sorts a vector,
 %   using the quick sort algorithm
 %
if (from < to)
        [p, a] = partition(a, from, to);
        quicksort(a, from, p);
        quicksort(a, p + 1, to);
   end
   b = a;
 function [1, b] = partition(a, from, to)
 %  This function partitions a vector for
 %   the quick sort algorithm
  pivot = a(from);
  i = from - 1;
  j = to + 1;
  while (i < j)
     i = i + 1;
     while (a(i) < pivot)
        i = i + 1;
     end
     j = j - 1;
     while (a(j) > pivot)
        j = j - 1;
     end
     if (i < j)
        temp = a(i);     % swap(a, i, j)
        a(i) = a(j);
        a(j) = temp;
     end
  end
1 = j;
b = a;
```

Table 125—Code for Quick Sort

22.3. Merge Sort

Merge Sort is another O(NlogN) algorithm that achieves speed by dividing the original vector into two "equal" halves. Equality, of course, is not possible when there are an odd number of objects to be sorted, in which case, the length of the "halves" will differ by at most 1. The heart of the Merge Sort algorithm is the technique used to re-unite the now sorted halves of the vector. This function is called "merge." Its objective is to merge together two sorted vectors. Since the two parts are sorted, the smallest object can only be at the head of one of these two vectors. The smallest item is removed from its place and added to the result vector. This process continues until one of the two halves is empty, in which case the remaining half (whose values all exceed those in the result vector) is copied into the result.

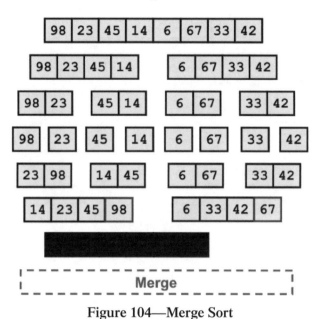

Figure 104—Merge Sort

The merge sort algorithm itself, like quick sort, is recursive, as illustrated in Figure 104:

· the terminating condition is a vector with length less than 2, which is already sorted.
· The recursive part invokes the merge function on the recursive call to merge the two halves of the vector.
· The process converges because the halves are always smaller than the original vector.

The code for merge sort is shown in Table 126.

```
function b = mergesort(a)
%
%    This function sorts a column array, using the merge sort
%    algorithm
%
    b = a;
    sz = length(a);
    if sz > 1
        szb2 = floor(sz / 2);
        first = mergesort(a( 1 : szb2));
        second = mergesort(a( szb2+1 : sz));
        b = domerge(first, second);
    end
function b = domerge(first, second)
%
%    Merges two sorted arrays into the array to be sorted by this
%    merge sorter.                                    (Continued)
```

Table 126—Code for Merge Sort

```
%      @param first the first sorted array
%      @param second the second sorted array
%
% merge both halves into the temporary array
     iFirst = 1;
     % next element to consider in the first array
     iSecond = 1;
     % next element to consider in the second array
     out = 1;
     % next open position in a
     % as long as neither i1 nor i2 past the end, move
     % the smaller element into a
     sf = size(first);
     ss = size(second);
     while (iFirst <= sf(1)) & (iSecond <= ss(1))
         if first(iFirst) < second(iSecond)
            b(out,1) = first(iFirst);
            iFirst = iFirst + 1;
         else
            b(out,1) = second(iSecond);
            iSecond = iSecond + 1;
         end
         out = out + 1;
     end
%    disp(sprintf('iF: %d; s1: [%d,%d]; iS: %d; s2: [%d,%d]', ...
%        iFirst, size(first), iSecond, size(second) ) );
     % note that only one of the two while loops
     % below is executed
     % copy any remaining entries of the first array
     while iFirst <= sf(1)
         b(out,1) = first(iFirst);
         out = out + 1;
         iFirst = iFirst + 1;
     end
     % copy any remaining entries of the second array
     while iSecond <= ss(1)
         b(out,1) = second(iSecond);
         out = out + 1;
         iSecond = iSecond + 1;
     end
```

Table 126—Code for Merge Sort *(Continued)*

22.4. Bucket Sort

A discussion of sorting techniques would not be complete without discussing Bucket Sort. This is also an O(NlogN) algorithm that is very frequently used for sorting physical piles of papers such as students' examination papers by the student's numerical ID. The process begins with a stack

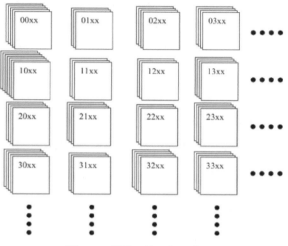

of un-sorted papers, each with an identifier consisting of a number or a unique name. One pass is made through the stack separating the papers into piles based on the first digit or character of the identifier. Subsequent passes sort each of these piles by subsequent characters or digits until all the piles have a small number of papers that can be sorted by insertion or selection sorts. The piles can then be reassembled in order. Figure 105 illustrates the situation at the end of the second sorting pass when piles for the first digit have also been separated by the second digit.

Figure 105—Bucket Sort

There are a number of reasons this technique is popular for sorting papers:

· There is a minimal amount of "paper shuffling" or bookkeeping;
· The logarithm in the O(NlogN) is either 10 (numerical identifier) or 26 (alphabetic identifier), thereby providing a "constant multiplier" speed advantage;
· Once the first sorting pass has been completed, one can use multi-processing (in the form of extra people) to perform the remaining passes in parallel, thereby reducing the effective performance to O(N) (given sufficient parallel resources).

22.5. Performance Analysis

In order to perform a comparison of the performance of different algorithms, a script was written to perform each sort on a vector of increasing length containing random numbers. The script started with a length of 4 and continued doubling the length until it reached 32,768. To obtain precise timing measurements, each sort technique was repeated sufficient times to obtain moderately accurate timing measurements with MATLAB's internal millisecond clock. In order to eliminate common computation costs, it was necessary to measure the overhead cost of the loops themselves and subtract that time from the times of each sort algorithm.

Figure 106 is a typical plot of the results of this analysis illustrating the relative power of O(NlogN) algorithms vs O(N^2) algorithms. The plot on a log-log scale shows the relative time[2] taken by the Selection Sort, Insertion Sort, Merge Sort and Quick Sort algorithms, together with MATLAB's internal sort method. Also on the chart are plotted trend lines for O(N^2) and O(NlogN) processes. We can make a number of observations from this chart:

1. Since the scales are each logarithmic, it is tempting to claim that there is "not much difference" between O(N^2) and O(NlogN) algorithms. Looking more closely, however, it is clear that for 100,000 items, the O(N^2) sorts are around 1,000 times slower than the O(NlogN) algorithms.
2. The performance of most of the algorithms is extremely erratic below 100 items. If you are sorting small amounts of data, the algorithm does not matter.
3. The Selection Sort and Insertion Sort algorithms clearly demonstrate O(N^2) behavior.
4. The performance of the Merge Sort and Quick Sort algorithms is less clear. They appear to have O(NlogN) performance when N is in the modest size range, but are tending towards O(N^2) as N gets above 50,000. This is an artifact of the MATLAB implementation of functions that does not permit a function direct access to an array passed as a parameter. Every recursive call is therefore penalized by having to copy the result array back to the calling function.
5. Clearly, the internal MATLAB sort function is closely tracking the O(NlogN) performance curve, indicating that it is programmed efficiently to take advantage of direct access to the array data.

22.6. Applications

This section discusses the circumstances under which you might choose to use one or the other of the sorting algorithms presented above. The first and most obvious question is why one would not always use the built-in MATLAB `sort()` function. Clearly, whenever that function would work, you should use it. However, its applicability is limited to sorting numbers in an array, and you will come across circumstances where you need to sort more complex items. You might, for example, have a structure array of addresses and telephone numbers that you wish to sort by last name, first name or telephone number. In this case, the internal sort program does not help, and you have to create your own sort.

It has been shown that the theoretical lower bound of sorting is O(NlogN). Consequently, we should not be looking for a generalized sorting algorithm that improves on this performance. However, within those constraints, there are circumstances under which each of the sorting techniques discussed above performs best.

---

[2] The actual performance of each sort technique was multiplied by an arbitrary factor to align its curve approximately with the trend lines. For example, the MATLAB sort was scaled by a factor of 1,000 to compare its shape to that of the other algorithms.

22.6.1. Insertion Sort

Insertion Sort is the fastest means of performing incremental sorting. If a very small number of new items, say, M, are being added to a sorted collection of size N, the process will be O(M*N) which will be fastest as long as M < log N.

22.6.2. Quick Sort

As its name suggests, this is the quickest of the sorting algorithms, and should normally be used for a full sort. However, it has one significant disadvantage. Its performance depends on a fairly high level of randomness in the distribution of the data in the original array. Consequently, if there is a significant probability that your original data might be already sorted, or partially sorted, you Quick Sort is not going to be quick. You should use Merge Sort.

22.6.3. Merge Sort

Since its algorithm does not depend on any specific characteristics of the data, Merge Sort will always turn in a solid O(N logN) performance. You should use it whenever you suspect that Quick Sort might get in trouble.

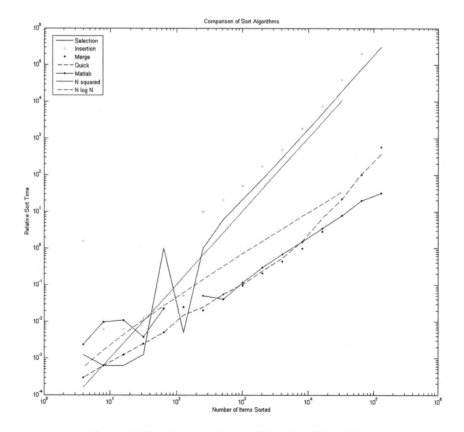

Figure 106—Comparison of Sorting Algorithms

22.6.4. Bucket Sort

It is possible to write the Bucket Sort algorithm in either MATLAB or Java to attempt to take advantage of its apparent performance improvements over the more conventional algorithms above. However, some practical problems arise:

- In practice, the manipulation of the arrays of arrays necessary to sort by this technique is quite complex;
- The performance gained for manual sorts by "parallel processing" stacks using multiple people cannot be realized easily, and
- The logic for extracting the character or digit for sorting is going to detract from the overall performance.

We therefore recommend that the use of Bucket Sort be confined to manually sorting large numbers of physical objects.

22.7. Examples

22-1   On the list of attributes below, check all that apply to both Quick Sort and Merge Sort:
   a. Defined recursively
   b. $O(N^2)$
   c. Linear search
   d. Requires an Array
   e. Second law of Thermodynamics
   f. $O(N \log N)$
   g. Defined iteratively
   h. Binary Search
   i. Requires a Collection with random access
   j. Divide and Conquer strategy

22-2   Which sorting algorithm makes use of a pivot when sorting?

22-3   Sort the following array using the algorithms listed below. Show all of the vectors (excluding the empty ones) created at each step.

   [5 4 10 2 9 6 3 7 8 1]

   a. Using merge sort
   b. Using quick sort
   c. Using insertion sort

PART III

OBJECT-ORIENTED PROGRAMMING

For every tree is known by his own fruit. For of thorns men do not gather figs, nor of a bramble bush gather they grapes.

Luke 6:44

23. OBJECT-ORIENTED PROGRAMMING

In Parts I and II of this text, we saw MATLAB as a means for manipulating *arrays*—sometimes in the guise of vectors or matrices, character strings or cell arrays. Furthermore, the manipulation performed was conducted by writing scripts that sometimes call functions—either the functions built into MATLAB, or functions we create ourselves. This type of programming is referred to as being in the procedural paradigm—functions and scripts being a form of procedure.

This part of the text considers a different paradigm altogether—the object-oriented (OO) paradigm. In this programming style, we will still begin in a script, but the scripts that we write will usually create and interact with *objects* rather than *arrays*.

23.1. Background

Languages that express the essential elements of the OO paradigm have been around since the 1960s when Simula was first developed. However, in the 1980s and 1990s, as massive software projects and especially Graphical User Interfaces (GUIs) became commonplace, OO emerged as the paradigm of choice for designing and developing large software systems. Major software systems (like the various releases of Microsoft Windows™) faced enormous design and integration challenges that could not be met by conventional programming practices. They needed language-imposed management of the interaction between large and small collections of programs and data.

A secondary requirement in efficiently developing large software systems is to be able to re-use core software modules without rewriting their entire contents. OO principles allow core modules to be re-used in three ways:

- Re-used intact, because the definitions of how to use them are precisely recorded,
- Re-used and extended, adding specific custom capabilities not found in the original module, but still using all of the original capabilities, or
- Re-used and redefined, replacing a few attributes of the general module by more specific definitions, while retaining all of the original characteristics.

The OO paradigm emerged as the framework that made large, reliable software systems possible. We should note here that OO encompasses far more than the syntax of any particular language, and far more than its core concepts touched briefly in this section of the book. OO is first of all a design issue. OO design takes advantage of the tenets and concepts of OO languages to produce good software system designs, from which good software systems can be built.

Many books are available to students wishing to pursue this theme further. However, a book on Computer Science concepts would not be complete without a serious treatment of, and some practical exposure to, OO concepts. As we study OO concepts and their MATLAB implementation[1], it should be in the light of realizing the power of these concepts, and their place in the development of significant software systems.

23.2. Definitions

In general, we will use the following definition of terms:

- *A Class* is the generic description of, for example, a Toyota Prius, indicating the nature of the car, the fact that one must specify a color and body style, and defining the functional relationships between, for example, the speed and fuel consumption.
- *An Object* is an instance of a class in the same way that one specific Toyota Prius is an instance or example of the Toyota Prius design, with a specific identification number, color and body style, and more concretely, with its own values for its current location, speed, fuel contents, etc.
- *An Attribute* is a data component of the class definition that will have a specific value in an object of that class at a given time. For example, all cars will have a speed, but you must examine a particular car to determine its current speed.
- *A Method*, much like a MATLAB function, is a procedural abstraction attached to a class that enables manipulation of the attributes of a particular object. Unlike a MATLAB function, methods have access not only to their own workspace, but also to the attributes of the class of which they are a part.
- *Encapsulation* is actually the core of good OO design. It is the process of packaging together attributes and methods in such a way that you define and control the interfaces through which outside users (other objects) can access the attributes of your objects.
- *Inheritance* is the characteristic that enables the re-use and/or extension of core facilities. It is the facility by which a general, core class can be extended to add more specific attributes and methods, perhaps redefining the behavior of a few existing methods, but retaining access to the original, unmodified behavior.
- *A Parent Class* is the class from which other classes inherit characteristics.
- *Child Classes* are classes derived from parent classes by inheritance[2]. Of course, grandchild classes can also inherit from child classes, etc.

---

[1] It should be noted here that the MATLAB implementations in this text were designed to remain as close as possible to a style that permits ready translation to more conventional OO language implementations (Java, C++, or C#). Where possible, we will footnote typical Java implementations of the MATLAB software artifacts.

[2] Some OO languages permit child classes to inherit from more than one set of parents—a practice that can cause significant logical challenges. Other languages (Java, for one) enforce single inheritance chains, but provide alternate mechanisms (interfaces) for enforcing other common behaviors. We will see interface-like characteristics in our MATLAB code examples.

· **Polymorphism**[3] is the ability to treat all the children of a common parent as if they were all instances of that parent. It has two important aspects:

1. All objects that are children of a parent class must be treated collectively as if they were all instances of the parent, but also,
2. Individually, the system must reach the specific child methods when called for.

23.3. Concepts

23.3.1. Behavioral Abstraction

Behavioral Abstraction is the central concept in OO programming. We discussed **Data Abstraction** as the ability to group together disparate data items as arrays or structures that permit us to discuss 'the temperature readings for July' or 'the information about that CD' without having to enumerate all the details. We also referred to functions as implementing **Procedural Abstraction** whereby we could collect a number of recurring instructions, group them together and invoke them without reiterating all the details.

Behavioral abstraction combines these two abstractions, allowing us to encapsulate not only related data items, but also the operations that are legal to perform on those data items. In the terms defined above, we can visualize a class as the encapsulation of a number of attributes with the methods that operate on those attributes to describe the behavior of object.

23.3.2. Abstract Data Type

An **Abstract Data Type (ADT)** is a technique for describing the general character of a class without descending into specifics. The format of an ADT does not have to be graphical—there are good textual techniques for accomplishing the same objective. The specific ADT format we will use in this text is illustrated in Figure 107, where the data defined for the class are enclosed in the yellow box and the methods for operating on the data are described by the white rectangles. We will use this form to define the overall behavior of classes before diving into the detailed implementation.

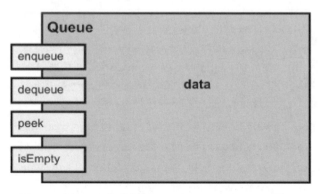

Figure 107—ADT Illustration—A Queue Class

---

[3] From a Greek word meaning "taking many forms."

23.4. MATLAB Observations

The basic MATLAB functionality we have already used actually exhibits some interesting behaviors. Consider, for example, the plus operator, **A + B**. Depending on the actual nature of **A** and **B**, this might have very different effects. For example, if **A** is an array, its actual type (referred to in the MATLAB workspace window as its **class**) is **double**. MATLAB actually interprets **A + B** as **plus(A, B)**, or applying the **plus** method to the class **A**. Depending on the nature of **B**, this operation may have very different results:

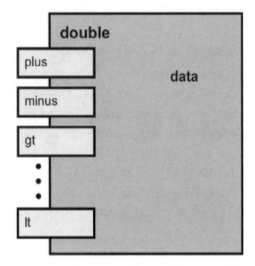

- If **A** is **1x1** (really, a scalar value), the operation will succeed when B is just about anything.
- If **A** is any sized array, the operation will only succeed if **B** is a scalar, or the same size as **A**.
- Otherwise, the operation will fail with an error message.

Figure 108—ADT for the Class Double

These seem to be obvious statements, but are actually quite profound, and fundamental to our understanding of OO. This means that what we have previously considered to be an "open collection" of numbers is actually a collection "protected from the world" by a set of methods that "understand" what can, and cannot, be done with the data. (Figure 108).

23.5. Categories of Classes

In general, classes fall into two categories: either classes that model individual objects—whether physical or abstract—such as vehicles, bank accounts or GUI widgets, or classes that model collections of things like arrays or queues. It is important to keep these two categories of model separate, but to provide for the fact that collection classes need to be able to hold objects of many different types—individual objects, and other collection objects.

For example, if we were intending to model traffic flow in a city, we might begin by considering the city map as a collection of streets and intersections. The role of a street object would be to contain and organize the vehicles moving on that street; the role of an intersection object (which might temporarily contain vehicles) is primarily to move vehicles from one street to another. Since one of the attributes of each vehicle should be the route it is currently following, the intersection should query a vehicle to discover which direction it should turn.

23.5.1. Modeling Objects

We talk generically about the vehicles on the streets. In general, a vehicle would have a size, a heading, a location, a speed and a route plan. It would have a method for moving along a street, and perhaps a generic method for drawing it when necessary. Specific vehicles would have specific constraints—motor-cycles might have a higher maximum speed, for example. If we were drawing the vehicles on the streets, each specific vehicle would also have its own specific drawing method. So a **Vehicle** class would encapsulate the basic data about a specific vehicle with methods like **draw(...)** and **move(...)**.

23.5.2. Modeling Collections

When we look harder at the behavior of vehicles on a street (excluding overtaking, accidents etc.) they behave as if they were in a queue. They join at the back of the queue, and arrive in order at the intersection at the other end of the street. So the streets really become containers of collections of vehicles with a specific behavior that we might describe as a queue. So a **Queue** class would encapsulate objects it currently contains with methods like **enqueue(...)** and **dequeue(...)** as illustrated in Figure 107.

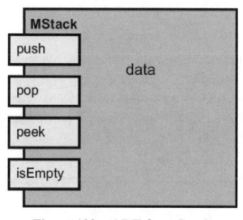

Figure 109—ADT for a Stack

Similarly, if we were, for example, emulating a Polish Notation calculator, we would need a stack to hold the intermediate values. We might visualize a stack[4] class **MStack**, as illustrated in Figure 109. By convention, we refer to the process of adding data to a Queue as enqueuing, but to a stack as pushing, and removing data as dequeuing and popping respectively.

Finally, there are advanced processing applications that require a special kind of queue called a Priority Queue. Imagine, for example, a process for organizing print jobs where you decide that people should not have to wait so long for small print jobs while long print jobs complete. When a job was enqueued for printing, it would therefore be put in the queue ahead of the larger jobs. This is a priority queue.

23.5.3. Objects within Collections

A street will process each vehicle generically by traversing its queue contents, but the vehicle specific characteristics will govern their actual behavior. In later chapters, we will discuss the

---

[4] Actually, since MATLAB has a predefined Stack class, we will name our stack class MStack.

MATLAB implementation of such a model that integrates objects with object collections; but first, we will separately consider modeling objects and collections with simple examples.

23.6. MATLAB Implementation of Classes and Objects

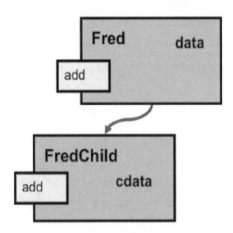

Figure 110—Example Classes

MATLAB actually does a very creditable job implementing the OO language characteristics detailed in section 23.2 above. We will consider the very simple pair of classes shown in Figure 110. Both the parent class, **Fred**, and the child class, **FredChild**, contain one data item, and host one method named **add**. The parent **add** method adds the value provided to its local data storage. The child **add** method adds both to its own data, and to the parent's data.

The following paragraphs indicate in this context how MATLAB implements the OO characteristics enumerated in Section 23.2 above.

23.6.1. MATLAB Classes

A Class in MATLAB is a collection of functions (the methods of that class) stored as .m files in a specific subdirectory of the current workspace. For example, if we were modeling the class named **Fred** illustrated above, all of the public methods (those you want to be accessible from outside the class) must be stored in a directory named **@Fred**. There are two ways to withhold public access to methods. If you need a private utility for use by only one of **Fred**'s methods, it can be included as a local function inside that method definition file. Utilities to be shared by more than one method but not from outside the class can be stored in a subdirectory named **private**. MATLAB requires the following methods to be present:

- A constructor—a method named the same as the class (**Fred** in our example) that may contain parameters used to initialize the object and returns the completed object[5]. However, it must make provisions for two features: calling the constructor with no parameters, and calling the constructor to copy another object of the same class—accomplished by calling the constructor with the object to copy as the only parameter. The Fred constructor is illustrated in Table 127.
- A **display(...)** method used by MATLAB whenever an assignment is made to a variable of this class without the semicolon to suppress the display.

---

[5] Java constructors normally don't return the object—they just initialize its attributes.

- A `char(...)` method[6] returning a string describing the content of this object. Typically, the `display(...)` method merely contains `disp(char(...))`, but this method also allows functions like `fprintf(...)` to display the object as a string.
- `set` and `get` methods for any attributes accessible by child classes.
- Other methods required by the class specification.

23.6.2. MATLAB Objects

An Object in MATLAB is created in a test script or a method of another class by assigning to a variable a call to the constructor of the required class with or without initializing parameters. For example, `myFred = Fred` would create an object `myFred` with default values of its attributes. Having created the object, its methods are called by invoking them by name with `myFred` as the first parameter[7]. For example, to display the object, one might use:

```
fprintf('the object is %s\n', char(myFred) );
```

23.6.3. MATLAB Attributes

Attributes in MATLAB are stored in a structure we will refer to as the attribute structure that actually becomes typed as the object. The structure is made into an object by casting its type in the class constructor. This is illustrated in Table 127.

```
function frd = Fred(data)
% @Fred\Fred class constructor.
% frd = Fred(data) creates a Fred containing data
% could also be a copy constructor:
%    newF = Fred(oldF) copies the old Fred oldF
if nargin == 0      % did the user provide data?
   frd.value = 0;  % set the attribute
   frd = class(frd,'Fred'); % cast as a Fred
elseif isa(data, 'Fred') % copy constructor?
   frd = data;
else
   frd.value = data;    % data provided
   frd = class(acct,'Fred');
end
```

Table 127—Constructor for the Fred Class

---

[6] Java enthusiasts might recognize this as `toString()` except that MATLAB does not automatically invoke `char(...)` if it is expecting a string but sees an object.

[7] Most OO implementation languages use the "structure access" style for invoking methods on an object like: `myFred.char()`.

Notes:

1. We must allow for the case where the constructor is called with no arguments. This is indicated when **nargin** is 0.
2. The function **class(...)** casts the structure in the first argument to the type provided in the second argument.
3. The function **isa(...)** determines whether a given object is of the type specified. This detects the copy constructor intended to replicate a given object of the same type.

23.6.4. MATLAB Methods

A method in MATLAB is written like a function, stored in the class folder, and obeys all the normal rules of functions. The object attributes are presented to the method as its first parameter (which is actually an attribute structure). If the method changes any attributes of the object, it is necessary to return the updated attribute structure to the calling program[8]. In this text, we have chosen the *tunneling back* approach as illustrated in Table 128 that illustrates the code to add something to the data stored in an object of type Fred. After performing the addition, the line:

```
assignin('caller', inputname(1), frd)
```

is the command that tunnels back. It first obtains the name of the variable provided to this method using **inputname(1)**, then assigns the updated attribute structure **frd** to that name in the caller's workspace.

```
function add(frd, data)
% @Fred\add to add data to its value.
% add(frd, data)
    frd.value = frd.value + data;
    assignin('caller', inputname(1), frd);
```

Table 128—Fred's Add Method

23.6.5. Encapsulation in MATLAB Classes

Encapsulation is accomplished in MATLAB by storing all the methods for a class in the folder named for the class (**@Fred** in the example).

---

[8] There is no nice, smooth way to accomplish this. The method must either return the new attribute structure to the calling program which exposes the uglies to the caller, or hides the uglies from the caller by "tunneling back" to the caller's workspace.

23.6.6. Inheritance in MATLAB Classes

Inheritance is accomplished in the MATLAB constructor for the child class. A local variable is first initialized as an instance of the parent class. The class cast method that creates the new child object includes this parent instance as a third parameter. The end result of this manipulation is an additional attribute in the child class that has the same name as the parent class, and contains a reference to the parent object. When the child class needs access to the methods of the parent[9], it refers to these methods by way of this reference. Table 129 shows the code for the child constructor, with notes to follow.

```
function fc = FredChild(data, cd)
% @FredChild class constructor.
%   fc = FredChild (data, cd) creates a FredChild
%     whose parent value is data, and local attribute
%     is dc
% could also be a copy constructor:
%   fc = FredChild ( ofc ) copies the account ofc
if nargin == 0
   super = Fred;                          % Note 1
   fc.cdata = 0;                          % Note 2
   fc = class(fc, 'FredChild', super);    % Note 3
elseif isa(data, 'FredChild')
   fc = data;
else
   super = Fred(data);                    % Note 4
   fc.cdata = cd;                         % Note 5
   fc = class(fc, 'FredChild', super);    % Note 6
end
```

Table 129—Fred Child Constructor

Notes:

1. When constructing a default child, first construct a parent object with default contents.
2. Then set the child data items to default values, and
3. Include the parent object in the class cast to establish the parent-child relationship.
4. The real constructor passes data to the parent, and
5. Keeps cd locally as the childData.
6. As with the default constructor, establish the parent-child link by passing the parent object to the class cast.

---

[9] MATLAB child classes cannot directly access the attributes of the parent. They are accessed and modified only by way of the parent's set and get methods.

23.6.7. MATLAB Parent Classes

A Parent Class is the class from which other classes inherit characteristics.

23.6.8. MATLAB Child Classes

Child Classes are classes derived from parent classes by inheritance[10]. Of course, grandchild classes can also inherit from child classes, etc. A child class cannot directly access the attribute structure of its parent. However, it can access the methods of the parent class by way of an attribute with the name of the parent class. This logic needs careful study. Examine the code for the child class's add method in Table 130, the diagram in Figure 111 and the explanatory notes.

```
function add(fc, value)
% add this value to both the child's and
%   parent's stored data
    fc.cdata = fc.cdata + value;        % Note 4
    parent = fc.Fred;                   % Note 5
    add(parent, value)                  % Note 6
    fc.Fred = parent;                   % Note 7
    assignin('caller', inputname(1), fc);  % Note 8
```

Table 130—Child Class Add Method

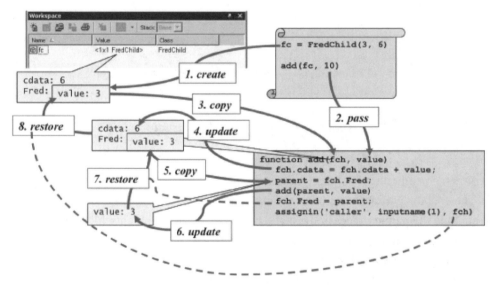

Figure 111—Functionality of a Child Class

---

[10] Some OO languages permit child classes to inherit from more than one set of parents—a practice that can cause significant logical challenges. Other languages (Java, for one) enforce single inheritance chains, but provide alternate mechanisms (interfaces) for enforcing other common behaviors. We will see interface-like characteristics in our MATLAB code examples.

Notes:

1. When a script creates an object, what appears in the workspace is an attribute structure whose class name is the name of the child class. Its attributes are the local data values for the child object and a special attribute with the name of the parent class. That parent class attribute contains the parent data items defined for this object.

2. When a child method is called, since the parameters are passed by value, the numerical parameters are copied in directly.

3. The original object is copied into the workspace of the child method, so the child method is working on a copy of the original object.

4. The child method can directly modify those parts of the attribute structure belonging to that child.

5. The child reaches the methods of the parent class via the attribute named for the parent class—in this case, **fc.Fred** This attribute contains the attributes of the parent object that are defined for this child class. Because this parent structure is an attribute structure, it cannot be directly passed as a parameter to the parent's methods. Rather, we must first extract a copy of the parent's attribute structure.

6. We then call the parent method with that copy, which modifies our local copy of the parent attributes.

7. Then, we put the copy of the parent attributes back into our local attribute structure.

8. Finally, since this method is also working with a copy of this object's attributes, these updated attributes must be copied back to the calling program / method.

23.6.9. Polymorphism in MATLAB

The two crucial aspects of *Polymorphism*[11] are

1. All objects that are children of a parent class must be treated collectively as if they were all instances of the parent, but also,

2. Individually, the system must reach the specific child methods when called for.

MATLAB achieves the first very naturally, because it ignores the type of all data until forced to operate on that data. The power of this polymorphic approach is this. Throughout MATLAB, all data objects are self-aware—of their data type and the methods they can implement. So objective 2 is achieved because when MATLAB calls a method on a particular object, it goes to that object for the method implementation.

A simple example might suffice. In the Fred class, in addition to the add and constructor methods discussed above, we implemented a **display(...)** method and a **char(...)** method to show

---

[11] From a Greek word meaning "taking many forms."

the contents of objects of type **Fred**. In the **FredChild** class, there is no **display(...)** method, but there is a **char(...)** method to return the contents both of this child, and of its parent class.

```
clear
clc
clear classes
f = Fred(20)              % Note 1
fc = FredChild(3, 6)      % Note 2
add(fc, 10)               % Note 3
fc                        % Note 4
```

Table 131—Fred Child Test Program

Notes:
1. Create an instance of the parent and show it by calling **display(...)** on the parent class. The display method calls char on this object which is a parent class.
2. Create and display a child object—note that this uses the display method on the parent because the child doesn't have one, but calls the char method on the child. Note also that the child char method invokes the parent's char method[12].
3. This changes the data in both parent and child by adding 10 to them, and
4. This displays the child again.

```
function display(frd)
%
disp(char(frd))
```

Table 132—@Fred\display.m

```
function str = char(frd)
%
str = sprintf('Fred with %d', frd.value );
```

Table 133—@Fred\char.m

```
function str = char(frdc)
%
str = sprintf('FredChild with %d containing %s', ...
         frdc.cdata, char(frdc.Fred) );
```

Table 134—@FredChild\char.m

---

[12] This is OK in this form because the parent attribute structure is not being modified.

```
Fred with 20
FredChild with 6 containing Fred with 3
FredChild with 16 containing Fred with 13
```

Table 135—Results in the Command Window

23.7. Examples

23-1 We want to create and test a class called *Payroll*, which includes the following:

  ❑ a constructor method that initializes the **payrate**
  ❑ a method named **totalCheck** that takes in the number of hours an employee works, multiplies it by the **payrate**, and returns the amount to be paid for the pay period

  a. Create the **Payroll** class in a directory **@Payroll**
  b. Write the constructor and **totalCheck** methods
  c. Write a script to test the **Payroll** class by creating a **Payroll** named **myPay** with a pay rate of 10.50 and displaying the hours and the pay for those hours from 10 to 80 in steps of 5 in the following format:

```
Hours          Pay
10             105.00
15             157.50
        etc.
```

23-2 We need a shopping assistant that will help with our grocery purchases. We will build it using the following steps:

  a. Create the class **Item** to represent a single item in a grocery cart. An item has the attributes **name** and **price**. You will need a constructor and a method **getPrice** that returns the price of an item.
  b. Write a short script to test the **Item** class.
  c. Create the class **Groceries** containing a cell array named **basket** that is initially empty.
  d. Write the method **add** in the **Grocery** class that consumes an object and adds it to the basket.
  e. Write the method **checkout** that consumes a tax rate percentage and calculates the total grocery purchase including that tax.
  f. Write a script to test your Grocery class with a suitable collection of items.

23-3 Suppose the information about a pirate is represented by a **Pirate** class containing two attributes: his name and the number of gold pieces he has, accessible by the methods `getName()` and `getGold()`. We need a function called ***richPirates*** that will accept a cell array of Pirate objects and return another cell array containing the names of all pirates with more than 100 gold pieces.

    a. Write the Pirate class and the necessary methods to access its fields.

    b. Write a test script that builds a cell array of pirates with random amounts of gold between 0 and 1,000 pieces, and lists the names and amounts of gold.

    c. Write the richPirates function according to the specification above.

    d. Add to the test script the ability to test richPirates.

24. MODELING OBJECTS

The overall goal of this section is to show a slightly more practical model without having to write too much code, and then illustrate inheritance by extension, and by redefining a small part. In particular, the emphasis will be on designing and gathering functionality in the parent class in order to minimize the amount of content in the child classes.

We will first see the ADT and MATLAB model for a simple bank account class, and then consider two techniques for extending that class—by extension to model a savings account, and then by redefinition to model an overdraft-protected account.

24.1. The Base Class

Figure 112 illustrates the ADT for a basic bank account class. While there are a number of attributes of a real account associated with the identity and ownership of that account, we will keep

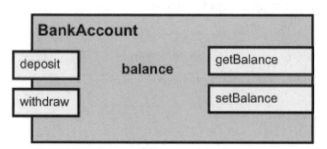

Figure 112—ADT for the Bank Account

things as simple as possible by considering just the balance on an account as the attribute of interest. The **deposit** and **withdraw** methods provide normal access to the account balance for external users. The **getBalance** and **setBalance** methods provide balance access for the derived classes.

All of the following files will be stored in the folder **@BankAccount** except the test program that should be in the work directory containing the class directories. Table 136 shows the constructor setting up the single attribute, the balance in the account.

```
function acct = BankAccount(data)
% BankAccount class constructor.
%   ba = BankAccount(amt) creates a bank account
%                           with balance amt
% could also be a copy constructor:
%   ba = BankAccount( oba ) copies the account oba
if nargin == 0
   acct.balance = 0;
   acct = class(acct,'BankAccount');                 (Continued)
```

Table 136—BankAccount Constructor

```
elseif isa(data, 'BankAccount')
   acct = data;
else
   acct.balance = data;
   acct = class(acct,'BankAccount');
end
```

Table 136—BankAccount Constructor *(Continued)*

Note:

A typical constructor as we saw in previous chapters.

```
function deposit(acct, amount)
% deposit to the account
        setBalance(acct, acct.balance + amount);
        assignin('caller', inputname(1), acct);
```

Table 137—The BankAccount Deposit Method

Note:

Any access to important data like the balance of an account should go through access methods to allow methods for validation and writing audit trails, etc. to be added in a central location.

```
function gets = withdraw(acct, amount)
% withdraw from the account
        gets = amount;
        if gets > acct.balance
            gets = acct.balance;
        end
        setBalance(acct, acct.balance - gets);
        assignin('caller', inputname(1), acct);
```

Table 138—The BankAccount Withdraw Method

Note:

In a typical account, withdrawals are limited to the amount in the account.

```
function ans = getBalance(ba)
% get the balance
ans = ba.balance;
```

Table 139—BankAccount getBalance Method

```
function setBalance(acct, amount)
% set the account balance
        acct.balance = amount;
        assignin('caller', inputname(1), acct);
```

Table 140—BankAccount setBalance Method

```
function display(ba)
% disp for the BankAccount class
% displays string representation of the account

disp(char(ba));
```

Table 141—BankAccount Display Method

```
function s = char(ba)
% toString for the BankAccount class
% returns string representation of the account

s = sprintf('Account with $%.2f\n', ba.balance );
```

Table 142—BankAccount Char Method

Note:

This string should be sufficiently generic to be able to be used by children classes.

```
moola = BankAccount(1000)
deposit(moola, 20.11)
fprintf('deposit 20.11 -> %s\n', char(moola) );
gets = withdraw(moola, 200);
fprintf('withdraw 200 -> $%.2f; %s\n', ...
    gets, char(moola) )
```

Table 143—BankAccount Test Script

```
Account with $1000.00
deposit 20.11 -> Account with $1020.11
withdraw 200 -> $200.00; Account with $820.11
```

Table 144—Test Results

24.2. Inheritance by Extension

Having invested significant effort in preparing the **BankAccount** class to be extended, writing a **SavingsAccount** class involves only the constructor and two methods. The **SavingsAccount**

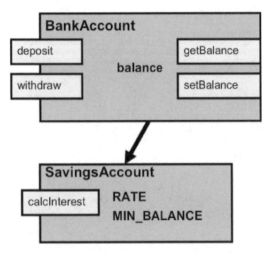

Figure 113—The SavingsAccount Class

class will have all the characteristics of a **BankAccount** plus the ability to calculate interest periodically. For simplicity, we will omit any time-sensitive calculations, and presume that the **calcInterest** is only run when appropriate. The interest will accumulate at a specified rate, and will only be applied if the account balance exceeds a given minimum balance.

The **SavingsAccount** class and its parent are illustrated in Figure 113. The only new code needed will be for the constructor (Table 145), the method that calculates the interest (Table 146) and the **char(...)** method to display its content (Table 147). Even that method will invoke the parent **char(...)** method for most of the work.

All the following files except the test script must be stored in the directory **@SavingsAccount**. Notice the following important characteristics:

1. The **calcInterest** method does not have to specifically request the **getBalance(...)** method of the parent because since there is no **getBalance** method on this class, the parent supplies it.

2. Similarly, the test program merely invokes the **deposit** method. Since the **SavingsAccount** doesn't have one, the parent **deposit** method is used.

3. On the other hand, the **char(...)** method does need to explicitly invoke the parent **char(...)** method in order to avoid recursive behavior.

4. Perhaps most challenging, notice that there is no **display(...)** method in this class, so the parent's **display(...)** method is called. However, it calls a **char(...)** method. Which **char(...)** method is invoked? The **SavingsAccount char(...)** method because its parameter is a **SavingsAccount** first, and a **BankAccount** second.

```
function acct = SavingsAccount(data)
% SavingsAccount class constructor.
%  ba = SavingsAccount(amt) creates a savings account
%                               with balance amt
% could also be a copy constructor:
%   ba = SavingsAccount( osa ) copies the account osa
if nargin == 0
   super = BankAccount;
   acct.RATE = 5;
   acct.MIN_BALANCE = 1000;
   acct = class(acct, 'SavingsAccount', super);
elseif isa(data,'SavingsAccount')
   acct = data;
else
   super = BankAccount(data);
   acct.RATE = 5;
   acct.MIN_BALANCE = 1000;
   acct = class(acct,'SavingsAccount', super);
end
```

Table 145—SavingsAccount Constructor

```
function int = calcInterest(acct)
% calculate the interest
if getBalance(acct) > acct.MIN_BALANCE
    int = acct.RATE * getBalance(acct) / 100;
else
    int = 0;
end
```

Table 146—SavingsAccount calcInterest Method

```
function s = char(sa)
% toString for the SavingsAccount class
% returns string representation of the account
s = sprintf( 'Savings %s', char(sa.BankAccount) );
```

Table 147—SavingsAccount `char(...)` Method

```
sa = SavingsAccount(2000)
deposit(sa, 3000);
fprintf('deposit 3000 -> %s\n', char(sa) );
intrst = calcInterest(sa);
deposit(sa, intrst);
fprintf('deposit interest %.2f -> %s\n', ...
            intrst, char(sa) );
```

Table 148—SavingsAccount Tests

```
Savings Account with $2000.00
deposit 3000 -> Savings Account with $5000.00
deposit interest 250.00
            -> Savings Account with $5250.00
```

Table 149—SavingsAccount Test Results

24.3. Inheritance by Redefinition

We now consider a further extension of the BankAccount family—a SavingsAccount with a guaranteed overdraft. Once overdraft privileges have been authorized, users of this account can withdraw as much as they want. Of course, if the resulting balance is negative, the bank applies an overdraft charge, thereby taking away even more of the money you don't have anyway.

The coding for this account will follow the general guidelines used above—a new constructor (Table 150), a method for permitting overdrafts to occur (Table 151), and a new **char(...)** method (Table 152). The data for this class will include a Boolean value indicating that overdraft has been approved for this particular account object. However, this account will also need its own withdraw method to implement the new withdrawal rules (Table 153).

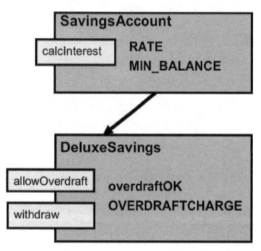

Figure 114—The Delux Savings Account

```
function acct = DeluxSavingsAccount(data)
% DeluxSavingsAccount class constructor.
%   ba = DeluxSavingsAccount(amt) creates an
%         account with balance amt
% could also be a copy constructor:
%   ba = DeluxSavingsAccount( oda ) copies oda
if nargin == 0
   super = SavingsAccount;
   acct.overdraftOK = false;
   acct.OVERDRAFT_CHARGE = 20;
   acct = class(acct,'DeluxSavingsAccount', super);
elseif isa(data,'DeluxSavingsAccount')
   acct = data;
else
   super = SavingsAccount(data);
   acct.overdraftOK = false;
   acct.OVERDRAFT_CHARGE = 20;
   acct = class(acct,'DeluxSavingsAccount', super);
end
```

Table 150—DeluxSavingsAccount Constructor

```
function allowOverdraft(acct, value)
% approve overdraft on DeluxSavingsAccount
   acct.overdraftOK = value;
   assignin('caller', inputname(1), acct);
```

Table 151—DeluxSavingsAccount allowOverdraft Method

```
function s = char(sa)
% toString for the DeluxSavingsAccount class
% returns string representation of the account

if sa.overdraftOK, strng = 'OK';
else, strng = 'off'; end
s = sprintf( 'Delux %s with overdraft %s', ...
   char(sa.SavingsAccount), strng );
```

Table 152—DeluxSavingsAccount char(...) Method

```
function gets = withdraw(acct, amount)
% withdraw from a DeluxSavings account
        if (amount < getBalance(acct))
                        || ~acct.overdraftOK
            parent = acct.SavingsAccount;
            gets = withdraw(parent, amount);
            acct.SavingsAccount = parent;
        else
            gets = amount;
            penalty = 0;
            if gets > getBalance(acct)
                penalty = acct.OVERDRAFT_CHARGE;
            end
            setBalance(acct,
                getBalance(acct) - gets - penalty);
        end
        assignin('caller', inputname(1), acct);
```

Table 153—Redefined Withdraw Method

Notes:
1. Like its predecessor, the **char(...)** method lets its parent classes generate much of the string, adding locally only the additional data values.
2. The redefined **withdraw(...)** method invokes the parent's **withdraw(...)** method if it can, but changes the balance by way of its **get** and **set** methods when it has to.
3. In particular, observe that when it can use the parent **withdraw(...)** method, it only reaches back one level to the **SavingsAccount** parent. The fact that this parent does not implement **withdraw(...)** and passes the call to its parent is not a concern for this child class.

24.4. Practical Example of Modeling

It would be wrong to leave this discussion without an example of a more practical application of these techniques. Figure 115 illustrates the inheritance hierarchy for a collection of vehicles that might be used, for example, in a traffic simulation.

24.4.1. A Vehicle Hierarchy

To simulate traffic dynamically, every vehicle must be able to be drawn, and to move in accordance with the rules that govern its behavior. Notice that many of the "simpler" actual vehicles do not contain their own **move** methods. Given a speed and heading for one of these vehicles, the generic vehicle **move** method can be applied. However, they all contain their own **draw** methods, because in general, drawing specific objects requires specific behavior in that **draw** method.

The more complex vehicles (a semi pulling a trailer, for example) do have their own draw methods, however, because in addition to moving the semi, the trailer must be moved in such a way that it remains attached to the semi. Similarly, a transporter trailer containing other vehicles must move all the other vehicles in a manner consistent with their remaining on the trailer.

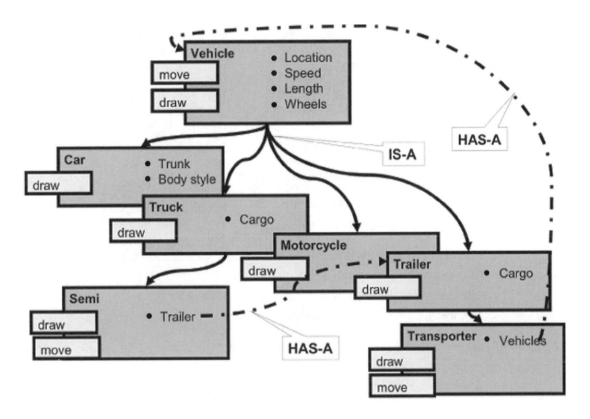

Figure 115—A Vehicle Hierarchy

24.4.2. The Containment relationship

There is one other practical consideration to note. Any practical hierarchy actually reflects two different relationships between classes. We discussed the Inheritance (IS-A) relationship in the paragraphs above—it is all about inheriting data and methods from a parent class, and is implemented in the child constructor. We illustrate here the other relationship—that of Containment (HAS-A) used to indicate a relationship of possession between objects. Two examples:

1. A Semi class has a trailer attached. There is no inheritance of data or methods between the Semi and trailer classes. Rather, one of the attributes peculiar to the Semi is a trailer object—that attribute can be accessed by set and get methods permitting the semi to move and draw its trailer.

2. A Transporter contains a collection of Vehicles. Its move and draw methods must be able to traverse that collection, calling the **move** or **draw** methods for the children as appropriate.

24.5. Examples

24-1 Write a class called **CS1371** with the following instructions.
   a. Create a directory @**CS1371**.
   b. It will have a variable called **myTA** that is a string.
   c. Create a constructor that initializes the value for **myTA** to the String passed in by the user.
   d. Write a **char()** method that returns a string in the form:

   > `'This is CS1371, and <myTA> is my TA'`

   e. Write a test script where you create a **CS1371** object and display its contents.

24-2 Modify the CS1371 class above according to the following:
   a. Add fields for your **name**, **test grade**, **final grade** and **overall grade**.
   b. Add **set** and **get** methods for these fields.
   c. Add the values of your test and final grades to the **char()** results.
   d. Add tests to your script for these fields.

24-3 Modify the test script above to create a cell array of **CS1371** objects. Use suitable names and test values.
   a. Write a function that accepts a **CS1371** object and computes a letter grade (tests = 35%, final = 65%).
   b. Write a function that maps this cell array by adding 20% to the test score of each student.
   c. Write a function that traverses the cell array and prints the overall averages as a table in the form:

   > `Name: <name>; grade: <A-F>`

   d. Add to your test script the function call to write out the original scores.
   e. Add to your test script the function call to raise the test scores and then print the results again.

24-4 Write a class Vehicle with the following attributes:

      a. type—a string

      b. color—a string

      c. owner—a string

Make sure it has set and get methods for these fields, a `char()` method to show a vehicle and a test script to create and display a cell array of vehicles.

25. DYNAMIC DATA STRUCTURES

Having dealt with the concept of modeling specific concrete or abstract objects, we turn to the process of defining dynamically sized collections of objects. The goal is to provide mechanisms that organize collections containing any kind of object—MATLAB basic classes, arrays or structures, cell arrays, or instances of our own classes as defined under the rules in Chapter 24.

25.1. Concepts

We will consider three concepts important to dynamic data structures: static memory allocation on the activation stack, dynamic memory allocation from the heap, and dynamically linking objects to create dynamic structures.

25.1.1. Static Memory Allocation

Static memory allocation: In Section 1.4, we discussed in general the allocation of memory to application programs on a processor. The first of these approaches was the Activation Stack (stack for short). The stack is used to allocate memory frames that contain data local to a script or function call. Each overall application program (like MATLAB) is allocated one memory block for use as its stack. Each time a function is called, a frame of memory is allocated from the stack; when the function terminates, that memory is released from the stack as discussed in Section 13.1.2.

For example, in the middle of a solution to Example 6.1, the activation stack might look like that in Figure 116. The script containing the variables u, s and g calls the function roots with parameters A, B, and C. In the core of that function, the square root of a value is called. This would be the state of the stack before the sqrt function completes. The blue blocks indicate static data storage on the stack for the variables allocated in the script and functions.

sqrt	x =	815.2						
roots	A =	49.05	B	=	- 40	C	=	40
Ex6_1	u =	40	s	=	40	g	=	9.81

Figure 116—An Activation Stack

25.1.2. Dynamic Memory Allocation

Dynamic memory allocation: The second source of memory discussed in Section 1.4 is the heap. This is a single block of memory available to all the applications to be allocated and deallocated upon request from an application. For example, when we created a BankAccount object for test purposes, the command was:

```
moola = BankAccount(1000)
```

Figure 117 illustrates what actually happens when that command is executed:

1. A block of memory large enough to hold the data structure for a BankAccount is requested from the Heap;
2. The data are initialized by the code in the constructor;
3. The variable `moola` actually becomes a pointer, or reference, to that block of memory;
4. The allocated memory is retained as long as there is a reference somewhere (not necessarily the same one); and
5. When the last reference to that memory block is destroyed, the block is returned to the operating system's heap.

We cannot leave this concept without considering the "ordinary" variables in Figure 116 and Figure 117. Although it is convenient to introduce them initially as if they were statically allocated[1], recall that all MATLAB entities are in fact instances of classes. Even single numbers are 11 arrays. Each of the variables illustrated should in fact be viewed in the same style as the variable `moola` shown in Figure 117.

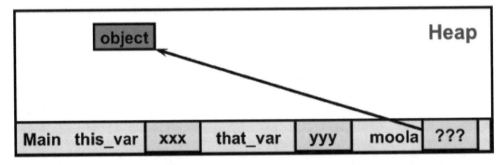

Figure 117—Dynamically Allocated Memory

---

[1] This is in fact true in Java where primitive variables of type int, double and Boolean are in fact stored on the stack.

25.1.3. Dynamic Data Structures

Dynamically linked memory: The power of these structures becomes evident when you consider the "simple" structure illustrated in Figure 118. References to objects on the heap are not confined to stack frames. Dynamically created objects can contain references to other similar, or dissimilar, objects. This chapter will demonstrate the implementation of the simplest of these structures, the linked list.

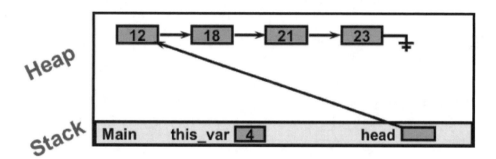

Figure 118—Dynamically Linked Data

25.2. Linked Lists

Linked lists are linear data structures implemented exactly as illustrated in Figure 118. Before we descend into the details of this implementation, it is important to identify a watershed in the style of the code presentation in this text. To this point, we have illustrated examples by showing all the code necessary to implement the examples. This has been possible so far because the code has been quite simple, and necessary because there was no good metaphor for summarizing the code. Now, the code is going to become more complex, but we have a metaphor for describing the code in a more concise manner—the ADT—than including all the listings.

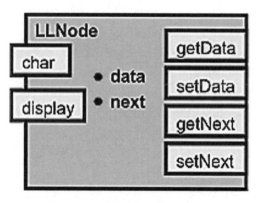

Figure 119—ADT for the LLNode

Here, we will review the ground rules under which we will use the ADTs as a metaphor for the bulk of the routine code[2], freeing us to concentrate on the methods of general interest. Consider one of the two basic classes necessary for implementing linked lists: the **LLNode** class illustrated

---

[2] All the necessary source code will be available on the support web site.

in Figure 119. When we include an ADT in this form, the implementation implied by its presence will be as follows:

- ❏ A class with the given name (**LLNode**) stored in the appropriate directory (**@LLNode**).
- ❏ Data items with the names and order shown in the ADT.
- ❏ Access methods with names built as shown, capitalizing the name of the data items.
- ❏ A constructor expecting initial values of the data items in the order indicated (**data** then **next**).
- ❏ If any of the data items are not provide to the constructor, by default the values will be set to null (**[]**).
- ❏ Other "expected" methods (**char** or **display** in this example) may be discussed if they have any interesting content.
- ❏ Other public methods will be identified on the left side of the ADT and the code presented and discussed.

Two classes are necessary to implement a linked list. The links themselves are all instances of the **LLNode** class. The container of all the linked list methods is a **LinkedList** class.

25.2.1. The LLNode Class

The purpose of the **LLNode** class is to contain references to data items and connect them in a linear list. The data items can be of any type, with two possible constraints. If the data are of type **double**, we have to make a special case in the **char(...)** method. Some methods that process the contents of the linked list may put other requirements on the contained objects.

Since the **LLNode** class has no really interesting methods, by the above ground rules, we need to include no code listings except the **char(...)** method. Here, we have to make a special case of contents with class **double** because **char(d)** when **d** is type **double** attempts to convert that **double** value to the ASCII code equivalent. If **d** is of any other type, **char(d)** will convert it to a string as needed.

```
function s = char(n)
% @LLNode\char(n) is the string representation
%                    of n.data
if strcmp(class(n.data), 'double')
    s = sprintf('%g', n.data);
else
    s = char(n.data);
end
```

Table 154—LLNode char(...) Method

25.2.2. The LinkedList Class

The purpose of the **LinkedList** class is to contain the head of the linked list (see Figure 118) and all the methods for processing the list. Figure 120 shows the ADT of the **LinkedList** class and its relationship to the **LLNode** class. The relationship is one of containment (HAS-A), not inheritance (IS-A). We will consider the methods of the **LinkedList** class in the context of the taxonomy of collection operations first introduced in Chapter 10.

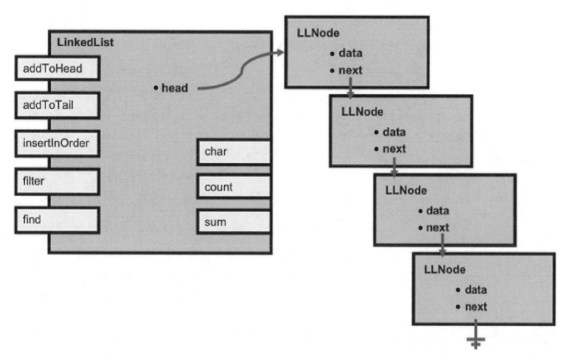

Figure 120—The LinkedList Class

25.3. Processing Recursive Data Structures

We could view the definition of a linked list as follows:

- A **LinkedList** is either empty (**[]**)
- Or an **LLNode** containing some data and a **LinkedList**.

Further, we could argue that we could model the template of a function for processing a linked list after that same structure, as shown in Table 155. See the notes to follow.

```
<function and return> processNode(here)
% recursive processing
if isempty(here)
    <reached the end>
else
    ... getData(here) ...
        ... processNode( getNext(here) ) ...
end
```

Table 155—Template for Processing a Linked List

Notes:

1. The parameter passed to the recursive function could be named **here** to remind us that the recursive program is moving through the list.
2. We test for the empty state with MATLAB's built-in function **isempty(...)**.
3. There will be some actions to take when we reach the end of the list, and
4. Until then, we may do something with the **data** value in the current node, and then recursively process using the **next** value of the node.

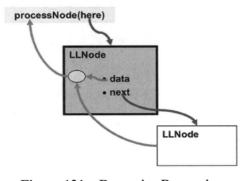

Figure 121—Recursive Processing

We might also consider the view in Figure 121 where processing the whole list is accomplished by repetitively processing the values of a single node:

· Check for the end of the list (here is null),
· Make the recursive call via next,
· Combine the result from the recursive call with the data at this node, and
· Return the result to the calling program.

26. IMPLEMENTING A LINKED LIST IN MATLAB

This chapter will discuss specifically the implementation of the Linked List and some derived classes.

26.1. Building a Linked List

There are three techniques for building a Linked List depending on how you intend the data to be added. The most straightforward is adding to the head of the list. However, this presents the last data item added as the first to be seen when traversing or searching the list. Consequently, we will also consider adding to the tail of the list and inserting in order. While adding to the head or tail of the list impose no constraints at all on the nature of the data in the list, adding in order presumes that we have a means for comparing two of the objects being inserted.

26.1.1. Adding at the Head of the List

Table 156 shows the method for adding to the head of a list. As long as the user has supplied the parameter data, it creates a new **LLNode** containing the **data** provided and the existing **head** of the list and makes that the new list **head**.

```
function addToHead(ll, data)
% @LinkedList\addToHead.
%    addToHead(ll, data) adds data to
%              the head of a LinkedList object
    if nargin > 1
        setHead(ll, LLNode(data, getHead(ll) ));
        assignin('caller', inputname(1), ll);
    end
```

Table 156—Adding to the Head

26.1.2. Adding to the Tail of the List

It is theoretically possible to add to the tail of a linked list either iteratively[1] or recursively. Recall the "myopic view" illustrated in Figure 121, and then apply that view to adding to the tail of a list. The **addToTail** method in the LinkedList class merely passes the head of the list to its recursive local function, **addToTailR**, and stores the new head of the list when that function completes.

---

[1] This is certainly true in Java that permits LLNodes to be modified "on the fly."

The helper function performs the addition of the data according to the logic described below. Table 157 shows these methods.

```
function addToTail(ll, data)
% @LinkedList\addToTail.
%   addToTail(ll, data) adds data to the
%                      tail of a LinkedList object
if nargin > 1
    setHead( ll, addToTailR(getHead(ll), data) );
    assignin('caller', inputname(1), ll);
end


function nl = addToTailR(here, data)
% recursive add to tail
if isempty(here)
    nl = LLNode(data);
else
    nl = LLNode( getData(here), ...
                 addToTailR(getNext(here), data));
end
```

Table 157—Adding to the Tail of a Linked List

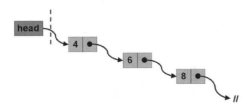

Figure 122—Initial List

All the processing is done by the recursive module using the myopic view illustrated in Figure 121, and the template in Table 155. Consider, for example, the existing list shown in Figure 122.

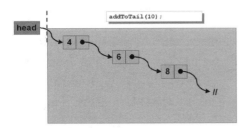

Figure 123—First Recursive Call

If we wanted to add the value 10 to the tail of the list, the first recursive call comes by way of the head of the list to the first node, the one containing the value 4 as shown in Figure 123. Since we are seeking the end of the list, the recursive calls continue.

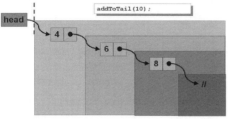

Figure 124—At the End of the List

Finally, the recursive calling reaches the end of the list, illustrated in Figure 124. The action at the end of the list is to create a new node with the data provided (the 10) and null for the next node.

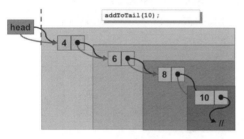

Figure 125—Returning the New List

Each recursive call then returns to its caller a copy of its original node linked to the emerging list provided from the recursive call. Finally, the new list fully formed is provided to the wrapper function that stores the new list as its head value.

26.1.3. Adding to the List in Order

Adding to the list in order is structurally similar to adding to its end, since we must allow for the possibility that the data must be added at its end. It must, however, also allow for finding a link that must come after the new data in the list. In this case, the method builds a new node containing the new data item, with the complete list from here to the end as the next link.

This process also places an additional demand on the data in the list. Whereas any data item can be added to the head or tail of the list, if the list is to be ordered, each data item must be able to respond to[2] the test **A >= B**. Clearly, numbers and characters (including vectors) are equipped to do so. User-defined classes are enabled to respond to this operator by including the method **ge(A, B)**. Table 158 shows the **ge(...)** method that enables a **BankAccount** (and any of its child classes) to be compared to another account, or to a numerical value.

```
function ans = ge(acct, data)
% compare this account to another account or a number
if isa( data, 'BankAccount') % children also respond
    comparison = getBalance(data);                    (Continued)
```

Table 158—ge(...) Operator for the BankAccount Class

---

[2] Java enthusiasts will recognize this as the Comparable interface.

```
else
    comparison = data;
end
ans = (getBalance(acct) >= comparison);
```

Table 158—ge(...) Operator for the BankAccount Class *(Continued)*

As with **addToTail(...)**, the **addInOrder(...)** method hands the head of the list to a recursive local function, and retrieves the new head of the list. Table 159 shows the method for adding to the tail of a list. This method also uses a recursive helper function.

```
function addInOrder(ll, data)
% @LinkedList\addInOrder.
%    ll = addInOrder(ll, data) adds data in order
%                        in a LinkedList object
if nargin > 1
    setHead( ll, addInOrderR(ll.head, data) );
    assignin('caller', inputname(1), ll);
end

function nl = addInOrderR(here, data)
% recursive add in order
if isempty(here)
    nl = LLNode(data);
elseif getData(here) >= data
    nl = LLNode(data, here);
else
    nl = LLNode( getData(here), ...
                 addInOrderR(getNext(here), data));
end
```

Table 159—Linked list addInOrder(...) Method

26.2. Traversing a Linked List

Since a traversal does not change the list, it is possible to perform a list traversal either iteratively or recursively. In order to illustrate iterative processing on a list, we will implement the **char(...)** method on a **LinkedList** class iteratively using the while loop template illustrated in Table 160.

```
<function and return> processLinkedList(theList)
% iterative processing
<initialize the loop exit test>
<initialize the data result>
while <stay in the loop>
    <process the data>
<move forward>
end
<return the results>
```

Table 160—Iterative LinkedList Processing Template

Table 161 shows the **char(...)** method code that directly matches the above template:

- This function returns a character string s.
- The loop will move the variable here through the nodes of the list; its initial value will be the head of the list.
- The initial value of the result string is set to the identifier '**LL:** '.
- The loop continues as long as the **LLNode** reference here is not empty.

We process the data by appending the **char(...)** conversion of the **LLNode**[3] followed by a semicolon.

```
function s = char(ll)
% @LinkedList\char
% char(ll) is the string representation of the list
here = getHead(ll);
s = 'LL: ';
while ~isempty(here)
    s = [s char(here) ';'];
    here = getNext(here);
end
```

Table 161—The LinkedList char(...) Method

---

[3] By asking for the char of the **LLNode** rather than its data contents, we make it responsible for always returning a string. This permits the **LinkedList** to contain numbers—usually a problem because **char(n)** where **n** is class double will attempt an ASCII conversion of n.

26.3. Mapping a Linked List

In general, mapping a list is performed not as a general service to all **LinkedList** users, but rather as a specialized utility written for derived classes that use a **LinkedList** as their parent class. For example, suppose a bank keeps all its interest-bearing accounts in a class derived from the **LinkedList** class. Periodically, they need to traverse that list and add the interest generated by each account. Since the length of the list remains unchanged, but the contents change, this would be a mapping of the original list.

Table 162 illustrates such an update method.

```
function update(acct)
%  @SavingsAccount\update
%     update to the account by depositing
%     the interest due
   amount = calcInterest(acct);
   setBalance(acct, getBalance(acct) + amount);
   assignin('caller', inputname(1), acct);
```

Table 162—SavingsAccount update(...) Method

In order to update all the accounts in a list of **SavingsAccounts**, the mapping would follow the recursive template in Table 155 with the following tailoring required:

❑ As usual, the public method, **updateList**, merely launches the recursive helper, **updateR**, with the current head of the list and stores the new list returned as the new head.
❑ The helper returns an empty list when it reaches the end of the old list.
❑ Otherwise, it returns a new **LLNode** containing the result of updating the old data, using the recursive **updateR** call to update the rest of the list.

The resulting code is shown in Table 163.

```
function updateList(acctList)
%  @SavingsAcctList\update
%     update to the accounts by depositing
%     the interest due
   setHead( acctList, updateR(getHead(acctList)) );          (Continued)
```

Table 163—Mapping a SavingsAccount List

```
    assignin('caller', inputname(1), acctList);


function newLst = updateR(here)
% recursive update helper
if isempty(here)
    newLst = [];
else
    newLst = LLNode( update( getData(here) ), ...
                    updateR( getNext(here) ) );
end
```

Table 163—Mapping a SavingsAccount List *(Continued)*

26.4. Filtering a Linked List

As with mapping a list, filtering can only be performed as service to specialized collections derived from the **LinkedList** class. The contents of the derived class must provide a method **keep(...)** that determines whether to keep a particular item on the list.

For example, we continue the idea of a list of bank accounts[4] in a class derived from the **LinkedList** class. Perhaps the bank wishes to remove all accounts with a negative balance for this list. They would merely have to provide the **keep(...)** method shown in Table 164 and then implement the generic **LinkedList** filter discussed below.

```
function ans = keep(acct)
% @BankAccount\keep
%    keep an account with a non-negative balance
    ans = getbalance(acct) >= 0;
```

Table 164—BankAccount keep(...) Method

To filter items in a generic list, we will again follow the recursive template in Table 155 with the following tailoring required:

- As usual, the public method, **filter**, launches the recursive helper, **filterR**, with the current head of the list and stores the new list returned.

---

[4] Since we are not making any use of child account features, we can use any type of BankAccount, and store the keep(...) method in the bankAccount class.

- The helper returns an empty list when it reaches the end of the old list.
- Otherwise, if it should keep this data item, it returns a new **LLNode** containing the old data, using the recursive **updateR** call to update the rest of the list.
- Otherwise, it returns the result from applying **updateR** recursively to the rest of the list.

The resulting code is shown in Table 165.

Table 166 is a script to test the filtering function—note that as far as the outside world is concerned, filtering is done "in place" in the **LinkedList** class. So to keep a copy of all the accounts before applying the filter, we use the copy constructor,

```
goodAccts = LinkedList(BAList);
```

```
function filter(ll)
% @LinkedList\filter
%     filter the list by removing all items
%     returning false from their keep method
    setHead( ll, filterR(getHead(ll)) );
    assignin('caller', inputname(1), ll);
function newLst = filterR(here)
% recursive filter helper
if isempty(here)
    newLst = [];
elseif keep(getData(here))
    newLst = LLNode( getData(here), ...
                    filterR( getNext(here) ) );
else
    newLst = filterR( getNext(here) );
end
```

Table 165—Generic LinkedList **filter(...)** Method

```
BAList = LinkedList;
s = BankAccount;
addToHead(BAList, s)
moola = BankAccount(-1000);
addToHead(BAList, moola)
sa = SavingsAccount(2000);
addToHead(BAList, sa)
dsa = DeluxSavingsAccount(2000);
allowOverdraft(dsa, true);                          (Continued)
```

Table 166—Testing the **filter(...)** Function

```
gets = withdraw(dsa, 3000);
addToHead(BAList, dsa)
fprintf('accounts: %s\n', char(BAList) )
goodAccts = LinkedList(BAList);
filter(goodAccts);
fprintf('\ngood accounts: %s\n', char(goodAccts) )
```

Table 166—Testing the `filter(...)` Function *(Continued)*

26.5. Folding a Linked List

Unlike the previous list operations, folding can be performed as a service in the **LinkedList** class. We illustrate this by the **sum(...)** method. It does constrain the contents of the list to those classes that respond to the method **plus(...)**. In general, **plus(...)** permits the programmer to add the current object either to another object of the same class or to some other object that can be added to a **double** value.

For example, we continue the idea of a list of bank accounts[5] in a **LinkedList**. Perhaps the bank wishes to sum all accounts in this list. They would merely have to provide the **plus(...)** method shown in Table 167, and then implement the generic **LinkedList** sum discussed below.

```
function ans = plus(ba, item)
% @BankAccount\plus
% add this bank account to another item:
%   either another BankAccount, or something
%   else that can be added to a double
if isa(item,'BankAccount')
    addend = getBalance(item);
else
    addend = item;
end
ans = addend + getBalance(ba);
```

Table 167—BankAccount `plus(...)` method

To sum items in a generic list, we will again follow the recursive template in Table 155 with the following tailoring required:

---

[5] Since we are not making any use of child account features, we can use any type of BankAccount, and store the plus(...) method in the BankAccount class.

- As usual, the public method, **sum**, merely launches the recursive helper, **sumR**, with the current head of the list and passes the total on to its caller.
- The helper returns 0 when it reaches the end of the old list.
- Otherwise, it returns the result from adding[6] the current data value to the result of applying **sumR** recursively to rest of the list.

The resulting code is shown in Table 168.

```
function total = sum( list )
% @LinkedList\sum
% total the items in a list
total = sumR( getHead(list) );

function sum = sumR(here)
% recursive list adder
if isempty(here)
    sum = 0;
else
    sum = getData(here)...
        + sumR(getNext(here));
end
```

Table 168—Generic LinkedList **sum(...)** Method

26.6. Searching a Linked List

Unlike the previous list operations, searching can be performed as a service in the **LinkedList** class. We illustrate this by the **find(...)** method. It does constrain the contents of the list to those classes that respond to the method **eq(...)**. The **eq(...)** method is invoked whenever a program used the '**==**' operator, and can be applied to primitive data types, and added to all more complex classes. The user of this operation is required only to decode how a user class will determine whether an object of that class responds to the equality test for some data. Bank account equality could be determined by account number, telephone number, etc.

To find an item in a list, we will again follow the recursive template in Table 155 with the following tailoring required:

---

[6] In MATLAB, this causes the plus function to be applied to the data item and the running total.

- As usual, the public method, **find**, launches the recursive helper, **findR**, with the current head of the list and the item to be found, **item**. When the recursive call completes, it passes the result to its caller.
- The helper returns **[]** when it reaches the end of the old list.
- Otherwise, if the item sought matches this item in the list, it returns that item.
- Otherwise, it returns the result from finding the item on the rest of the list, using **findR** recursively.

The resulting code is shown in Table 169. Table 170 is the code to test the find method. It populates a **LinkedList** with random numbers between 0 and 19, and then checks to see if the value 10 is on the list. Running it repeatedly will verify that the find method is operating correctly.

```
function result = find( list, item )
% @LinkedList\find
% find an item on a list
result = findR( getHead(list), item );


function result = findR(here, item)
% recursive list adder
if isempty(here)
    result = [];
elseif getData(here) == item
    result = getData(here);
else
    result = findR(getNext(here), item);
end
```

Table 169—LinkedList find (...) Method

```
lst = LinkedList;
for it = 1:20
    num = floor( 20*rand );
    addToHead( lst, num );
end
fprintf('list is %s\n', char(lst));
ans = find(lst, 10);
if isempty(ans)
    ans = -1;
end
fprintf('find 10 returned %d\n', ans );
```

Table 170—Test the find (...) Method

26.7. Queues

We referred in Section 23.5.2 to the need for Collection objects to implement the **Queue** (Figure 107) and **MStack** (Figure 109) classes. These next two sections show simple implementations of each making use of the **LinkedList** class as its parents. Once the **LinkedList** class has been created with all the data support methods likely to be required, a **Queue** class can quickly be derived as a child class merely by implementing the standard class framework and two methods, each of which merely invoke the appropriate parent methods as indicated.

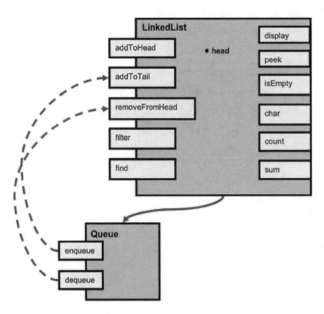

Figure 126—Queue Implementation

The complete code for the **Queue** class is therefore its standard infrastructure plus the simple **enqueue(...)** and **dequeue(...)** methods as shown in Table 171 and Table 172. To be honest, since the method **peek(...)** is needed by both the **Queue** and **MStack** classes, this "extremely complex" method (Table 173) was added to the **LinkedList** class. We will test the **Queue** and **MStack** classes together in the next section.

```
function enqueue(q, data)
% @Queue\enqueue
% enqueue onto a queue
   addToTail(q, data);
   assignin('caller', inputname(1), q);
```

Table 171—Queue `enqueue(...)` Method

```
function ans = dequeue(q)
% @Queue\dequeue
% dequeue from a Queue
   ans = removeFromHead(q);
   assignin('caller', inputname(1), q);
```

Table 172—Queue `dequeue(...)` Method

```
function ans = peek(lst)
% @LinkedList\peek
% peek at the head of the list
  ans = getData(getHead(lst));
```

Table 173—LinkedList `peek(...)` Method

26.8. Stacks

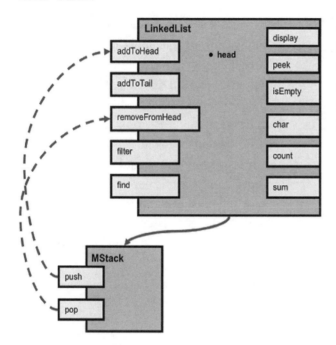

As indicated above, we can also implement the **MStack** class as its basic infrastructure (constructor and possibly a **char(...)** method) and the **push(...)** and **pop(...)** methods listed as Table 175 and Table 176.

Table 174—MStack implementation

```
function push(stk, data)
% @MStack\push
% push onto a stack
  addToHead(stk, data);
  assignin('caller', inputname(1), stk);
```

Table 175—Stack `push(...)` Method

```
function ans = pop(stk)
% @MStack\pop
% pop from a stack
   ans = removeFromHead(stk);
   assignin('caller', inputname(1), stk);
```

Table 176—Stack pop(...) Method

26.9. Priority Queues

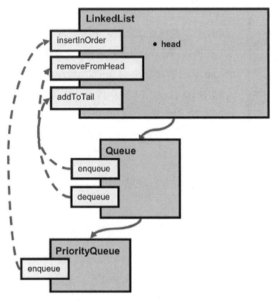

It would not surprise many people that implementing a priority queue[7] is best accomplished by extending the **Queue** class, and invoking a different **LinkedList** method for the Priority Queue **enqueue(...)** method. This is an excellent example of extension by redefinition—allowing the parent classes to provide all the infrastructure and operational requirements except the one specific new capability required. Figure 127 illustrates this implementation, and Table 177 illustrates the one method required.

Table 178 shows a suitable test script for these three collections, and Table 179 shows the results from the command window.

Figure 127—Priority Queue Implementation

```
function enqueue(pq, data)
% @PriorityQueue\enqueue
%      enqueue onto a queue
   addInOrder(pq, data);
   assignin('caller', inputname(1), pq);
```

Table 177—Priority Queue enqueue(...) Method

---

[7] Priority Queue behavior is defined in Section 23.5.2.

```
stk = MStack;
fprintf('is stack empty? %d\n', isEmpty(stk) );
for ix = 1:10
    push(stk, ix);
end
fprintf('is stack empty? %d\n', isEmpty(stk) );
stk
fprintf('pop from stack -> %d leaving %s\n', ...
    pop(stk), char(stk) );
fprintf('peek stack -> %d leaving %s\n', ...
    peek(stk), char(stk) );
q = Queue;
fprintf('is queue empty? %d\n', isEmpty(q) );
for ix = 1:10
    enqueue(q, ix);
end
fprintf('is queue empty? %d\n', isEmpty(q) );
q
fprintf('dequeue -> %d leaving %s\n', ...
    dequeue(q), char(q) );
fprintf('peek at queue -> %d leaving %s\n', ...
    peek(q), char(q) );
while ~isEmpty(q)
    push(stk, dequeue(q));
end
fprintf('stack with whole queue is %s\n', ...
                                char(stk) );
pq = PriorityQueue;
for ix = 1:10
    value = floor(100*rand);
    fprintf(' %g:', value );
    enqueue(pq, value );
end
fprintf('\npriority queue is %s\n', char(pq) );
```

Table 178—Stack, Queue and Priority Queue Test Script

```
is stack empty? 1
is stack empty? 0
MStack: 10;9;8;7;6;5;4;3;2;1;
pop from stack -> 10 leaving MStack:
                        9;8;7;6;5;4;3;2;1;
peek stack -> 9 leaving MStack: 9;8;7;6;5;4;3;2;1;
is queue empty? 1
is queue empty? 0
Queue: 1;2;3;4;5;6;7;8;9;10;
dequeue -> 1 leaving Queue: 2;3;4;5;6;7;8;9;10;
peek at queue -> 2 leaving Queue: 2;3;4;5;6;7;8;9;10;
stack with whole queue is MStack:
          10;9;8;7;6;5;4;3;2;9;8;7;6;5;4;3;2;1;
 82: 91: 11: 81: 90: 15: 12: 76: 72: 65:
priority queue is PriorityQueue:
                    11;12;15;65;72;76;81;82;90;91;
```

Table 179—Test Results

26.10. Summary of Ideas

The examples above are intended to illustrate the power of inheritance. The most powerful characteristic of a good OO design is its ability to use inheritance effectively. Once you have invested some effort in a solid infrastructure, it is stunningly simple to implement very capable, reliable classes of your own by extending existing classes.[8]

26.11. Examples

26-1 Write a MATLAB function called **myFilter** that takes in a queue of numbers and returns a 'filtered' queue containing only numbers divisible by 3.

26-2 Write and test a method that copies all the entries from the cell array of **CS1371** objects (see example 24-1) to a **LinkedList**.
   a. What kind of process is this? (Folding? Mapping?)
   b. Is this restricting the nature of the data in any way?

---

[8] This is the real power of Java. It provides an enormous collection of libraries well cataloged and indexed to enable specific mechanisms to be found and extended.

26-3 Write another method to copy the data, inserting each item from the Cell Array *in order* into the **LinkedList**. You will need a **gt(...)** method in the **CS1371** class to compare the overall averages.

26-4 Rewrite the **char(...)** method for the **LinkedList** class in recursive form. Call it **rchar(...)** and test it thoroughly.

26-5 Rewrite the recursive **rchar(...)** method for the **LinkedList** class concatenating the recursive result before the local data instead of after it. Test this version thoroughly. What do you learn about the ordering of the data?

26-6 Write and test a method to find the number of items in a **LinkedList**.

26-7 Write and test a method to find the average of the items in a **LinkedList**. Your **CS1371** class will need an **add(...)** method.

26-8 Write and test a method to find the bank account with the largest balance in a **LinkedList** of **BankAccounts**.

26-9 Write an iterative version of **find(...)** for the **LinkedList** class using a while loop.

26-10 Write an iterative version of **sum(...)** for the **LinkedList** class using a while loop.

26-11 Write the class **ArrayQueue** that conforms to the **Queue** ADT, but is implemented using a Cell Array instead of inheriting from the **LinkedList** class.

26-12 Write the class **ArrayStack** that conforms to the **Stack** ADT, but is implemented using a Cell Array instead of inheriting from the **LinkedList** class.

26-13 We want write a script to model the situation in the library where students are always standing in line waiting for a computer. Follow these steps:

    a. Write the code for a class **Student** whose only data of interest are the **name**, provided to the constructor, and a Boolean variable **atComputer**, initialized to false. Its **char(...)** method should show the name and whether they are at a computer.

    b. Create a **Queue** object called **ComputerLine**.

    c. Write a function **nextStudent** which consumes a **Queue** of **Student** objects and **dequeues** the first student in line. It should then set that student's **atComputer** field to **true** using the **setAtComputer** method in **Student**. It should return the **Queue** after the first student has been removed.

    d. After a while, a student may get tired of checking his email and playing solitaire, so he decides to leave the library. Create another **Queue** called **ExitLine** that tracks the order of in which students leave the library.

e. Create a function called **leaveComputer** which consumes a **Queue** and a student, and adds the student to the **Queue**, also setting the student's **atComputer** field to false. The function should return the new **Queue**.

f. Use the **Queue** objects **ComputerLine** and **ExitLine** to keep track of the students in the following scenario. To help keep track of the students, it may be helpful to adopt a convention of **Jim = Student('Jim');** when creating objects.

Notes:

❏ Assume that as soon as a computer opens up, the first person in line takes it.

❏ When more than one student arrives, take their arrival in the order of their names as listed.

❏ Use the functions nextStudent and leaveComputer in the simulation; nextStudent uses the ComputerLine Queue; leaveComputer uses ExitLine

Scenario:
```
Jim arrives at the library and wants to use a computer.
All of them are taken, but he is the first in line.
He is soon joined by his friend Jaime.
They start chatting about CS1 and how much fun they're
having in the class.
A computer opens up.
Three more students arrive in line—Andy, Amy, and Allison.
They find it amusing that their names all being with A.
Todd arrives in the line.
A computer opens up.
Jim is done checking his email and leaves; his computer is
open
Rachel and Ryan arrive next, followed by David.
A computer opens up.
Andy realizes he forget to transfer his files to the acme
server and sprints back to his dorm. His computer is now
open.
Two more computers open up.
Mike and Matt arrive in the line.
Jaime heads off to class; her computer is now open.
Todd finishes checking espn and leaves; his computer is
open.
Andy makes it back to the library, but he has to wait in
the line.
```

Hint: For diagnostic purposes, you might want to show the contents of each Queue after each of the above steps.

a. In the code above, the first student waiting in line always took the next available computer. However, we are now going to account for those students who have a preference for what type of computer they want to use—either a Mac, a PC, or no preference. When a computer opens up, the first available student in the line whose preference matches that computer type will go to the computer. Therefore, it is not always the student at the front of the line.

b. Add a **prefers** field to the **Student** class initialized in the constructor to either **'Mac'**, **'PC'**, or **'either'**.

c. Add an **eq(...)** method to the **Student** class comparing a String parameter with the **prefers** field of the Student object. Be sure to account for **'either'** correctly.

d. Modify the **char()** method to print out the additional information of the type of computer the student **prefers**.

e. The **ComputerLine** will be modeled using an enhanced **EQueue**, instead of a **Queue**. Write the **Equeue** class extending the **Queue** class plus a **delete(q, value)** method. The **delete(...)** method will start at the front of the **Equeue** and search for a student matching the value.

f. Modify the **nextStudent** function keeping the following in mind:
   ❑ It should take in a String that represents the type of computer (**'Mac'** or **'PC'**) that has opened up.
   ❑ The student is deleted from the list, and his **atComputer** field is set to true.

g. Perform the following simulation in the test program of this class:

```
Jarrett, after an excruciating day of basketball practice,
comes to the library to finish up some studying. To his dis-
appointment, all the macs (his preference) were in use.
Jarrett decides he'll wait in line until one opens up.
After a few minutes, Will and Ismail show up at the
library. They both prefer either type of computer, but all
the PCs are full as well.
Jarrett, Will, and Ismail take some time to discuss why
they are awesome, and suddenly a pc opens up.
Reggie (mac) and Calvin (pc) then arrive to email all their
friends and family about destroying UGA in football.
A mac opens up.
Luke (pc) then arrives, tells everyone how tall he is and
gets in line.
A mac opens up.
3 members of the Mac User Association of America (named
Arnie, Hector, and Vincent) then arrive and obnoxiously let
everyone know why they use macs and why everyone else
should use macs.
```

```
Will finishes with his pc and leaves. His computer is now
open.
A mac opens up.
Mary (either), sad that the only purpose of her existence
is to illustrate a homework problem, decides to join the
line.
Ismail and Jarrett finish with their macs.
Soon after, 3 members of the Mac Haters of Georgia Tech
(John, Jake, and Joe) get in line
A pc opens up.
Calvin finishes reading articles about himself on ramblin-
wreck.com and leaves his pc.
A mac opens up.
A pc opens up.
Hector and Vincent finish posting to their mac lovers news-
groups and leave their computers.
```

26-14 Your job is to build a **Dealership** class to model the purchase of new cars for several people. It will have three queues, one named **onOrder** (vehicles that have been placed on order), one named **inTransit** for vehicles that are in route to their owner, and one named **delivered** that will be a queue of vehicles that have been delivered. Your class **Dealership** needs the following methods.

   a. **addToOrder**—takes in a **Vehicle** and enqueues it onto the **onOrder** queue.

   b. **finishedVehicle**—deletes the first **Vehicle** from **onOrder** and enqueues it onto **inTransit**.

   c. **deliveredVehicle**—deletes the first **Vehicle** from **inTransit** and enqueues it onto delivered.

   d. A method **printout()** to display the vehicles.

   e. Test it with the following script:

```
Autos = Dealership();
Susan = Vehicle('sedan', 'green', 'Susan');
Jim = Vehicle('truck', 'blue', 'Jim');
Mike = Vehicle('coupe', 'red', 'Mike');
Ron = Vehicle('convertible', 'silver', 'Ron');
Anna = Vehicle('sedan', 'yellow', 'Anna');
Amy = Vehicle('convertible', 'black', 'Amy');
addToOrder(Autos, Susan);
addToOrder(Autos, Jim);
finishedVehicle(Autos);
addToOrder(Autos, Mike);
deliveredVehicle(Autos);
finishedVehicle(Autos);
```

```
finishedVehicle(Autos);
addToOrder(Autos, Ron);
deliveredVehicle(Autos);
addToOrder(Autos, Anna);
addToOrder(Autos, Amy);
finishedVehicle(Autos);
printout(Autos);
```

26-15   What is printed by the following code block?

```
q = Queue; % make a new queue
s = MStack; % make a new stack
array = [ 2 1 6 8 9];
for k = 1:5
        enqueue(q, array(k));
end
for k = 1:5
        temp = dequeue(q);
        push(s, temp);
end
for k = 1:5
        temp = pop(s);
        disp(temp)
end
```

27. BINARY TREES

We move to a slightly more complex dynamic data structure—the binary tree. Where each node of a LinkedList contains only one child node, a binary tree has two child nodes, normally referred to as the left and right nodes, as illustrated in Figure 128.

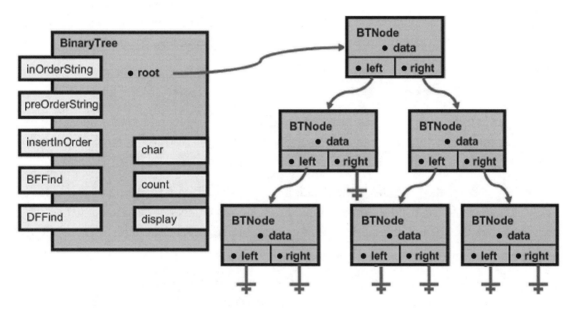

Figure 128—Structure of a Binary Tree

Within this structure, we need to consider two cases: one—a Binary Tree—where the data in the tree exhibit no apparent organization, and one—a Binary Search Tree (BST)—where the data are organized for efficient searching.

27.1. Concepts

A Graph: The most general form of dynamic data structure is a graph—an arbitrary collection of nodes connected by edges. A street map is a good example of a graph where the intersections are the nodes, and the streets are the edges. The edges may be directional to indicate that the graph can be traversed at that point in only one direction (like a one-way street). The edges may also have a value associated with them to indicate, for example, the cost of traversing that edge. For a street map, this could be either the distance, or perhaps in a more sophisticated system, the travel time—a function of the distance, the speed limit and the traffic congestion. Graphs are not required to be completely connected, and they can obviously contain cycles—closed loops in which the unwary algorithm could get trapped. Graphs also have no obvious starting and stopping points.

A path on a graph is a connected list of edges that is the result of traversing a graph.

N-ary Tree: While a graph is the most general form of dynamic structure, it is also the most complex to process. We therefore step back to simpler situations first. A tree is best thought of as an acyclic graph—a good example would be a family tree tracing the descendants from a common ancestor. An N-ary Tree is one where each node can contain an arbitrary number of links to other nodes.

The Root: Since no cycles are permitted in trees, there has to be a common anchor point like the head of a linked list. We refer to the anchor point of a tree as its root.

Leaves: just as there is one node that begins the tree, there will in general be many nodes that terminate the traversal of a tree because they have no child links. We refer to these nodes as the leaves. A linked list, by contrast, had only one leaf.

Binary Tree: We make one more simplification before we can start analyzing the behavior of trees—it is convenient at the beginning to limit the maximum number of child nodes to two. This greatly reduces the amount of logic required to traverse a tree. An ancestral tree—tracing from a child back up its lineage is a good example of a binary tree.

Binary Search Tree: a Binary Search Tree (BST) is an important specialization of a binary tree where the data are ordered in a very specific way to facilitate searching for information in the tree. We will discuss the impact of that ordering below. However, this is a good place to point out that if the data items in the tree are complex, one cannot order the data in the tree on all the components of the data. For example, it might be useful to organize Student objects in a BST ordered by their student ID. As we will see soon, this greatly speeds the process of searching by ID for a student, but is no help at all searching for other criteria like name or telephone number.

27.2. Processing Binary Trees

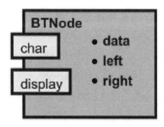

Figure 129—A Binary Tree Node

When discussing linked lists, we discovered that there are occasions in which one could iteratively process the list, especially if the list is not being changed. There are similar opportunities once we start processing graphs or trees. However, we first consider processing binary trees recursively. Figure 129 illustrates the content of the node with which we can construct a Binary tree. Omitted for clarity are the `set/get` methods for the `data`, `left` and `right` attributes.

We determine how to process a Binary Tree based on its formal definition:

- A **BinaryTree** is either empty (**[]**)
- Or a **BTNode** containing a data item and two **BinaryTrees** named **left** and **right**

Further, we could argue that we could model the template of a function for processing a binary tree after this definition, as shown in Table 180.

```
<function and return> processBTNode(here)
% recursive processing
if isempty(here)
    <reached the end>
else
    ... getData(here) ...
        ... processBTNode( getLeft(here) ) ...
        ... processBTNode( getRight(here) ) ...
end
```

Table 180—Template for Processing a Binary Tree

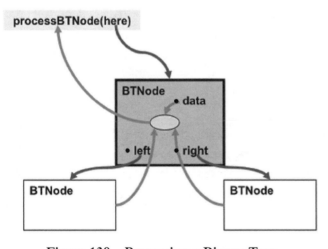

Figure 130—Processing a Binary Tree

Figure 130 illustrates the operation of this recursive process on a particular BTNode. Just as with processing linked lists, the accomplishments of a recursive operation on a binary tree are governed by the logic implemented in the recursive call. In general, processing a node involves a recursive call to process the left child, a recursive call to process the right child and then some logic to combine these two results with the data in this particular node. The results are then returned to the calling node.

27.3. Processing Binary Search Trees

The definition of a BST is as follows:

- A **BST** is either empty ([])
- Or a **BTNode** containing a data item and two **BSTs** named **left** and **right** where all the data in the left sub-tree are less[1] than the data at this node, and all the data in the right sub-tree are greater than this node.
- Equal data items are not permitted in BSTs[2,3].

Notice that this is a recursive definition so that the ordering requirement continues throughout the BST.

The template and diagram for processing a BST is identical to Table 180 and Figure 130. As we see specific applications processing these trees, there are times when we can take advantage of the ordering of the data to reduce the amount of processing.

In each of the sections to follow, some of the discussions may apply only to one type of tree or the other.

27.4. Traversing a Binary Tree

We will consider three different techniques for traversing a Binary Tree. Two are depth-first traversals—so called because each traversal reaches recursively down paths to the leaves of the tree. The other is a breadth-first traversal that is performed iteratively and travels across the tree generations.

27.4.1. Depth-first Traversal

When traversing a LinkedList, the process was simple because there was only one child. The only choice you could make was to append the recursive result from the rest of the list before or after the local data value. When traversing a binary tree, there are three pieces of data to combine: the local data item (D), the result from the left branch (L) and the result from the right branch (R).

---

[1] This restricts the nature of the data items to those that can respond to gt(...), lt(...) and eq(...).

[2] This requirement drives the nature of the information stored in a BST—there needs to be a high probability that the index will be unique, so that equality becomes either a data item to be ignored, or an error to be analyzed. Good indices would be a telephone number or student ID. Bad indices would be first and last names in any combination, since uniqueness is not guaranteed.

[3] It is technically possible, but beyond the scope of this text, to construct a BST where the data item stored is a collection of items, all of which satisfy a specific equality test. The structure of the BST would then continue to satisfy this requirement, while its implementation would add equal items to the local collection. Traversal and search then become considerably more complex, of course.

In general, they can be combined in 6 different combinations: D—L—R, L—D—R, L—R—D, D—R—L, R—D—L, R—L—D. All 6 will give different results, but only two are actually useful to implement.

- The L—D—R sequence is referred to as an "in-order traversal" because if the tree is a BST, it will visit the nodes in their assigned order in the tree. This traversal is normally used unless there is a good reason not to[4].
- The D—L—R sequence is referred to as a "pre-order traversal" because it touches the data first before performing either recursion. This form of traversal is used when serializing a BST because it preserves the tree structure.

```
<function and return> inOrder(here)
% processing items in order
if isempty(here)
    <return the empty answer>
else
<combine the following>
... inOrder(getLeft(here)) ...
... getData(here) ...
... inOrder(getRight(here)) ...
end
```

Table 181—Recursive BinaryTree Processing Template

By convention in this text, the `char(...)` conversion of these more complex collections will not traverse the collection. Specific methods traversing the collections will be used. Table 182 shows the `inOrderString(...)` method that directly matches the above template. For comparison,

- As usual, the wrapper function merely invokes the recursive process with the tree root.
- Both functions return a character string.
- The recursive function concatenates the result of left recursion with the `char(...)` of the local node and the result of the right recursion.
- The `BTNode char(...)` function takes care of presenting the string value of double types using the `%g` conversion.

---

[4] For our current purposes, the only reason not to use in-order traversal is if the traversal is for the purpose of serializing a BST (writing it to a file for archiving purposes). If you used an in-order traversal for this, the data would be in order. If you subsequently inserted that data an item at a time back into an initially empty BST, the result would not be the original BST, but rather a linear tree!

```
function str = inOrderString(bt)
% @BinaryTree\inOrderString
%    str = inOrderString(bt)
str = RinOrderString(bt.root);

function str = RinOrderString(here)
%  recursive in-order processing
if isempty(here)
    str = '';
else
    str = [ RinOrderString(getLeft(here)) ' ' ...
            char(here) ' ' ...
            RinOrderString(getRight(here)) ];
end
```

Table 182—The Binary Tree `inOrderString(...)` Method

```
function str = preOrderString(bt)
% @BinaryTree\preOrderString
%    str = preOrderString(bt)
str = RPreOrderString(bt.root);

function str = RPreOrderString(here)
%  recursive in-order processing
if isempty(here)
    str = '';
else
    str = [ char(here) ' ' ...
            RPreOrderString(getLeft(here)) ' ' ...
            RPreOrderString(getRight(here)) ];
end
```

Table 183—The Binary Tree `preOrderString(...)` Method

27.4.2. Breadth-first Traversal

Breadth-first traversal permits data in the tree to be accessed a generation at a time. It uses a simple, but effective, iterative template that uses a queue to store the children of each generation. Table 184 shows the template for this process.

```
<function and return> BFTraversal(btree)
% @BinaryTree\BFTraversal
q = Queue;      % create a queue
enqueue(q, getRoot(btree) );
< initialize the result>
while !isEmpty(q)
node = dequeue(q);
<operate on getData(node)>
enqueue(q, getLeft(node));
enqueue(q, getRight(node));
end
< return the result>
```

Table 184—Template for Breadth-first Traversal

Table 185 shows the code that produces a string representation of the tree using a breadth-first traversal. This is slightly complicated by the need to keep up with the layers in the tree. What is pushed onto the queue is a cell array containing a number—the level of the tree—with the node to be processed.

- All the children are pushed with the value of the next level.
- A new line is inserted into the string when the level changes.
- Whenever the level changes, we halve the number of spaces to be written between the items on a row.
- Since it is possible for leaves to appear in the printout, they are marked by '--'.

```
function str = BFTString(bt)
% @BinaryTree\BFTString
%  tree traversal including formatting lines
q = Queue;
enqueue(q, {0, bt.root} )
level = -1;
sp='                                                     ';
str = '';
nsp = 64;
while ~isEmpty(q)
    v = dequeue(q);
    if v{1} ~= level        % set the tree level
```

(Continued)

Table 185—Breadth-first String Generator

```
        level = v{1};
        str = [str '\n'];
        nsp = ceil(nsp / 2);
    end
    node = v{2}; % insert the data we just dequeued
    if isempty(node)
        str = [str sp(1:nsp) '--'];
    else
        str = [str sp(1:nsp) char(node)];
        % enqueue the children of this node
        enqueue(q, {level+1, getLeft(node)  });
        enqueue(q, {level+1, getRight(node) });
    end
end
```

Table 185—Breadth-first String Generator *(Continued)*

27.5. Building a BST

Since the structure of Unordered Binary Trees usually has some specific meaning not evident from the data content itself, they are not usually built dynamically. For our purposes, they will be created in the test script. It is very common, however, to build a BST by inserting data items one at a time.

Building the BST consists of a repetitive insertion of data into an initially empty BST. The major technical challenge for inserting into a BST is where to place the new node and retain the ordering of the data. This ordering cannot be guaranteed when inserting at the root, or inserting at some intermediate layer of the tree. The only place one can safely add to a BST and retain its ordering is to recursively find the leaf node at which to add a new node containing the new data. This code is listed in Table 186. This code will function well for any tree content object that can respond to the equality test and the greater than test.

```
function insert(bst, n)
% @BST\insert
setRoot(bst, rInsert(getRoot(bst), n) );
assignin('caller', inputname(1), bst);


function node = rInsert(here, n)
% recursive insertion into a BST
```
(Continued)

Table 186—Inserting into a BST

```
if isempty(here)
    node = BTNode(n);
elseif getData(here) == n
    node = here;
elseif getData(here) > n
    node = BTNode(getData(here), ...
                  rInsert(getLeft(here), n), ...
                  getRight(here));
else
    node = BTNode(getData(here), ...
                  getLeft(here), ...
                  rInsert(getRight(here), n));
end
```

Table 186—Inserting into a BST *(Continued)*

Notice the following features:

- As with any operation that changes a dynamic data structure, the whole structure is always replaced.
- A new **BTNode** is created and returned when the recursion reaches a leaf node.
- We must test for equality to avoid adding duplicate keys. A policy decision is needed to decide whether to announce an error here or merely (as in this code) exit without adding a new node. Notice that the existing node must still be returned to add the rest of that structure to the new resulting structure.
- We compare the current node's data to the value to insert to decide whether the insertion happens to the left or right of this node.
- Whichever direction is chosen, a new node is created with the same data value as the current node, the same left or right subtree to the side not changed, and a recursive call to the side that is changed.

27.6. Mapping a Binary Tree

In general, mapping a binary tree is performed not as a general service to all **BinaryTree** users, but rather as a specialized utility written for derived classes that use a **BinaryTree** as their parent class. For example, suppose a bank keeps all its interest-bearing accounts in a class derived from the **BinaryTree** class. Periodically, they need to traverse that tree and add the interest generated by each account. Since the size of the tree remains unchanged, but the contents change, this would be a mapping of the original tree.

Table 187 illustrates such an update method. In order to update all the accounts in a tree of **SavingsAccounts**, the mapping would follow the recursive template in Table 180 with the following tailoring required:

- As usual, the public method, **updateTree**, merely launches the recursive helper with the current root of the tree and stores the root returned as the new root.
- The helper returns an empty tree when it reaches a leaf of the old tree.
- Otherwise, it returns a new **BTNode** containing the result of updating the old data, using the recursive updateR call to update the rest of the tree.

The resulting code is shown in Table 187.

```
function updateTree(acctTree)
% @SavingsAcctTree\update
%     update to the accounts by depositing
%     the interest due
    setHead(acctTree, updateR(getRoot(acctTree)) );
    assignin('caller', inputname(1), acctTree);


function newTree = updateR(here)
% recursive update helper
if isempty(here)
    newTree = [];
else
    newTree = BTNode( update( getData(here) ), ...
                      updateR( getLeft(here) ), ...
                      updateR( getRight(here) ));
end
```

Table 187—Mapping a SavingsAccount Tree

27.7. Filtering a BST

We do not, in general, filter Binary Trees. These trees are static in nature, and rarely need maintenance. If maintenance is required, this is usually done manually in the code that reconstructs the tree. We can, however, filter a BST in a restricted sense—removing one node at a time, while preserving the ordering of the BST. Figure 131 illustrates this process.

When removing an item from a BST, there are three cases to consider depending on the location in the tree of the item to be removed.

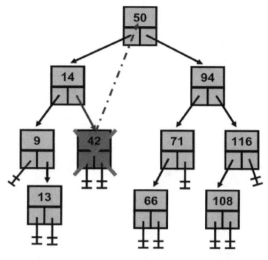

Figure 131—Deleting from a BST

- **No children:** Consider, for example, removing the node containing 13. Since it has no children at all, it can be removed simply by replacing its link in the node containing 9 with [].
- **One child node:** Removing a node with one child node (such as those with value 9 or 71) is also simple. We merely replace its parent node reference with a reference to the surviving child node.
- **Two children nodes:** The logic for removing a node with both children present is a little more challenging. Consider removing the node with value 50. We must first find the largest node in its left sub-tree, the value 42, (or the smallest in its right sub-tree, in this case, the 66). We place

its node data in the node we are removing, and then delete that node from the tree. This latter deletion will be one of the simpler cases above.

```
function delete(bst, n)
% @BST\delete
setRoot(bst, rDelete(getRoot(bst), n) );
assignin('caller', inputname(1), bst);


function node = rDelete(here, n)
%
if isempty(here)              % not in the tree
    node = [];
elseif getData(here) == n     % found it
    node = deleteThis(here);
elseif getData(here) > n      % look left
    node = BTNode(getData(here), ...
                rDelete(getLeft(here), n), ...
                getRight(here));
else                          % look right
    node = BTNode(getData(here), ...
                getLeft(here), ...
                rDelete(getRight(here), n));
end
```

Table 188—Deleting from a BST Part I—Finding and Repairing

```
function node = deleteThis(here)
%
left = getLeft(here);
right = getRight(here);
if isempty(left)
    node = right;
elseif isempty(right)
    node = left;
else
    [value rest] = deleteLargest(left);
    node = BTNode(value, rest, right);
end


function [value node] = deleteLargest(here)
%
right = getRight(here);
if isempty(right)
    value = getData(here);
    node = getLeft(here);
else
    [value, node] = deleteLargest(right);
end
```

Table 189—Deleting from a BST Part II—Finding the Node

```
nn = input('How many nodes? ')
bst = BST( BTNode(50) );
for in = 1:nn
    insert(bst, ceil(100*rand));
end
fprintf('number is %d (started with %d)\n',...
                        count(bst), nn+1 );
fprintf('largest number is %d\n', ...
                        largest(bst) );
fprintf('pre-order list is %s\n', ...
                    preOrderString(bst) );
fprintf('in-order list is %s\n', ...
                    inOrderString(bst) );
fprintf('breadth-first list: %s\n', ...
                    BFTString(bst));
n = 1;                                        (Continued)
```

Table 190—Testing the BST Functions

```
while n > 0
    n = input('number to find: ');
    if n > 0
        ans = find(bst, n)
        BSTdelete(bst, n);
        fprintf('number is %d (started with %d)\n',...
                        count(bst), nn+1 );
        fprintf('in-order list is %s\n',...
                        inOrderString(bst) );
        fprintf(' bst with %d removed: %s\n', ...
                        n, BFTString(bst));
    end
end
```

Table 190—Testing the BST Functions *(Continued)*

27.8. Folding a Binary Tree

Unlike the previous tree operations, folding can be performed as a service in the **BinaryTree** class. We illustrate this by the **count(...)** method. To count items in a binary tree, we will again follow the recursive template in Table 180 with the following tailoring required:

- As usual, the public method, **count**, merely launches the recursive helper, **rCount**, with the root of the tree and passes the total to its caller.
- The helper returns 0 when it reaches a tree leaf.
- Otherwise, it returns the result from adding 1 to the result of applying **rCount** recursively to left and right subtrees.

The resulting code is shown in Table 191.

```
function ans = count(bt)
% @BinaryTree\count
ans = rCount(bt.root);



function ans = rCount(here)
%   recursive counting a binary tree
if isempty(here)
    ans = 0;
else
    ans = 1 + rCount(getLeft(here)) ...
            + rCount(getRight(here));
end
```

Table 191—Generic BinaryTree Count Method

27.9. Searching Binary Trees

We need to consider searching both the ordinary binary tree and the BST[5]. In the same way as we categorized traversal, searching an ordinary binary tree may be accomplished either breadth-first or depth first.

27.9.1. Breadth-first Search

The breadth-first search method **BFFind** will follow the iterative, breadth-first template in Table 184 with the following tailoring required:

- It first creates a **queue** and enqueues the tree root.
- As long as that **queue** is not empty (indicating failure) or the dequeued item is not what we seek, it continues enqueueing the children of the current node.

The resulting code is shown in Table 192.

27.9.2. Depth-first Search

Depth-first search can also be accomplished iteratively using a **MStack** instead of a **Queue**, as illustrated with the **DFFind** method. The code is illustrated in Table 193.

```
function ans = BFFind(bt, what)
% @BinaryTree\BFFind
q = Queue;
enqueue(q, bt.root )
found = false;
ans = [];
while ~found && ~isEmpty(q)
    node = dequeue(q);
    % check the data we just dequeued
    found = (node == what);
    if ~found
    % enqueue the children of this node
```
(Continued)

Table 192—Binary Tree Breadth-first Find Method

---

[5] We should observe again that a BST ordered by some particular data attribute can be searched efficiently for items with that particular attribute. However, to find items by some other criteria requires it to be treated as a regular Binary Tree.

```
        left = getLeft(node);
        if ~isempty(left)
            enqueue(q, left );
        end
        right = getRight(node);
        if ~isempty(right)
            enqueue(q, right );
        end
    end
end
if found
    ans = getData(node);
end
```

Table 192—**Binary Tree Breadth-first Find Method** *(Continued)*

```
function ans = DFFind(bt, what)
% BinaryTree\DFFind
st = MStack;
push(st, bt.root )
found = false;
ans = [];
while ~found && ~isEmpty(st)
    node = pop(st);
    % check the data we just popped
    found = (node == what);
    if ~found
    % push the children of this node
        left = getLeft(node);
        if ~isempty(left)
            push(st, left );
        end
        right = getRight(node);
        if ~isempty(right)
            push(st, right );
        end
    end
end
if found
    ans = getData(node);
end
```

Table 193—**Binary Tree Depth-first Find Method**

27.9.3. Searching a BST

BST search takes advantage of the ordering of the data to eliminate half of the tree at each search step as shown in Table 194. Obviously, the data items in the tree must provide both an **eq(...)** method and a **gt(...)** method.

```
function ans = find(bst, n)
% @BST\find
ans = rFind( getRoot(bst), n);



function ans = rFind(here, n)
%
if isempty(here)
    ans = [];
elseif getData(here) == n
    ans = getData(here);
elseif getData(here) > n
    ans = rFind(getLeft(here), n);
else
    ans = rFind(getRight(here), n);
end
```

Table 194—BST Search

27.10. Combining Complex Operations

When the stated problem is a little more complex than the ordinary operations indicated above, it is tempting to expand the code for a single operation. For example, suppose we were asked to put into a cell array the names of all foreigners in Prince William's ancestral tree[6]. It would be possible to modify the fold method on the FamilyTree to apply the condition that the person's nationality be not British, and then add their name to a cell array of names. However, it seems that a regular traversal of the tree extracting all the data into a cell array, and then filtering that cell array to remove all the non-British subjects might take a little longer, but would be much more robust and comprehensible.

---

[6] See the file royalAncestors.m in the code archive.

27.11.Examples

27-1 Draw the final Binary Search Tree that results from the following numbers being inserted into an initially empty BST. (Note: the first number listed is the first one inserted into the BST, etc.)

[10 7 9 11 6 39 12 42 2 16 31]

27-2 Answer the following with regards to the tree below:
   a. Draw the tree with the value 10 inserted.
   b. Draw the tree with the root deleted.

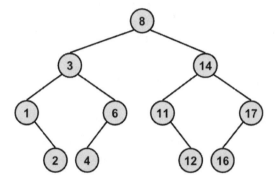

27-3 We need to determine whether a binary tree contains any item less than a certain value. Answer the following questions:
   a. Give the *recursive definition* of a **binary tree.**
   b. Using the recursive definition of a **binary tree**, write an efficient method called **findLessThan(val)** that returns **true** if there is some node in the binary tree that contained a value less than **val**.
   c. What would the running time (the *Big "O"*) of your **findLessThan** method be?
   d. Rewrite **findLessThan(val)** to take advantage of the sorted nature of a BST.

27-4 Consider the following "binary search tree."

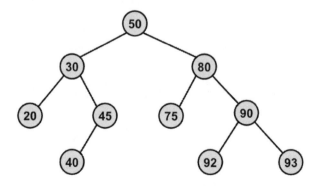

a. Which node in the tree is out of place?

b. Draw the tree with the incorrect node in the correct place (moving only the wrong node).

c. From the original tree (with the incorrect node), draw the resulting tree were you to delete the root.

27-5   We want to build and test a script that manipulates a BST of **Students** sorted alphabetically by name.

a. Extend the **Student** class created in the examples of Chapter 26, calling the new class **BSTStudent**. Change the **eq(...)** method to check for equality of the name, and add a **gt(...)** method to compare names in order, and have the **char(...)** method merely show you the name.

b. Create a new **BST** object called **myBST**.

c. Initialize a counter to 0.

d. Continue generating and adding students to the BST until 50 have been added. Since duplicates are not allowed in the BST, you will need to generate a random name using the function provided, and search the BST to see if that name is in there. If it is not there, add it to the BST and increment the count.

e. Print out **myBST** when you are done. You should see a list of 50 names in alphabetical order.

27-6   We want to experiment with saving and resorting data in a BST. Perform the following steps:

a. Build a **BST** containing about 50 random integers in the range **1..99** (could be less than 50 if you refuse to add duplicate numbers.) Display the **BST** using the built-in **BFS print** method.

b. Modify the in-order traversal to traverse the tree putting each data item into a vector of numbers.

c. Build another tree inserting the items from that vector, and display this new tree. What do you observe?

d. Now, traverse the original tree using pre-order traversal putting the numbers into a vector as before.

e. Build a third tree using this vector as the data source, and display it as before. What do you observe?

f. What lesson can you draw from this exercise?

28. N-ARY TREES

We move to an even more complex dynamic data structure—the N-ary tree, removing the previous restriction on the number of children permitted. Where each node of a binary tree has two child nodes, an N-ary tree will in general contain a collection of 0 or more child nodes, as illustrated in Figure 132. We discussed the place of the N-ary tree concept among other dynamic data structures in Section 27.1 above.

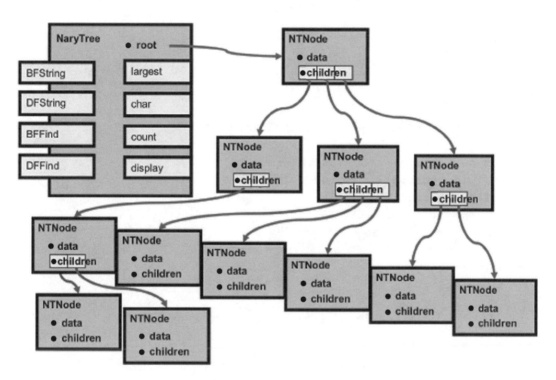

Figure 132—Structure of an N-ary Tree

28.1. Processing N-ary Trees

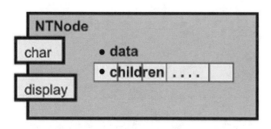

Figure 133—An N-ary Tree Node

As with binary trees, there are opportunities to use either iterative processes or recursive processes. However, we first consider processing N-ary trees recursively. Figure 133 illustrates the content of the node with which we construct an N-ary tree. Omitted for clarity are the **set/get** methods for the **data** and **children** attributes.

We determine how to process an N-ary Tree based on its formal definition:

- An **N-aryTree** is an **NTNode** containing a data item and a collection (that might be empty) of **NTNodes** named **children**[1]

This is a slightly different formal definition than we have seen before, because it introduces the idea of a collection of child nodes. A very strong way to decompose this definition for processing is to consider two separate parts of the node—the data part and the collection of children, and build a separate function for processing each part. The template for processing an N-ary tree then becomes mutually recursive, as shown in Table 195.

```
<function and return> processNTNode(here)
% mutually recursive processing
    ... getData(here) ...
        ... processNTChildren( getChildren(here) ) ...


<function and return> processNTChidren(ch)
% traverse the collection, processing each child
<initialize the result>
<traverse the collection>
    <extract the child node thisch>
    <insert processNTNode(thisch) in the result>
<end traversal>
<return the result>
```

Table 195—Template for Processing an N-ary Tree

Figure 134 illustrates the operation of this recursive process on a particular NTNode. Since the children of this node are a collection of references to other NTNodes, we define a separate method for processing that collection[2] to accumulate the results from the child nodes. The main function then combines this summary of the child results with the data at this node, and returns the result to the calling node.

---

[1] Notice that having a collection of children actually simplifies the processes because the collection of children can be empty, thereby removing the possibility (except at the root of an empty tree) that the node to process is ever empty.

[2] While it is possible to use any collection capable of holding generalized objects, we have chosen in this text to use a cell array to hold the collection of children.

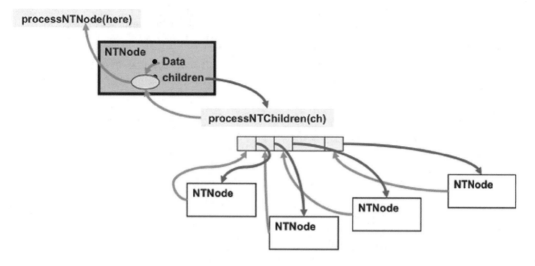

Figure 134—Processing an N-ary Tree Node

28.2. Traversing an N-ary Tree

We will consider both depth-first and breadth-first techniques for traversing an N-ary Tree. For simplicity, we will adopt the iterative approach using queues and stacks to manage the traversal.

28.2.1. Depth-first traversal

Table 196 shows the template for depth-first traversal on an N-ary tree. It is the typical iterative approach using a stack to organize the data. In order to maintain the "natural" left-right appearance of the traversal, the children should be pushed onto the stack in reverse order so that they are popped off the stack in forward order.

```
<function and return> DFTraversal(ntree)
% @BinaryTree\BFSTraversal
st = MStack;      % create a stack
push(st, getRoot(ntree) );
< initialize the result>
while !isEmpty(st)
node = pop(st);
<operate on getData(node)>
<traverse the children in reverse order>
      push(st, <each child>);
    end
end
< return the result>
```

Table 196—Iterative N-ary Tree Depth-first Traversal

Since by convention in this text, the `char(...)` conversion of these more complex collections will not traverse the collection, we must use specific methods traversing the collections to create strings. Table 182 shows the `DFString(...)` method that performs the traversal using a stack.

```
function str = DFString(nt)
% @NaryTree\DFString
%   depth-first tree traversal
st = MStack;
push(st, nt.root )
str = '';
while ~isEmpty(st)
    node = pop(st);
    str = [str '; ' char(node)];
    % push the children of this node
    ch = getChildren(node);
    for ind = length(ch):-1:1
            push(st, ch{ind} );
    end
end
```

Table 197—The N-ary Tree `DFString(...)` Method

28.2.2. Breadth-first Traversal

Breadth-first traversal permits data in the tree to be accessed a generation at a time. It uses a simple, but effective, iterative template that uses a queue to store the children of each generation. Table 198 shows the template for this process.

```
<function and return> BFTraversal(ntree)
% @NaryTree\BFTraversal
q = Queue;      % create a queue
q.enqueue(getRoot(ntree) );
< initialize the result>
while !isEmpty(q)
node = dequeue(q);
<operate on getData(node)>
<traverse the children>
        enqueue(q, <each child>);
    end
end
< return the result>
```

Table 198—Template for N-ary Tree Breadth-first Traversal

Table 199 shows the code that produces a string representation of the tree using a breadth-first traversal. As with the binary tree breadth-first traversal, this is slightly complicated by the need to keep up with the layers in the tree.

```
function str = BFString(nt)
% @NaryTree\BFString
%  tree traversal including formating lines
q = Queue;
enqueue(q, {0, nt.root} )
level = -1;
sp = '                              ';
str = '';
nsp = 64;
while ~isEmpty(q)
    v = dequeue(q);
    % set the tree level
    if v{1} ~= level
        level = v{1};
        str = sprintf('%s\n', str);
        nsp = ceil(nsp / 2);
    end
    % insert the data we just dequeued
    node = v{2};
    if isempty(node)
        str = [str sp(1:nsp) '—'];
    else
        str = [str sp(1:nsp) char(node)];
        % enqueue the children of this node
        ch = getChildren(node);
        for ind = 1:length(ch)
            enqueue(q, {level+1, ch{ind}  });
        end
    end
end
end
```

Table 199—Breadth-first N-ary Tree String Generator

28.3. Building an N-ary Tree

Since the structure of N-ary Trees usually has some specific meaning not evident from the data content itself, they are not usually built dynamically. For our purposes, they will be created in the test script. The motivation example in this text will be a segment of the British royal family tree. A fuller version of this tree is provided for the students in the code collection.

28.4. Folding an N-ary Tree

We will illustrate here two examples of mutually recursive methods to fold or summarize an N-ary tree. The first, `count(...)`, is of course independent of the content of the tree. The second, `largest(...)`, will find the "largest" item in the tree. Our test data for this will be a family tree containing person objects whose comparisons are performed on their age. This method will therefore find the oldest person in the family tree.

28.4.1. Counting an N-ary Tree

To count items in an N-ary tree, we will follow the recursive template in Table 195 with the following tailoring required:

- The public method, `count`, checks for an empty tree, then launches the recursive helper, `countChild`, with the root of the tree and passes the total to its caller.
- The `countChild` helper adds one to the result of counting its children.
- The `countChildren` helper traverses the collection of children accumulating the number of children in each subtree.

The resulting code is shown in Table 200.

```
function ans = count(nt)
% @NaryTree\count
if isempty(nt.root)
    ans = 0;
else
    ans = countChild(nt.root);
end


function ans = countChild(here)
% count the child node
ch = getChildren(here);
ans = 1 + countChildren( ch );
function ans = countChildren(ch)
% count the children nodes
ans = 0;
for index = 1:length(ch)
    ans = ans + countChild( ch{index} );
end
```

Table 200—Generic N-ary Tree `count(...)` Method

28.4.2. Finding the Largest Item in an N-ary Tree

To find the largest item in an N-ary tree, we will again follow the recursive template in Table 195 with the following tailoring required:

- The public method, **largest**, checks for an empty tree, then launches the recursive helper, **largestChild**, with the root of the tree and passes the result to its caller.
- The **largestChild** helper invokes the **largestOfChildren** method to find its largest child (which could be empty if there are no children).
- The **largestOfChildren** helper uses a recursive call to **largestChild** method to find the largest child in each subtree. It checks that there are children, sets the largest to the largest child in the first child subtree, and traverses the rest of the collection of children comparing the largest child in each subtree.

The resulting code is shown in Table 201.

```
function ans = largest(nt)
% @NaryTree\largest
% returns the largest item in the tree
if isempty(nt.root)
    ans = [];
else
    ans = largestChild(nt.root);
end


function ans = largestChild(here)
% returns the data item that is the largest child
thisch = getData(here);
ch = getChildren(here);
ch1 = largestOfChildren( ch );
if ~isempty(ch1) && (ch1 > thisch)
    ans = ch1;
else
    ans = thisch;
end


function ans = largestOfChildren(ch)
% returns the data item that is the largest child
l = length(ch);
```
(Continued)

Table 201—Finding the Largest in an N-ary Tree

```
if l == 0
    ans = [];
else
    ans = largestChild(ch{1});
    for index = 2:length(ch)
        chld = largestChild(ch{index});
        if chld > ans
            ans = chld;
        end
    end
end
```

Table 201—Finding the Largest in an N-ary Tree *(Continued)*

28.5. Searching an N-ary Tree

We need to consider searching both the N-ary tree either breadth-first or depth first. As with the traversals, these searches are done iteratively with queues and stacks respectively.

28.5.1. Breadth-first Search

The breadth-first search method **BFFind** will follow the recursive template in Table 198 with the following tailoring required:

- It first creates a **queue** and enqueues the tree root.
- As long as that **queue** is not empty (indicating failure) or the dequeued item is not what we seek, it continues enqueueing the children of the current node.

The resulting code is shown in Table 202.

```
function ans = BFFind(nt, what)
% NaryTree\BFFind
q = Queue;
enqueue(q, nt.root )
found = false;
ans = [];
while ~found && ~isEmpty(q)
    node = dequeue(q);
    % check the data we just popped
```
                                                                (Continued)

Table 202—N-ary Tree Breadth-first Find Method

```
        found = (node == what);
        if ~found
        % push the children of this node
            ch = getChildren(node);
            for ind = 1:length(ch)
                enqueue(q, ch{ind});
            end
        end
    end
end
if found
    ans = getData(node);
end
```

Table 202—N-ary Tree Breadth-first Find Method *(Continued)*

28.5.2. Depth-First Search

Depth-first search can also be accomplished iteratively using a **MStack** instead of a **Queue**, as illustrated with the **DFFind** method. The code is illustrated in Table 203.

```
function ans = DFFind(nt, what)
% @NaryTree\DFFind
st = MStack;
push(st, nt.root )
found = false;
ans = [];
while ~found && ~isEmpty(st)
    node = pop(st);
    % check the data we just popped
    found = (node == what);
    if ~found
    % push the children of this node
        ch = getChildren(node);
        for ind = length(ch):-1:1
            push(st, ch{ind});
        end
    end
end
if found
    ans = getData(node);
end
```

Table 203—N-ary Tree Depth-first Find Method

28.6. Testing the N-ary Tree Methods

To test these N-ary tree methods, we built a short royal family database as shown in Table 205. These person objects were then collected into an N-ary tree by building the nodes illustrated in Table 204. We could then test the N-ary tree methods using the script in Table 206. Clearly, `BFFind` can also be used for searching.

```
N1_01 = NTNode(William);
N1_02 = NTNode(Henry);
N1_03 = NTNode(Peter);
N1_04 = NTNode(Zara);
N1_05 = NTNode(Beatrice);
N1_06 = NTNode(Eugenie);

N2_02 = NTNode(Charles);
setChildren(N2_02,{N1_01, N1_02});
N2_03 = NTNode(Anne);
setChildren(N2_03,{N1_03, N1_04});
N2_04 = NTNode(Andrew);
setChildren(N2_04,{N1_05, N1_06});
N2_05 = NTNode(Edward);
N2_06 = NTNode(David);
N2_07 = NTNode(Sarah);

N3_01 = NTNode(ElizabethII);
setChildren(N3_01,{N2_02, N2_03, N2_04, N2_05});
N3_02 = NTNode(Margaret);
setChildren(N3_02,{N2_06, N2_07});

N4_01 = NTNode(GeorgeVI);
setChildren(N4_01,{N3_01, N3_02});
```

Table 204—Royal Family Tree

```
William = Person('William', 1982, -1, [], ...
    'Prince of Wales');
Henry = Person('Henry', 1984, -1, [], ...
    'Prince of Wales');
```
(Continued)

Table 205—Short Royal Family

```
Peter = Person('Peter', 1977, -1, [], ...
    'Phillips');
Zara = Person('Zara', 1981, -1, [], ...
    'Phillips');
Beatrice = Person('Beatrice', 1988, -1, [], ...
    'Princess of York');
Eugenie = Person('Eugenie', 1990, -1, [], ...
    'Princess of York');
Charles = Person('Charles', 1948, -1, [], ...
    'Prince of Wales');
Anne = Person('Anne', 1950, -1, [], ...
    'Princess Royal');
Andrew = Person('Andrew', 1960, -1, [], ...
    'Duke of York');
Edward = Person('Edward', 1964, -1, [], ...
    'Earl of Wessex');
David = Person('David', 1961, -1, [], ...
    'Viscount Linley');
Sarah = Person('Sarah', 1964, -1, [], ...
    'Lady Armstrong-Jones');
ElizabethII=Person('Elizabeth II', 1926, -1, [], ...
    'Queen of the United Kingdom ...');
Margaret = Person('Margaret', 1930, 2002, [], ...
    'Princess');
GeorgeVI = Person('George VI',1895,1952, [], ...
    'King of the United Kingdom ...');
```

Table 205—Short Royal Family *(Continued)*

```
family = NaryTree(N4_01)
fprintf('%s has %d descendants!\n', ...
 show(getData(getRoot(family))), count(family) - 1 );
fprintf('oldest member is %s\n', ...
                        show( largest(family) ) );
fprintf('depth-first list: %s\n', ...
                        DFString(family));
fprintf('breadth-first list: %s\n', ...
                        BFString(family));
lookFor = input('Depth First find: ', 's' );
```
(Continued)

Table 206—Testing the Royal Family Tree

```
while length(lookFor) > 0
    val = DFFind(family, lookFor);
    if isempty(val)
        disp('not found');
    else
        fprintf('depth-first find %s -> %s\n',...
                        lookFor, show(val));
    end
    lookFor = input('Depth First find: ', 's' );
end
```

Table 206—Testing the Royal Family Tree *(Continued)*

28.7. Examples

28-1. Write a recursive version of the depth-first string generator for an N-ary tree, and check that the answers match those from the iterative version in the text.

28-2. Write an iterative version of the N-ary tree **count(...)** method.

28-3. We would like to find out who in the royal family tree was youngest when they ascended the throne.
   a. Extend the Person class used in the royal family tree to include the year at which this individual ascended to the throne (if they did). If not, use –1 for the year of ascension.
   b. Change the comparison method in the Person class to compare ages at ascension to the throne, bearing in mind the –1 value for those who did not reign.
   c. You can determine the year of ascension for a monarch from the year of death of their predecessor on the throne. Add these values to the data set.
   d. If you have done this correctly, you should be able to run the largest(. . .) method unchanged to find the monarch who was the youngest to ascend the throne.

29. GRAPHS

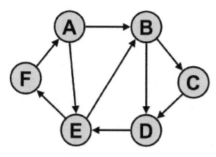

Figure 135—A Typical Graph

As we discussed in 27.1 above, graphs are the most general form of dynamic data structure. A simple graph might be visualized as an N-ary tree in which it is permitted to close cycles with the child links, as shown in Figure 135. As usual, we refer to the connection points A ... F as the Nodes. The lines connecting the nodes are referred to as Edges. On a typical graph, edges may be directional as shown here, or bidirectional, and they may have weights or costs associated with them, such as a length or a travel time.

Graphs occur frequently in everyday life as illustrated by the Underground map in Figure 136. The design of this map was motivated by the need to travel from any one station to any other, changing to different lines at most twice.

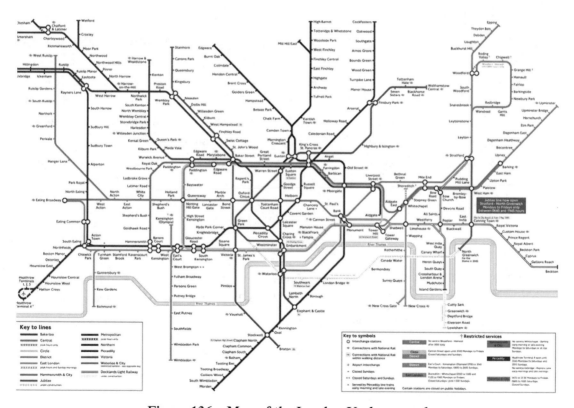

Figure 136—Map of the London Underground

Operations on graphs are more complex to code than operations on trees, because of two complicating factors:

- With cycles permitted in the data, there is no natural starting point like a 'head' or 'root.' Consequently, we have to specify a place on the graph to start a search, as well as the node to find.
- There are also no natural 'leaf nodes' where a search might terminate. Consequently, processing a graph must have a means of determining that being at a given node is the 'end of the line.' Typically, this is accomplished by maintaining a visited path as we progress around the graph. Each time a node is visited, we check to see whether that node is already on the visited path. If so, we refuse to return to that node. A leaf node is then one from which there is no edge to a node that has not already been visited.
- Having the starting point of a tree search "on the edge of the data" limits the direction in which a traversal or search can proceed. This actually masks the worst characteristics of depth-first and breadth-first path search techniques which are exposed when you put the starting place for a search in the middle of a graph rather than the edge.

29.1. The End of the Line ...

As the dynamic data structures have become more and more general, and therefore more complex, and difficult to process, we have steadily reduced the type of operations we expect to perform on them. We will confine our interest in graph operations to considering a number of search techniques.

Furthermore, there is a fundamental limitation in MATLAB's ability to construct graphs in the manner in which we constructed N-ary trees in Table 204. This limitation prevents us from constructing graphs in the same manner to test our code. While it might be possible to rewrite a significant amount of code to make graph processing possible, this is probably not practical for an introductory text. Consequently, we will consider graph algorithms only conceptually, without actually writing MATLAB code.

29.2. Searching Graphs

We will first generalize the iterative templates for performing depth-first and breadth-first search, and then discuss a simple extension to these techniques that will find the optimal path in a way that neither depth-first nor breadth-first techniques can guarantee. The generalizations involve the following:

- Since the test for "leaf nodes" requires knowledge of the path used to reach any place on the graph, the items to be maintained on the queue or stack must be a list of nodes that is the current path.
- Before considering any node, we must determine whether that node is currently on the path being maintained.

• There must be some indication for each problem of which order to use in selecting the edges to the children of the current path.

For a simple, consistent example, consider the graph in Figure 137. We wish to find a path from A to H, and all edges are bidirectional. When choosing the edges to the next child, the children should be taken in alphabetic order of the node letters. The numbers indicate the relative cost of including that edge in the resulting path. Of course, neither the DFS or BFS algorithms take any notice of the edge cost, they only consider reaching the nodes.

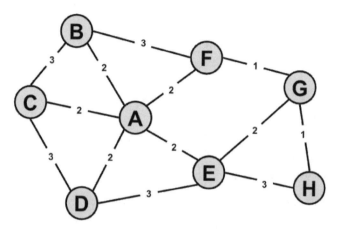

Figure 137—Typical Graph Example

29.2.1. Depth-first Graph Search

The basic depth-first algorithm is shown on Table 207.

```
- create a stack
- push onto the stack a path containing the origin
- while the stack is not empty
- pop a path off the stack
- if this is the path to the destination, quit
- else
    - traverse the children in reverse order
    - if the child is not on the path,
        - add it to the path
        - push the new path onto the stack
    - end
        - end
- end
```

Table 207—Depth-first Graph Search

Table 208 indicates the contents of the stack as this algorithm proceeds.

Table 208—Depth-first Stack Trace

Step	Action	Considering:	Stack contents
1	Push the starting location		A
2	Pop a path	A	[]
3	Push the children in reverse order	A	A – B
			A – C
			A – D
			A – E
			A – F
4	Pop a path	A – B	A – C
			A – D
			A – E
			A – F
5	Push the children in reverse order (not A—been there)	A – B	A – B – C
			A – B – F
			A – C
			A – D
			A – E
			A – F
6	Pop a path	A – B – C	A – B – F
			A – C
			A – D
			A – E
			A – F
7	Push the children in reverse order (not A or B—been there)	A – B – C	A – B – C – D
			A – B – F
			A – C
			A – D
			A – E
			A – F
8	Pop a path	A – B – C – D	A – B – F
			A – C
			A – D
			A – E
			A – F

Step	Action	Considering:	Stack contents
9	Push the children in reverse order (not A or C—been there)	A – B – C – D	A – B – C – D – E A – B – F A – C A – D A – E A – F
10	Pop a path	A – B – C – D – E	A – B – F A – C A – D A – E A – F
11	Push the children in reverse order (not A or D—been there)	A – B – C – D – E	A – B – C – D – E – G A – B – C – D – E – H A – B – F A – C A – D A – E A – F
12	Pop a path	A – B – C – D – E – G	A – B – C – D – E – H A – B – F A – C A – D A – E A – F
13	Push the children in reverse order (not A or C—been there)	A – B – C – D – E – G	A – B – C – D – E – G – F A – B – C – D – E – G – H A – B – C – D – E – H A – B – F A – C A – D A – E A – F
14	Pop a path	A – B – C – D – E – G – F	A – B – C – D – E – G – H A – B – C – D – E – H A – B – F A – C A – D A – E A – F

Step	Action	Considering:	Stack contents
15	No children to push – A, B and G already on the path	A – B – C – D – E – G – F	A – B – C – D – E – G – H A – B – C – D – E – G A – B – C – D – E – H A – B – F A – C A – D A – E A – F
16	Pop a path—the answer!—Not the shortest, but an answer	A – B – C – D – E – G – H	A – B – C – D – E – H A – B – F A – C A – D A – E A – F

29.2.2. Breadth-first Graph Search

The basic breadth-first algorithm is shown Table 209.

```
- create a queue
- enqueue a path containing the origin
- while the queue is not empty
- dequeue a path
- if this is the path to the destination, quit
- else
    - traverse the children
    - if the child is not on the path,
        - add it to the path
        - enqueue the new path
    - end
        - end
- end
```

Table 209—Breadth-first Graph Search

The behavior of this algorithm for our simple graph is shown in Table 210.

Table 210—Breadth-first Queue Trace

Step	Action	Considering:	Queue contents
1	Enqueue the starting location		A
2	Dequeue a path	A	[]
3	Enqueue the children	A	A – B
			A – C
			A – D
			A – E
			A – F
4	Dequeue a path	A – B	A – C
			A – D
			A – E
			A – F
5	Enqueue the children (not A)	A – B	A – C
			A – D
			A – E
			A – F
			A – B – C
			A – B – F
6	Dequeue a path	A – C	A – D
			A – E
			A – F
			A – B – C
			A – B – F
7	Enqueue the children (not A)	A – C	A – D
			A – E
			A – F
			A – B – C
			A – B – F
			A – C – B
			A – C – D
8	Dequeue a path	A – D	A – E
			A – F
			A – B – C
			A – B – F
			A – C – B
			A – C – D

Step	Action	Considering:	Queue contents
9	Enqueue the children (not A)	A – D	A – E
			A – F
			A – B – C
			A – B – F
			A – C – B
			A – C – D
			A – D – C
			A – D – E
10	Dequeue a path	A – E	A – F
			A – B – C
			A – B – F
			A – C – B
			A – C – D
			A – D – C
			A – D – E
11	Enqueue the children (not A) T his last enqueue gives the answer— we could enqueue a lot of paths after this one, but this will be the first path out of the queue with the answer, so we might as well take it now!	A – E	A – F
			A – B – C
			A – B – F
			A – C – B
			A – C – D
			A – D – C
			A – D – E
			A – E – D
			A – E – G
			A – E – H

29.2.3. Optimal Graph Search

To calculate the optimal path, we will use a version of Dijkstra's algorithm, as shown in Table 211. The key to the algorithm is the use of a Priority Queue described in Section 26.9 above. Paths are placed on the priority queue using the overall path length as the sorting criterion. Consequently, the algorithm works in a manner similar to breadth-first search, except that paths are considered shortest first.

```
- create a priority queue
- enqueue a path containing the origin with length 0
- while the queue is not empty
- dequeue a path
```
(Continued)

Table 211—Dijkstra's Algorithm for Optimal Path Search

```
- if this is the path to the destination, quit
- else
    - traverse the children
    - if this child is the destination, quit
    - if the child is not on the path,
        - add it to the path
        - calculate the new length
        - enqueue the new path at that length
    - end
        - end
- end
```

Table 211—Dijkstra's Algorithm for Optimal Path Search *(Continued)*

The behavior of Dijkstra's algorithm is shown in Table 212.

Table 212—Queue Trace of Dijkstra's Algorithm

Step	Action	Considering:	Queue contents
1	Enqueue the starting location		(0) – A
2	Dequeue a path	A	[]
3	Enqueue the children	A	(2) – A – B
			(2) – A – C
			(2) – A – D
			(2) – A – E
			(2) – A – F
4	Dequeue a path	(2) – A – B	(2) – A – C
			(2) – A – D
			(2) – A – E
			(2) – A – F
5	Enqueue the children	(2) – A – B	(2) – A – C
			(2) – A – D
			(2) – A – E
			(2) – A – F
			(5) – A – B – C
			(5) – A – B – F
6	Dequeue a path	(2) – A – C	(2) – A – D
			(2) – A – E
			(2) – A – F
			(5) – A – B – C
			(5) – A – B – F

Step	Action	Considering:	Queue contents
7	Enqueue the children (not A)	(2) – A – C	(2) – A – D (2) – A – E (2) – A – F (5) – A – B – C (5) – A – B – F (5) – A – C – B (5) – A – C – D
8	Dequeue a path	(2) – A – D	(2) – A – E (2) – A – F (5) – A – B – C (5) – A – B – F (5) – A – C – B (5) – A – C – D
9	Enqueue the children (not A)	(2) – A – D	(2) – A – E (2) – A – F (5) – A – B – C (5) – A – B – F (5) – A – C – B (5) – A – C – D (5) – A – D – C (5) – A – D – E
10	Dequeue a path	(2) – A – E	(2) – A – F (5) – A – B – C (5) – A – B – F (5) – A – C – B (5) – A – C – D (5) – A – D – C (5) – A – D – E
11	Enqueue the children (not A)	(2) – A – E	(2) – A – F (5) – A – B – C (5) – A – B – F (5) – A – C – B (5) – A – C – D (5) – A – D – C (5) – A – D – E (5) – A – E – D (5) – A – E – G (5) – A – E – H

Step	Action	Considering:	Queue contents
12	Dequeue a path	(2) – A – F	(5) – A – B – C
			(5) – A – B – F
			(5) – A – C – B
			(5) – A – C – D
			(5) – A – D – C
			(5) – A – D – E
			(5) – A – E – D
			(5) – A – E – G
			(5) – A – E – H
13	Enqueue the children (not A)	(2) – A – F	(3) – A – F – G
			(5) – A – B – C
			(5) – A – B – F
			(5) – A – C – B
			(5) – A – C – D
			(5) – A – D – C
			(5) – A – D – E
			(5) – A – E – D
			(5) – A – E – G
			(5) – A – E – H
			(5) – A – F – B
14	Dequeue a path	(3) – A – F – G	(5) – A – B – C
			(5) – A – B – F
			(5) – A – C – B
			(5) – A – C – D
			(5) – A – D – C
			(5) – A – D – E
			(5) – A – E – D
			(5) – A – E – G
			(5) – A – E – H
			(5) – A – F – B
15	Enqueue the children (not F)	(3) – A – F – G	(4) – A – F – G – H
			(5) – A – B – C
			(5) – A – B – F
			(5) – A – C – B
			(5) – A – C – D
			(5) – A – D – C
			(5) – A – D – E
			(5) – A – E – D

15	Enqueue the children (not F)		(5) – A – E – G
			(5) – A – E – H
			(5) – A – F – B
			(6) – A – F – G – E
16	Dequeue a path—the shortest to the destination!	(4) – A – F – G – H	(5) – A – B – C
			(5) – A – B – F
			(5) – A – C – B
			(5) – A – C – D
			(5) – A – D – C
			(5) – A – D – E
			(5) – A – E – D
			(5) – A – E – G
			(5) – A – E – H
			(5) – A – F – B
			(6) – A – F – G – E

29.3. Examples

29-1 Consider the following graph and answer the questions below.

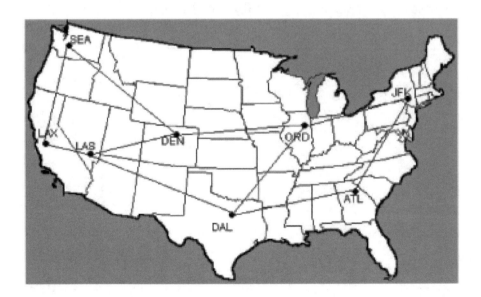

a. What is the final path if you do a DFS from ATL to SEA considering the airports in alphabetical order?

b. What is the final path if you do a BFS from ATL to SEA considering the airports in alphabetical order?

29-2 Consider the following graph:

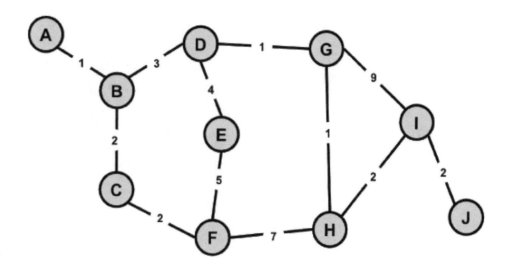

a. Perform a DFS on the graph above, starting at node A and ending at node J. When choosing the order of the child nodes, take them in increasing order of the edge weights, starting with the smallest. Give the final path resulting from the DFS and the path cost.

b. Using the same rules, compute the path and path cost resulting from a BFS.

c. Using the same rules, compute the path and path cost resulting from an optimal search using the Dijkstra algorithm.

30. COST OF COMPUTING

A book about computing would not be complete without summarizing what computer programs can, and cannot, do. As the chapters progressed, we discussed a number of data collections and a number of operations on those data collections. We also discussed Big O, the basic technique for evaluating the computing cost of an algorithm.

In this chapter, we first summarize the computing cost of the classic operation types on the several data collections. We will then discuss in general the subject of computability, and will conclude with a discussion of a very special class of problem—the N-P Complete problem.

30.1. Comparing Algorithms and Collections

Figure 138 illustrates the Big O performance of the most common operations we have discussed on the common data collections. In summary, any traversal, mapping, folding or filtering is O(N) because all the data items have to be touched to perform these operations. Inserting (the critical component of building) into unstructured collections is usually O(1) because it doesn't matter where in the collection the new data are placed. Searching is O(N) unless the structure facilitates a binary search, and sorting is O(N log N) unless the structure cannot support random access, in which case, insertion sort must be used with O(N^2).

Operation	Array	Sorted Array	Structure	Linked List	Binary Tree	BST	N-ary Tree	Graph
Traverse	N	N	X	N	N	N	N	X
Insert	1	N	1	1	1	Log N	X	X
Map	N	N	N	N	N	N	N	X
Filter	N	N	N	N	X	N	X	X
Fold	N	N	N	N	N	N	N	X
Search	N	Log N	X	N	N	Log N	N	N
Sort	N log N	N log N	X	N^2	X	X	X	X

Figure 138—Performance of Operations on Collections

30.2. Reasonableness of Algorithms

As we discussed while presenting the big O discussion, the performance of algorithms really doesn't matter for small amounts of data. However, in the information age in which we now live, we are confronted daily with enormous amounts of data, and computer scientists are busy polishing algorithms to process these massive amounts of data efficiently. For example, it is only in recent years that the telephone company has made national telephone directories available for search. Before then, you first had to know the area code before you could ask for a person's phone number, because the national listing was too cumbersome to search.

Even with the best algorithms available, however, there are cases where exact solutions are not computable in reasonable amounts of time.

30.2.1. Polynomial Algorithms

We tend to think of algorithms where the Big O has N to a constant power as being "OK." However, consider some algorithm that is $O(N^5)$. With 256 items of data and a processor the performs one operation in a microsecond (10^{-6} sec), this algorithm would take about 1.1 million seconds, 12.7 days, to complete. Probably something to avoid, but it could be worse.

30.2.2. $O(2^N)$

You probably heard the story of the peasant who did a good deed for the king. The king, not being that bright, offered to do anything the peasant wanted. The peasant, being a bit too greedy for his own health, suggested that they take a chess board and put a grain of rice on the first square. Each day for the next 63 days, they would put on the next square double the number of grains on the previous square. If one were to chart the number of grins of rice involved, the chart would look like:

Day	Grains
1	1
2	2
3	4
4	8
5	16
6	32
.	
.	
.	
63	9,223,000,000,000,000,000
64	18,450,000,000,000,000,000

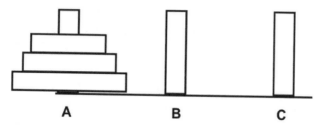

Figure 139—Towers of Hanoi

If you could produce a grain of rice every nanosecond (10^{-9} sec), it would take 585 years just to produce the grain for the last square.

Of course, the king cut off the peasant's head when he realized ...

The Towers of Hanoi problem is also $O(2^N)$. Consider the child's puzzle toy in Figure 139. The objective is to move all the rings from peg A to peg C. However, they can only be moved one ring at a time, and you cannot put a larger ring on top of a smaller ring.

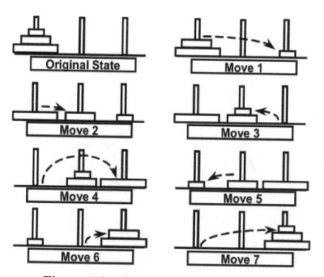

Figure 140—Towers of Hanoi Solution

Figure 140 illustrates the solution with 3 rings. Unfortunately, when you realize what is happening, you notice that for each ring you add, you have to move all the smaller rings twice to get the new ring from A to B and then B to C–$O(2^N)$.

So with 64 rings and moving one ring every microsecond, it would take 584,000 years to finish the puzzle.

But it could be worse ...

30.2.3. O(N!)

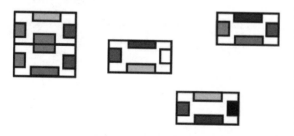

I need to tell you the sad story of our bathroom floor. Our decorating advisor came across this new kind of tile with random patterns. The general idea is that you want to match the patterns at the tile edges. So I measured the bathroom floor, and discovered I would only need 25 tiles to do the job. I went to our local DIY store, bought a box of tiles and promised that I would have the bathroom retiled by dinner time. Fortunately, I decided not to spread the adhesive until I had the pattern figured out.

I picked the first tile at random, placed it in one corner, and went through the other 24 looking for a match to the first edge. This repeated with the second, third and fourth tiles down to the last one, and wouldn't you know it, the last one didn't fit. Had to start over again with a new configuration... How many combinations are there to try? Yes, N!, and 25! works out to be 15,500,000,000,000,000,000,000,000 (roughly). So if I could try one combination every microsecond, I would be at this for 470 billion years!

30.2.4. Unreasonable Algorithms

Although the computation time of polynomial algorithms (where the Big O has N raised to a constant power) can get quite nasty, we class them as *reasonable* algorithms. Those algorithms, however, exponential algorithms where N gets into the exponent in some form are classed as *unreasonable*. While we don't really care about the run-time performance for very small amounts of data, the worst of the exponential algorithms take an enormous amount of time even on a really fast computer, as illustrated in Figure 141.

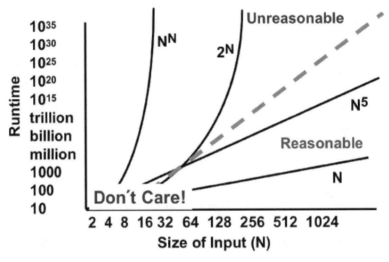

Figure 141—Reasonable and Unreasonable Algorithms

Would a faster computer help, or a large cluster of computers, or both? All these approaches merely improve the Big O by linear amounts—if you really need to solve the kind of problem where these algorithms are invoked, you have to ue sophisticated approximation techniques.

30.3. Tractability of Problems

Since algorithms are really only there to solve problems, we also need some way to assess the advisability of even starting to solve a problem whose solution might end up being unreasonable. We turn from the performance of algorithms to assessing the tractability of problems.

30.3.1. Definitions

We consider first two definitions:

- The upper bound of a problem is the Big O of the best algorithm that has ever been found to completely solve the problem.
- The lower bound of a problem is the Big O of the best proof mathematicians can develop that the solution to this class of problem must be at least this complexity.

For example, a trivial lower bound would be O(1) since if you were smart enough, you could always write down the right answer immediately.

30.3.2. Closed vs. Open Problems

There are some classes of problem where the upper and lower bounds have the same Big O value. For example, mathematicians are satisfied that the best sorting algorithm will be O(N log N). Since we already have sorting algorithms of O(N log N), this indicates that sorting is a closed problem—there is no room for improving the state of the art. Does this mean that there will never be better sorting algorithms? No—there will always be linear improvements such as the progress from Merge Sort to Quick Sort. But the improvement will not affect the Big O.

There are other problems where the upper and lower bounds have not yet met—they are still open for better algorithms or better proofs.

30.3.3. More Definitions

This leads us to the following definitions:

- A problem is said to be tractable if its upper and lower bounds are at worst polynomial.
- A problem is said to be intractable if its upper and lower bounds are both exponential.

30.4. N-P Complete Problems

The definitions of Section 30.3.3 above leave an obvious hole. What do we do with problems whose upper bound is exponential—there is not yet a polynomial algorithm that solves the problem completely—yet the lower bound is polynomial—the mathematicians cannot prove that the solution has to be exponential. This is in fact an enormous class of problems—perhaps larger than any other class of problem—referred to as N-P Complete.

30.4.1. Yet More Definitions

To understand this description of problems, we need a few more definitions:

- A solution is said to be deterministic if at each step of the way, there exists some logic indicating which choice to make without looking forward to the rest of the solution.

- A solution is said to be non-deterministic if no logic exists indicating which choice to make without looking forward to the rest of the solution.
- Perhaps the most remarkable attribute of this class of problem is that all N-P complete problems can be expressed in the same notation—statements in propositional calculus. This means that the problems are deemed to be Complete—that is, transformable from one to another.

N-P Complete stands for that set of problems that is **N**on-Deterministic, should have a **P**olynomial solution, and is a **Complete** set.

30.4.2. Illustrations

The world of science and engineering is overflowing with N-P complete problems that are being solved approximately every day:

- The Traveling Salesman Problem (TSP)—compute the shortest route for a traveling salesman to visit all of the cities in his territory.
- The map coloring problem—find the algorithm that will color a given map with arbitrary boundaries using only four different colors with no two adjacent regions the same color[1].
- 2-D arrangement problems—cutting out a random selection of parts from a sheet of metal with minimal waste.
- Bin packing—arranging odd-shaped items as densely as possible in a given space.
- Planning problems—scheduling classes at a school for the most efficient use of classroom space and teacher hours.
- Scheduling airline service or delivery trucks minimizing the distance traveled to accommodate a specific passenger or cargo demand.
- The clique problem—finding the largest set of vertices in an undirected graph in which there is an edge between every pair of vertices.

All of these problems and many more of their cousins are approximated every day of the week thousands of times. The inefficiency of the solutions to these problems is a permanent drain on the national economy.

30.4.3. The Opportunity

Either lower the upper bound of one of these problems, or develop a proof that raises its lower bound, and you will be famous overnight. They will name buildings after you.

---

[1] This is easily done if you restrict the number of regions that can intersect at a point to 4.

PART IV

APPENDICES

31. MATLAB RESERVED WORDS AND SYMBOLS. [1]

Special Characters	Matrix Definition	Section
{ }	Define a cell array	8.2.1
[ ]	concatenate vectors and arrays	4.2.2
( )	used in statements to group operations	
	used to identify the formal and actual parameters of a function	7.3.2
	used with an array name to identify specific elements	4.2.4
'	encloses a literal character string	12.2
	transposes an array	11.1
;	separates rows in an array definition	11.2
	suppresses output when used in commands	2.2.5
:	used to generate vectors	4.2.2
	used in slicing vectors	4.3.6

Special Characters	Operators Used in MATLAB Calculations	Section
=	assignment operator—assigns a value to a memory location—not the same as an equality test	1.6.4
%	indicates a comment in an M-file	3.2
+	scalar and array addition	4.3.1
−	scalar and array subtraction	4.3.1
*	matrix multiplication	16.3.1
.*	array multiplication	4.3.1
/	matrix division	16.3.2
./	array division	4.3.1
^	matrix exponentiation	16.2.3
.^	array exponentiation	4.3.1

Commands	Formatting Commands	Section
format compact	sets format to compact form	2.2.8
format long	sets format to 14 decimal places	2.2.8
format long e	sets format to 14 exponential places	2.2.8
format loose	sets format back to default, noncompact form	2.2.8

---

[1] Appendix A of Etter, Kuncicki & Moore "Introduction to MATLAB® 7" ISBN 0-13-147492-8.

Commands	Formatting commands	Section
format short	sets format back to default, 4 decimal places	2.2.8
format short e	sets format to 4 exponential places	2.2.8

Commands	Basic Workspace Control	Section
ans	default variable name for results of MATLAB calculations	1.6.4
clc	clears command screen	2.2.2
clear	clears workspace	4.3.6
exit	terminates MATLAB	help exit
help	invokes help utility	help
load	loads the workspace from a file	17.1
quit	terminates MATLAB	help quit
save	saves variables in a file	17.1
who	lists variables in the workspace	2.2.3
whos	lists variables and their sizes	2.2.3

Names	Special Constants	Section
eps	smallest possible difference between two floating point numbers	help eps
i	unit imaginary number—sqrt(-1)	help complex
inf	infinity	help inf
j	unit imaginary number—sqrt(-1)	help complex
Nan	not a number	help Nan
pi	ratio of the circumference of a circle to its diameter	help pi

Functions	Elementary Math	Section
abs	computes the absolute value	help abs
ceil	rounds to the nearest integer toward positive infinity	help ceil
erf	calculates the error function	help erf
exp	computes the value of e^x	help exp
fix	rounds to the nearest integer toward zero	help fix
floor	rounds to the nearest integer toward minus infinity	help floor
log	computes the natural log	help log
log10	computes the log base 10	help log10
log2	computes the log base 2	help log2
rem	calculates the remainder in a division problem	help rem

Functions	Elementary Math	Section
round	rounds to the nearest integer	help round
sign	determines the sign (positive or negative)	help sign
sqrt	calculates the square root of a number	help sqrt

Functions	Trigonometry	Section
asin	computes the inverse sine (arcsine)	help asin
cos	computes the cosine	help cos
sin	computes the sine	help sin
sinh	computes the hyperbolic sine	help sinh
tan	computes the tangent	help tan
	MATLAB includes all the common trigonometric functions. Only the most common are listed here	Search help for 'trigonometry'

Functions	Data Analysis	Section
cumprod	computes a cumulative product of the values in an array	help cumprod
cumsum	computes a cumulative sum of the values in an array	help cumpsum
max	finds the maximum value and its position in an array	help max
mean	computes the average of the elements in an array	help mean
median	finds the median of the elements in an array	help median
min	finds the minimum value and its position in an array	help min
prod	multiplies the values in an array	help prod
std	determines the standard deviation	help std
sum	totals the values in an array	help sum

Functions	Random Numbers	Section
rand	calculates evenly distributed random numbers	help rand
randn	calculates normally distributed (Gaussian) random numbers	help randn

Functions	Two-Dimensional Plots	Section
bar	generates a bar graph	help bar
barh	generates a horizontal bar graph	help barh
contour	generates a contour plot	help contour

Functions	Two-Dimensional Plots	Section
`hist`	generates a histogram	`help hist`
`loglog`	generates an x-y plot, with both axes scaled logarithmically	`help loglog`
`pie`	generates a pie chart	`help pie`
`plot`	creates an x-y plot	15.2
`polar`	creates a polar plot	`help polar`

Functions	Two-Dimensional Plots	Section
`semilogx`	generates an x-y plot, with the x-axis scaled logarithmically	`help semilogx`
`semilogy`	generates an x-y plot, with the y-axis scaled logarithmically	`help semilogy`

Functions	Three-Dimensional Plots	Section
`bar3`	generates a three-dimensional bar graph	`help bar3`
`barh3`	generates a horizontal three-dimensional bar graph	`help barh3`
`mesh`	generates a mesh plot of a surface	15.3.2
`peaks`	creates a sample matrix used to demonstrate graphing functions	15.3.2
`pie3`	generates a three-dimensional pie chart	`help pie3`
`plot3`	generates a three dimensional line plot	
`sphere`	example function used to demonstrate graphing	`help sphere`
`surf`	generates a surface plot	15.3.2
`surfc`	generates a combination surface and contour plot	15.3.2

Special Characters	Control of Plot Appearance	Section
Indicator	**Line Type**	
–	solid	15.2
:	dotted	15.2
–.	dash-dot	15.2
—	dashed	15.2
Indicator	**Point Type**	
.	point	15.2
o	circle	15.2
x	x-mark	15.2
+	plus	15.2
*	star	15.2

Indicator	Point Type	
s	square	15.2
d	diamond	15.2
v	triangle down	15.2
^	triangle up	15.2
<	triangle left	15.2
>	triangle right	15.2
p	pentagram	15.2
h	hexagram	15.2

Indicator	Color	
b	blue	15.2
g	green	15.2
r	red	15.2
c	cyan	15.2
m	magenta	15.2
y	yellow	15.2
k	black	15.2

Functions	Figure Control	Section
axis	freezes the current axis scaling for subsequent plots or specifies the axis dimensions	15.2
figure	opens a new figure window	help figure
grid off	turns the grid off	help grid
grid on	adds a grid to the current and all subsequent graphs in the current figure	help grid
hold off	instructs MATLAB to erase figure contents before adding new information	help hold
hold on	instructs MATLAB **not to** erase figure contents before adding new information	help hold
legend	adds a legend to a graph	15.2
shading flat	shades a surface plot with one color per grid section	15.3.2
shading interp	shades a surface plot by interpolation	15.3.2
subplot	divides the graphics window up into sections available for plotting	15.2
text	adds a textbox to a graph	15.2
title	adds a title to a plot	15.2
xlabel	adds a label to the x-axis	15.2
ylabel	adds a label to the y-axis	15.2
zlabel	adds a label to the z-axis	15.2

Functions	Figure Color Schemes	Section
autumn	colormap for surface plots and images	15.3.2
bone	colormap for surface plots and images	15.3.2
colorcube	colormap for surface plots and images	15.3.2
cool	colormap for surface plots and images	15.3.2
copper	colormap for surface plots and images	15.3.2
flag	colormap for surface plots and images	15.3.2
hot	colormap for surface plots and images	15.3.2
hsv	colormap for surface plots and images	15.3.2
jet	default colormap	15.3.2
pink	colormap for surface plots and images	15.3.2

Functions	Figure Color Schemes	Section
prism	colormap for surface plots and images	15.3.2
spring	colormap for surface plots and images	15.3.2
summer	colormap for surface plots and images	15.3.2
white	colormap for surface plots and images	15.3.2
winter	colormap for surface plots and images	15.3.2

Special Characters	Comparison Operators	Section
<	less than	4.3.2
<=	less than or equal to	4.3.2
>	greater than	4.3.2
>=	greater than or equal to	4.3.2
==	equal to	4.3.2
~=	not equal to	4.3.2

Special Characters	Logical Operators	Section
&	Element-wise logical AND (vectors)	4.3.2
&&	Short-circuit logical AND (scalar)	5.2.3
|	Element-wise logical OR (vectors)	4.3.2
||	Short-circuit logical OR (scalar)	5.2.3
~	not	4.3.2

Special Characters	Format Control	Section
%e	exponential notation	12.2.5
%f	fixed point, or decimal notation	12.2.5

Special Characters	Format Control	Section
`%g`	either fixed point or exponential notation	12.2.5
`%s`	character string	12.2.5
`\n`	linefeed	12.2.5
`\r`	carriage return	12.2.5
`\t`	tab	12.2.5
`\b`	backspace	12.2.5

Functions	Input/Output Functions	Section
`disp`	displays matrix or text	12.2.3
`fprintf`	prints formatted information	12.2.5
`input`	prompts the user to enter a value	12.2.4
`num2string`	converts an array into a string	`help num2string`

Functions	Timing	Section
`clock`	determines the current time on the CPU clock	`help clock`
`etime`	finds elapsed time	`help etime`
`pause`	pauses the execution of a program, until any key is hit, or for a specified number of seconds	`help pause`
`tic`	starts a timing sequence	`help tic`
`toc`	stops a timing sequence	`help toc`

Functions	Function Definition	Section
`function`	identifies an M-file as a function	7.3.2
`nargin`	determines the number of input parameters actually supplied by a function's caller	23.6.3
`nargout`	determines the number of output parameters actually requested by a function's caller	`help nargout`

Functions	Matrix Definition, Manipulation and Analysis	Section
`det`	computes the determinant of a matrix	`help det`
`diag`	extracts the diagonal from a matrix or (if provided with a vector) constructs a matrix with the given diagonal	11.2
`eye`	generates the identity matrix	16.3.2
`fliplr`	flips a matrix from left to right	`help fliplr`
`inv`	computes the inverse of a matrix	16.3.2
`length`	determines the largest dimension of an array	4.2.3

Functions	Matrix Definition, Manipulation and Analysis	Section
linspace	defines a linearly spaced vector	4.2.2
magic	generates a magic square	11.2
meshgrid	maps each of two vectors into separate two-dimensional arrays	15.3.2
ones	generates an array filled with the value 1	16.3.2
size	determines the dimensions of an array	11.1
sort	sorts the elements of a vector in ascending order	22.5
zeros	builds an array filled with the value 0	16.3.2

Functions	Data Types and Classes	Section
char	cast to a character type	12.2
	for numerical primitives, look up the ASCII character code	12.2
class	determine the data type of an object	23.6.3
double	cast to type double	
int8/16/32/64	cast to integer type with the specified number of bits	33.3
isa	tests for a given data type	23.6.3
isempty	tests for the empty vector []	25.3
uint8/16/32/64	cast to unsigned integer type with the specified number of bits	33.3

Functions	Numerical Methods	Section
diff	compute the differences between adjacent values in a vector	20.5.2
interp1	compute linear and cubic interpolation	20.1.2
polyfit	computes a least-squares polynomial	20.2.3
polyval	evaluates a polynomial	20.2.3
Spline	spline interpolation	20.1.2

CHAPTER THIRTY-TWO

1. THE ASCII CHARACTER SET

Originally, the American Standard Code for Information Interchange (ASCII) defined a mapping whereby a specific set of characters was assigned the numerical values 0:127. This was sufficient to represent the number symbols, the lower and upper case alphabet, and all the common punctuation marks. However, as the need arose to represent more international characters, this numerical range was inadequate, and the next 128 values were assigned to meet this need. There is not universal agreement on this second mapping. The following table shows the values used by MATLAB.

Then, more international issues arose with other complete alphabets, and the standard international character set now uses a 16 bit representation, of which the original ASCII set are the first 256.

	0	1	2	3	4	5	6	7	8	9
0	□	□	□	□	□	□	□	□	□	□
10	□	□	□	□	□	□	□	□	□	□
20	□	□	□	□	□	□	□	□	□	□
30	□	□	□	!	''	#	$	%	&	'
40	(	)	*	+	,	-	.	/	0	1
50	2	3	4	5	6	7	8	9	:	;
60	<	=	>	?	@	A	B	C	D	E
70	F	G	H	I	J	K	L	M	N	O
80	P	Q	R	S	T	U	V	W	X	Y
90	Z	[	\	]	^	_	`	a	b	c
100	d	e	f	g	h	i	j	k	l	m
110	n	o	p	q	r	s	t	u	v	w
120	x	y	z	{	|	}	~	□	□	□
130	□	□	□	□	□	□	□	□	□	□
140	□	□	□	□	□	□	□	□	□	□
150	□	□	□	□	□	□	□	□	□	□
160		¡	¢	£	¤	¥	¦	§	¨	©
170	ª	«	¬		®	¯	°	±	²	³
180	´	µ	¶	·	¸	¹	º	»	¼	½
190	¾	¿	À	Á	Â	Ã	Ä	Å	Æ	Ç
200	È	É	Ê	Ë	Ì	Í	Î	Ï	Ð	Ñ
210	Ò	Ó	Ô	Õ	Ö	x	Ø	Ù	Ú	Û
220	Ü	Ý	X	ß	à	á	â	ã	ä	å
230	æ	ç	è	é	ê	ë	ì	í	î	ï
240	ð	ñ	ò	ó	ô	õ	ö	÷	ø	ù
250	ú	û	ü	ý	þ	ÿ				

33. INTERNAL NUMBER REPRESENTATION

We will describe two different techniques whereby most computers today store the values of numbers: integers and floating-point. Integer storage has the nice property that it represents the exact value of the number stored, while floating-point storage only guarantees a certain number of bits of precision. There is an upper limit to the values that can be stored in both integer and floating-point form. However, significantly larger numbers can be stored in floating-point than in integers.

By default, MATLAB sets the storage of numbers to double precision floating-point representation. However, operations like reading images into MATLAB present the large volume of data in the more compact unsigned integer form.

33.1. Integers

Integers are represented in computer memory by blocks of data bits of various sizes. Since memory is allocated in 8 bit increments, usually referred to as 'bytes,' it is not surprising that integer storage comes in the same size increments. For a given size, the values of the data bits are represented in two different ways—signed or unsigned. Normally, of course, we expect a number to have both positive and negative values, and when the number of bits is large, this does not seem to have much impact.

However, when a small number of bits is used to store a value, one of those bits must be used to show that the number is positive or negative. The range of numbers that can be stored is therefore reduced by one bit, a factor of 2. Figure 142 illustrates the internal storage of 8 bit unsigned and signed values.

Unsigned 8 bit integer

Power of 2:	2^7	2^6	2^5	2^4	2^3	2^2	2^1	2^0
Value of bit is 1:	128	64	32	16	8	4	2	1
Example	0	0	1	0	1	1	0	1
			32		+ 8	+ 4		+ 1 = 45

Signed 8 bit integer

Power of 2:	sign	2^6	2^5	2^4	2^3	2^2	2^1	2^0
Value of bit is 1:	−128	64	32	16	8	4	2	1
Example	1	1	1	0	1	1	0	1
	−128 + 64 + 32				+ 8	+ 4		+ 1 = −9

Figure 142—Integer Number Representation

Clearly, for 8 bits, the maximum value is 127 signed, or 255 unsigned. If this is not sufficient storage, numbers can be stored in 16, 32 or 64 bit words, with the corresponding increase in the maximum stored size.

33.2. Floating Point Numbers

Floating-point numbers are stored either in single precision (32 bits) or double precision (64 bits) using the IEEE 754 standard. As the name suggests, the storage format includes a mantissa and an exponent, each expressed internally in a manner similar to integer storage. The fixed size of the mantissa leads to the fixed amount of precision of each storage type. The **float** data type gives 7 significant decimal digits; the **double** data type gives 15 significant decimal digits.[1]

For details of these storage types, I recommend a Web search for "IEEE 754 standard." At the time of writing, there was a good explanation at:

http://www.geocities.com/SiliconValley/Pines/6639/docs/fp_summary.html.

33.3. Parameters of Each Storage Type

Figure 143 describes the most commonly used storage types available in MATLAB, their minimum and maximum values, and the Java equivalent name.

MATLAB Name	Size(bytes)	Min value	Max value	Java name
uint8	1	0	255	unsigned byte
int8	1	-128	127	byte
uint16	2	0	65,535	unsigned short
int16	2	-32,768	32,767	short
uint32	4	0	4,294,967,295	unsigned int
int32	4	-2,147,483,648	2,147,483,647	int
uint64	8	0	18,446,744,073, 709,551,615	unsigned long
int64	8	-9,223,372,036, 854,775,808	9,223,372,036, 854,775,807	long
float	4	~-3.4E+38	~3.4E+38	float
double	8	~-1.7E+308	~1.7E+308	double

Figure 143—number formats

---

[1] Note that while this seems to be a large amount of precision, you must always design your programs to preserve that precision. If, for example, you were to subtract two numbers almost equal in value, the precision of the result will be significantly worse than that of the original numbers.

34. WEB REFERENCE MATERIALS

At the time of writing, the following web sites were available for additional programming tutorials and examples.

MathWorks:

http://www.mathworks.com/academia/student_center/tutorials/launchpad.html
http://www.mathworks.com/academia/student_center/tutorials/index.html#
http://www.mathworks.com/academia/student_center/homework/
http://www.mathworks.com/access/helpdesk/help/techdoc/MATLAB.html
http://www.mathworks.com/support/tech-notes/list_all.html

GT CoC:

http://www.cc.gatech.edu/classes/AY2004/cs1371_summer/
http://www.cc.gatech.edu/classes/AY2004/cs1371_spring/
http://www.cc.gatech.edu/~bbb/cs4495ta/MATLAB.html
http://www.cc.gatech.edu/classes/AY2002/cs7635_spring/tutorial/
http://www.cc.gatech.edu/ccg/people/helene/MATLAB/compiler2.pdf
http://www.cc.gatech.edu/ccg/people/helene/MATLAB/sgl_lib.pdf

GT ECE:

http://users.ece.gatech.edu/~bonnie/book/TUTORIAL/tutorial.html
http://users.ece.gatech.edu/~bonnie/book/TUTORIAL/tutorial.pdf
http://users.ece.gatech.edu/~bonnie/book/applets.html
http://www.eedsp.gatech.edu/Information/MATLAB_User_Guide/index.shtml

GT ME:

http://www.me.gatech.edu/me3015c/MATLAB/
http://www.me.gatech.edu/me3015c/notes/MATLAB1.pdf

GT AE:

http://www.ae.gatech.edu/~msmith/academic/ae2220/MATLAB.pdf

GT ChE:

http://dot.che.gatech.edu/information/research/issicl/che6500/files/MATLAB_primer.pdf
http://staff.ttu.ee/~alahe/aMATLAB.html

35. SOLUTIONS TO SELECTED EXAMPLES

The code that solves some of the examples from each chapter, together with the illustrative code in the text and the necessary data files, is found on the web site at *http://www.dms489.com/ Concepts_book.*

` 118, 132

" 111

% 35

& 44

&& 44, 57

( ) 45

: 46, 123

; 31, 118

[ ] 45

{ } 87

| 44

| | 44, 57

~ 45, 57

= 16, 45

Abstraction 13, 179

   behavioral 179

   data 14, 39, 179

   procedural 14, 75, 179

Activation stack 143

Ada 9, 15

Algorithm 14

ALU 4, 11

Array 117

   cell 87, 364

      operations 89

      uses 88

   concatenation 123

   diagonal 118

   elements 117, 120

   generic 87

   indexing 120

   linearizing 123

   operation 121

      arithmetic 121

   logical 122

   shorten 120

   slicing 124

   square 118

   string 138

   structure 97

   transpose 118

Assignment 15

Babbage, Charles 2

BASIC 9, 16

Big O 275

   algebra 278

   $O(1)$ 276

   $O(2^N)$ 278, 390

   $O(\log N)$ 276

   $O(N \log N)$ 281, 282

   $O(N)$ 276

   $O(N^2)$ 277

   $O(N!)$ 391

Boolean 44, 49, 126

C 8, 9, 136

C++ 8, 15, 136

Cast 133, 230

Casting 131

Cell array 87, 196, 364

Classes 19, 292

COBOL 9

Code block 55

Collection 39, 87, 117, 317, 346

   array 117

   binary search tree 346

   binary tree 346

   BST 346

   cell array 87

Collection (*cont.*)
 graph 345, 375
 heterogeneous 87
 homogeneous 39
 linked list 319
 matrix 179
 n-ary tree 346, 363
 priority queue class 295, 336
 queue class 295, 334
 stack class 294, 335
 structure 95
 structure array 97
 vector 39
Colossus 3
Command History 26
Command Window 25
Comments 35, 36, 77
Computer
 ALU 4, 11
 CPU 4, 11
 Hardware 4
 languages 7
 mainframe 4
 memory 3, 12, 317
 microcomputer 4
 network 5
 operating systems 5
 program
  executing 9
 software 5
  tools 6
 supercomputer 4
 utilities 6
 workstation 4
Concatenation 45, 123
Conditional 55
Coordinates
 rotation 186

Copy
 hard 4
 soft 4
Cost of computing 389
 closed and open problems 393
 lower bound 393
 N-P Complete problems 393
 polynomial algorithms 390
 reasonable algorithms 390
 tractable problems 393
 unreasonable algorithms 392
 upper bound 393
CPU 4, 11
Current Directory 31, 35
 Window 31
Curve fitting 188, 244, 249
Deleting from a BST 354
Document Window 31
Dynamic data structure 317
Edit Window 33
Encapsulation 75, 79, 292
Environment
 interactive 11
Equations
 simultaneous 188
Evaluation
 short-circuit 58
Exceptions 155
 catching 156
 handling 156
 throwing 155
Executing 9, 10
Expression
 logical 57
Fast Fourier Transform 211
Fibonacci Series 150
File I/O 193
 delimiters 193, 195

File I/O (*cont.*)

    saving data 197

    table of functions 194

Files

    m 35

    script 36

    text 35

for loops 66

FORTRAN 8, 16

Function

    invoking 77

    local 79, 146, 324

    multiple results 78

functions 75

Graph

    path 346, 376

Graphics Window 32

Heap 12, 318, 319

I/O 11, 12, 193

Images 225

    color mapped 226

    edge detection 234

    indexed 226

    true color 226

    types 226

Indentation 60

Indexing

    cell 88

    content 88

Instruction 8, 11

Iteration 65

Java 9, 15, 20

Key word

    all 58, 138

    and 57, 138

    ans 26, 47

    any 58, 138

    assignin 298

auread 194, 202

axis 165

case 59

catch 157

char 132, 133, 297, 320

class 298

clc 48, 49

clear 48, 49

clf 161

close 161

colorbar 172

colormap 171, 231

deal 91

diag 118

diff 261

disp 48, 134

end 46, 123, 125

eps 112

erf 190

error 158

eye 181

false 57

fft 212

fieldnames 98

figure 161

find 126

floor 68

for 65, 66

format 33

fprintf 136

function 77

getfield 99

grid 168

hidden 170

hold on 164

if 56

ifft 213

imread 194, 227

Key word (*cont.*)

`imwrite` 227
`input` 71, 80, 134
`inputname` 298
`int8` 133, 408
`interp1` 240
`inv` 184
`isa` 298
`isempty` 322
`isfield` 98
`legend` 164
`length` 41, 48, 118
`lightangle` 172
`linspace` 40
`load` 193
`magic` 119
`mesh` 169
`meshgrid` 169
`nargin` 298
`not` 57
`ones` 40, 118
`or` 57, 138
`otherwise` 59
`peaks` 171
`plot` 165
`plot3` 167
`polyfit` 190, 247
`polyval` 190, 247
`rand` 40, 118
`rmfield` 99
`save` 193
`setfield` 98
`shading flat` 170
`shading interp` 170
`size` 117, 230
`sort` 285, 287
`sound` 204

`spline` 242, 244
`sprintf` 136
`sscanf` 136
`strcmp` 137
`struct` 101
`subplot` 163
`surf` 170
`surfc` 171
`switch` 58
`title` 164
`true` 57
`try` 157
`uint8` 231, 408
`view` 173
`wavread` 202
`while` 69
`who` 30
`whos` 30
`xlabel` 164
`xlsread` 194, 195
`ylabel` 164
`zeros` 40, 118

Language
  interpreted 18
  Typed 18
Languages
  4GL 8
  Ada 9, 15
  assembly 7
  BASIC 9, 16
  C 8, 9, 136
  C++ 8, 15, 136
  COBOL 9
  compiled 10
  execution 10
  FORTRAN 8, 16
  generations 8

Languages (*cont.*)
high-level. 8
Java 9, 15, 20
machine 7
natural 8
Pascal. 9
Linked list 319, 321, 323
MATLAB implementation 323
node. 320
Linspace 40
Lisp 15
Logical expression 57
loop-and-a-half 65, 70
Mapping 75, 131
MATLAB
Command History 26
Command Window 25
Current Directory
Window 31
Document Window 31
Edit Window 33
Executing. 11
Getting Started. 23
Graphics Window 32
Start Button 33
Student Edition 24
Windows 24
Workspace Window. 27
Matrices. 179
Matrix
division 182, 184
exponentiation. 183
identity. 181
multiplication. 180
Memory. 12
dynamic allocation. 318
dynamically linked 319

management. 12
static allocation 317
Numbers
range of 40
Numerical methods 239
critical points 263
cubic spline interpolation 242, 244
curve fitting 244
differentiation 259
integration 254
interpolation. 239
least squares. 246
linear interpolation. 240
linear regression. 244
polynomial regression 247
Simpson's rule. 255
trapezoidal rule 255
Objects 19, 292
Object-Oriented Programming (OOP) . . . 291
abstract data type. 293, 319
ADT. 293, 319
attribute 292, 297
char(…) 297
child class 292, 300
class 298
constructor. 296
display(…) 296
encapsulation. 292, 298
get methods. 297
inheritance. 292, 299
MATLAB implementation 296
method. 292, 298
modeling collections 295, 317
modeling objects 295, 305
object. 292, 301
parent class 292, 300
polymorphism 293, 301

Object Oriented Programming (OOP)
set methods 297
Operation
  add in order in a linked list 325
  add to the head of a linked list 323
  add to the tail of a linked list 323
  breadth-first search of a
      binary tree 358
  breadth-first search of a graph 380
  breadth-first search of an
      n-ary tree 370
  breadth-first traversal of a
      binary tree 350
  breadth-first traversal of an
      n-ary tree 366
  build 107, 108
  build a linked list 323
  building a BST 352
  depth-first search of a binary tree 358
  depth-first search of a graph 377
  depth-first search of an n-ary tree 371
  depth-first traversal of a
      binary tree 348
  depth-first traversal of an
      n-ary tree 365
  filtering 107, 112
  filtering a BST 354
  filtering a linked list 329
  folding 107, 113
  folding a binary tree 357
  folding a linked list 331
  folding an n-ary tree 368
  in-order traversal of a
      binary tree 352
  inserting 107
  insert into a linked list 323
  inserting into a BST 352

mapping 107, 111
mapping a binary tree 353
mapping a linked list 328
optimal search of a graph 382
pre-order traversal of a binary tree 349
searching 107, 114
searching a binary tree 358
searching a BST 360
searching a graph 376
searching a linked list 332
searching an n-ary tree 370
sorting 107, 116, 279
traverse 65, 107, 279
traverse a linked list 326
traversing a binary tree 348
Palindromes 152
Paradigm
  Functional 15
  Object-Oriented 15
  Procedural 15
Parameters 76
Pascal 8, 9
Plaid 168
Plotting 161
  2-D 163
  3-D 166
Precedence
  operator 45
Priority queue 295, 336
Programming
  Functional 15
  Object-Oriented 15
  Procedural 15
Queue 293, 334, 337
RAM 4
Recursion 143, 321, 347, 364
  generative 150

Recursion (*cont.*)
mutual 149
tail 148
wrapper functions 146
Recursive data structures
processing 321, 347, 364
ROM 4
Scalar 42
Scope
global 79
local 79
variable 79
Script 35
run 35, 36
Short-circuit evaluation 58
Slicing 47
Sorting 279
analysis 285
applications 287
bucket sort 284
insertion sort 279
merge sort 282
quick sort 281
Sound 201
amplitude 201
filtering 221
frequency 201
frequency content 212
frequency spectrum 213
physics 201
playback 201
playback frequency 207
recording 201
sampling 202
stretching or shrinking 208
time domain 203
Stack 143, 295, 335, 337

activation 143
Start Button 33
String
arrays 138
character 131
comparing 137
concatenating 133
operations 133
slicing 133
Structure 95
array 98
Test first 65, 66
Test last 65, 69
Traversal 65
Tree
leaf 346
root 346
Typing 17
strong 19
untyped 18
weak 19
Variable names 16
Vector 39
column 118
concatenation 40, 45
creating 40
elements 39, 41
indexing 41
length 41
of indices 46
operations 42
arithmetic 42
logical 44
position 40
row 118
shortening 42
size 41

Vector (*cont.*)

   slicing 47

von Neumann 3

while loops 69

whos 30

Working Directory 27, 35

Workspace Window. 27